D0267931

AN INTRODUCTION
TO HUMAN GENETICS

AN INTRODUCTION
TO HUMAN GENETICS

H. Eldon Sutton   *The University of Texas*

HOLT, RINEHART AND WINSTON
New York   Chicago   San Francisco   Toronto   London

102329

NORTHWEST MISSOURI
STATE COLLEGE LIBRARY

to Beverly

Copyright © 1965 by Holt, Rinehart and Winston, Inc.
All rights reserved
Library of Congress Catalog Card Number: 65–12816

28233–0315

Printed in the United States of America

575.1
S 96i

PREFACE

The study of human genetics is no longer the pastime of a select few; rather, it has become the common meeting place for persons of diverse disciplines and training. As such, human genetics itself is a diverse subject. This is appropriate, since it is concerned with human variation.

A textbook of human genetics, if it is to serve as an introduction for students in such different areas as medicine and anthropology, must recognize that persons using it will have very different backgrounds. The genetic content of the text need not be altered to match each such background, but the illustrative material necessarily will vary with the class. For this reason, an attempt has been made in this text to reduce nongenetic material to a minimum. It is assumed that the instructor will supplement text assignments with suitable examples.

This text has resulted from the contributions of many persons. Although I must bear responsibility for the general organization and first draft, the many suggestions of reviewers have helped greatly in arriving at the final form. Drs. C. P. Oliver, Burke Judd, Herman Slatis, and Beverly J. Sutton read the entire draft. Comments on specific sections were made by Drs. Margery W. Shaw, Charles R. Shaw, Walter K. Long, and J. de Grouchy. The skillful manuscript surgery of Lee C. Cooper is gratefully acknowledged, as is the art work of Pauline G. West. I am indebted to the Literary Executor of the late Sir Ronald Fisher, F.R.S., Cambridge, and to Oliver & Boyd Ltd., Edinburgh, for their permission to reprint Table No. III from their book *Statistical Methods for Research Workers*. To all of these, my appreciation.

H. E. S.

Austin, Texas
January, 1965

v

CONTENTS

Chapter One

INTRODUCTION

The uniqueness of individuals has long been accepted in theory if not in practice. Each person has an appearance unlike that of any other person and thinks differently from other persons. Some differences are due primarily to variations in environment; others most certainly are not. Most undoubtedly reflect a combination of environmental and inherited differences.

With respect to biological variability, references still are made to nature versus nurture. Efforts have been made to compartmentalize traits as environmentally or genetically determined. Statements to this effect, if meant literally, are nonsense. Every trait is the result of a genetic potential expressed in a particular environment.

An example may help to emphasize the semantic difficulties that can arise: Human beings require a variety of amino acids and vitamins in their diet. These substances are manufactured by a variety of organisms, particularly plants. At some very early stage in animal evolution, mutations occurred that resulted in loss of the ability to synthesize these dietary components. This would not be of serious consequence for organisms that obtain their energy by consuming other organisms, thereby acquiring the essential compounds secondhand. But today, many persons suffer from malnutrition due to lack of one or more of these substances. We say that malnutrition results from an inadequate environment, but we could as well say that it is due to mutations that occurred millions of years ago and that led in turn to our inability to synthesize the missing nutrients.

The appropriate terminology depends on one's point of view. In general, we are not so much concerned with those attributes for which the entire population is uniform. Instead, we are concerned with the ways in which individuals differ. The major difference between well-nourished and malnourished persons is environmental; hence, malnutrition is said to be environmental. To be sure, there is evidence that some persons

102323

1

require more of a particular vitamin or amino acid than do others. There are rare pedigrees in which some persons avoid ricketts only by the consumption of very large amounts of vitamin D. This effect of genetic variation presumably is small compared to the dietary differences found when the whole population is considered.

The preceding example will serve to illustrate another facet of this problem: The subject of investigation by geneticists is *variation* within the population rather than some absolute attribute. It may be of theoretical interest to speculate about types of people who do not exist, but the only scale of variation available experimentally is the species as it does exist. If the species is uniform for a particular gene, the traits governed by that gene will not show genetic variation. These same traits may show the effects of differing environments, but the variation then would be entirely environmental and there would be no way to demonstrate the presence of genetic control.

Another example of rather complex interaction of environmental and genetic variation is found in various learned skills. There is strong evidence that major differences in intelligence reflect genetic differences, although many genes appear to be involved. Most persons can be taught to read, certainly an acquired ability. Their skill, however, will depend in part on the amount and kind of instruction and practice. If two groups of children matched for intelligence are exposed to different methods of instruction, differences in reading skill may be largely environmental. On the other hand, if students of widely different intelligence are exposed to a uniform method of instruction, then differences in reading skill will be largely genetic. A few individuals do not learn to read, regardless of the effort expended on them, because they do not have adequate ability. Others of high ability may learn to read with a minimum of instruction.

From the preceding discussion, it should be apparent that the subject of investigation is always variation and that attempts to ascribe variation to genetic or environmental factors is pointless without adequate reference to the nature of the population under investigation, the nature of the variable being investigated, and the type of environment to which the population is exposed.

In spite of these limitations, the science of genetics has made great advances. Within the last dozen years, the structure of deoxyribonucleic acid has been established, the effects of mutation on protein structure were discovered, many of the details of the functions of nucleic acids in protein synthesis have been worked out, and the genetic code has been partially established. Human genetics has participated in this great advance. Studies of human hemoglobins have been important to our understanding of the nature of inherited protein variations. And much has been learned about the effects of inheritance on human processes, both in normal variations and pathological conditions.

The study of human genetics necessarily includes a consideration of many other organisms that have been used to elucidate genetic principles. The short generation times of flies, bacteria, and viruses permit observations that are impossible in human beings. Many types of observations can be made in man, however, provided the experimenter understands the special methods appropriate to his needs. Several of the chapters in this book deal with the special techniques for investigating human beings. While some of these techniques may appear complicated, their use frequently permits simple statements regarding the action of genes in individuals and in populations.

THE LITERATURE OF HUMAN GENETICS

Original reports of research in human genetics are published in a great variety of journals. Most of the standard medical journals have articles from time to time—and with increasing frequency—that are concerned with inherited disorders. In addition, the following journals primarily publish articles on human genetics:

Acta Genetica et Statistica Medica
Acta Geneticae Medicae et Gemellologiae
American Journal of Human Genetics
Annales de Génétique
Annals of Human Genetics (formerly *Annals of Eugenics*)
Cytogenetics
Humangenetik (formerly *Zeitschrift für menschliche Vererbungs- und Konstitutionslehre*
Japanese Journal of Human Genetics
Journal de Génétique Humaine
Journal of Medical Genetics

The following list of textbooks and monographs will prove useful to students and investigators:

BOYD, W. C. 1950. *Genetics and the Races of Man.* Boston: Little, Brown and Co., 453 pp.

BOYER, S. H., IV (ed.). 1963. *Papers on Human Genetics.* Englewood Cliffs, N. J.: Prentice-Hall, 305 pp.

BURDETTE, W. J. (ed.). 1962. *Methodology in Human Genetics.* San Francisco: Holden-Day, 463 pp.

DOBZHANSKY, T. 1962. *Mankind Evolving*. New Haven: Yale University Press, 381 pp.

GEDDA, L. *De Genetica Medica*. Rome: Istituto Gregorio Mendel, seven volumes, 1961 and later.

HARRIS, H. 1959. *Human Biochemical Genetics*. New York: Cambridge, 310 pp.

HSIA, D. Y.-Y. 1959. *Inborn Errors of Metabolism*. Chicago: Yearbook Publishers, 358 pp.

LI, C. C. 1955. *Population Genetics*. Chicago: University of Chicago Press, 366 pp.

————. 1961. *Human Genetics*. New York: McGraw-Hill, 218 pp.

MCKUSICK, V. A. 1960. *Heritable Disorders of Connective Tissue*, 2d ed. St. Louis: C. V. Mosby, 361 pp.

————. 1961. *Medical Genetics, 1958–1960*. St. Louis: C. V. Mosby, 534 pp.

NEEL, J. V., and SCHULL, W. J. 1954. *Human Heredity*. Chicago: University of Chicago Press, 361 pp.

PENROSE, L. S. 1959. *Outline of Human Genetics*. New York: Wiley, 146 pp.

————. (ed.). 1961. *Recent Advances in Human Genetics*. London: J. and A. Churchill, 194 pp.

RACE, R. R., and SANGER, R. 1962. *Blood Groups in Man*, 4th ed. Oxford: Blackwell, 456 pp.

ROBERTS, J. A. F. 1963. *An Introduction to Medical Genetics*, 3d ed. New York: Oxford, 283 pp.

SORSBY, A. (ed.). 1953. *Clinical Genetics*. London: Butterworth, 580 pp.

STANBURY, J. B., WYNGAARDEN, J. B., and FREDRICKSON, D. S. (eds.). 1960. *The Metabolic Basis of Inherited Disease*. New York: McGraw-Hill, 1477 pp.

STEINBERG, A. G., and BEARN, A. G. (eds.). 1961–1964. *Progress in Medical Genetics*, Vols. I–III. New York: Grune and Stratton.

STERN, C. 1960. *Principles of Human Genetics*, 2d ed. San Francisco: W. H. Freeman, 753 pp.

SUTTON, H. E. 1961. *Genes, Enzymes, and Inherited Diseases*. New York: Holt, Rinehart and Winston, 120 pp.

Chapter Two

MENDELIAN INHERITANCE

Throughout recorded history, the transmission of physical traits from parents to offspring has been recognized. The explanations for such family resemblances have been varied and need not be of concern here. Of more interest is a consideration of why investigations by competent scientists failed for so long to reveal the laws of heredity.

A major barrier to recognition of the laws of heredity was the assumption of a blending of hereditary traits, whether or not such assumptions were formally stated. The progeny of a cross between two different parental types frequently are a blend of parental characteristics, and it was thought that the inherited factors which determine these characteristics must blend together, losing their separate identities in the process. The progeny in turn would transmit to their offspring factors essentially different from those received from their own parents. This misconception had its origin in part in the attempts of experimenters to work with physical characteristics that have subsequently proved to be very complex in their inheritance, being influenced by many genes. Even today, when the basic laws of heredity are well understood and sophisticated statistical methods are available, we still are largely unable to analyze complex traits in a manner that yields information regarding the action of individual genes.

The Austrian monk Gregor Mendel, working in a monastery in Brünn, succeeded where his predecessors had failed. A major factor in Mendel's success was his judgment in selecting for study traits that occur as clearly alternate forms rather than on a continuous scale of differences. For his investigations he used the garden pea (*Pisum sativum*), in which it is possible to control pollination. Among the traits he observed were round versus wrinkled seeds, yellow versus green cotyledons, white versus brown seed coats, inflated versus constricted seed pods, green versus yellow pods, axial versus terminal flowers, and long versus short stems.

5

For each of these traits, a single plant can be classified as belonging to one or the other category.

In 1865, after eight years of investigation, Mendel presented his conclusions before the Science Research Society at Brünn. Publication of his studies occurred the following year in the proceedings of that Society, but their significance was not immediately recognized and they lay forgotten until 1900. In that year, Karl Erich Correns, Hugo De Vries, and Tschermak von Seysenegg, each working independently, arrived at conclusions similar to those of Mendel. They also discovered his paper and recognized its great importance. The year 1900 thus marks the beginning of genetics as a science.

In his use of simple traits, Mendel was able to avoid the erroneous assumption that the factors of heredity transmitted by parents to their offspring are blended in the offspring. Furthermore, he recognized that the transmission of traits is a statistical process that can be fully described only in terms of probability. As a result of his studies, he formulated some generalizations that have become the foundations of the science of genetics. These generalizations usually are expressed as the *law of genetic segregation* and the *law of independent assortment*.

Although Mendel continued his scientific studies after publication of his work on garden peas, he soon became so involved in administration of the monastery that there was little time for research. He died in 1884 without the recognition he so richly deserved.

MENDEL'S LAW OF GENETIC SEGREGATION

Mendel observed that if he crossed two true-breeding strains that were different for one of the traits under observation, the progeny (the F_1, or first filial generation) were all identical to each other. Furthermore, the F_1 generation was identical to, or very similar to, one of the parental stocks. Mendel allowed the F_1 generation to fertilize itself, producing an F_2 generation. In contrast to the F_1, the F_2 generation was composed of two types of plants. The majority (three fourths) resembled the F_1 and, hence, one of the original parental types; the remainder (one fourth) resembled the other parental stock (Fig. 2–1). Further breeding of members of the latter group among themselves produced only offspring of the second parental type.

The recovery of traits in the F_2 generation that were not expressed in the F_1 clearly indicated that the hereditary factors contributed by each parent to the F_1 cross maintain their individuality, even though they may not influence the appearance of the F_1 plant. Mendel designated the

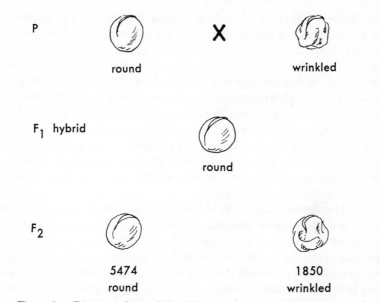

Figure 2-1. Diagram of one of Mendel's experiments with *Pisum sativum*, showing dominance of round seeds over wrinkled and recovery of wrinkled seeds in the F_2 generation.

expressed factor as the *dominant* form, the other factor the *recessive* form. In the F_1 generation, each individual receives both dominant and recessive factors from its parents, but only the dominant trait is expressed. In a mating of two F_1 plants, some of the offspring receive only recessive factors and hence express the recessive trait.

It will be useful at this point to introduce the concepts of *genotype* and *phenotype*. In 1911, W. Johannsen used the word *gene* to denote the unit factor of heredity. The genotype of an organism refers therefore to the kinds of genes possessed, regardless of whether or not they are expressed. The total complement of genes is called the *genome*. The phenotype refers to the observable individual. This may be largely genetically controlled for a given trait, or it may be the result of genetic and environmental variation acting together. Occasionally, it is possible to infer part of the genotype of an individual from his phenotype, but genotype cannot be observed directly. The alternate forms of a gene are designated *allelomorphs* or, more commonly, *alleles*. The position on a chromosome occupied by a particular series of homologous alleles is called the *locus* for those alleles.

As previously stated, those members of the F_2 generation that expressed a phenotype corresponding to the recessive parent produced only recessive offspring when bred among themselves. The members of the F_2 exhibiting a dominant phenotype proved to be of two types: If allowed to self-fertilize, one third of them produced only dominant offspring. The other two thirds behaved as the F_1 generation, producing offspring three fourths of which exhibited the dominant phenotype and one fourth the recessive phenotype. This indicated to Mendel that there were three types of offspring in the F_2 generation: one fourth with only recessive genes, one fourth with only dominant genes, and one half with both types. The seeds formed by the F_1 reflect a separation of the dominant and recessive genes into different gametes followed by chance recombination to form zygotes. The rules describing this separation of genes is known as the law of segregation.

The regular formation of dominant and recessive phenotypes in the F_2 and subsequent generations can be explained by assuming that each plant contains two alleles for each trait studied. If we represent the dominant form by A and the recessive by a, then a plant possessing the recessive phenotype would have an aa genotype. Plants with the dominant phenotype could be either AA or Aa. The original stocks used by Mendel were highly inbred and were therefore *homozygous* for most loci, either AA or aa. All plants in the F_1 generation would be *heterozygous* Aa, since they result from a cross of dominant $AA \times$ recessive aa. Each parent contributes equally to the offspring, whether it is the seed-bearing or pollinating parent.

The ratios in the F_2 can be explained by the assumption that each gene has an equal chance of appearing in a gamete, regardless of whether the gene is dominant or recessive. Thus an Aa plant would form equal numbers of A and a gametes (Fig. 2–2). Random assortment of A and a

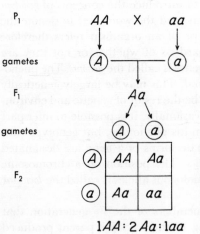

Figure 2–2. Diagram showing segregation of A and a in the gametes of the F_1 generation. All possible combinations of alleles occur in the F_2. The 2×2 chart in the F_2 generation is a convenient way of assuring that all possible combinations have been included and are in the correct proportions.

gametes into new individuals would result in genotypes in the ratio $1AA$: $2Aa:1aa$. The first two categories would be indistinguishable in phenotype, but two thirds would be of type Aa and therefore capable of segregating into A and a gametes. These predictions correspond exactly to Mendel's results.

Mendel knew nothing about chromosomes. He proposed that gametes have one of each pair of genetic determiners and that zygotes therefore have two, because this hypothesis was adequate to predict the experimental results. It was later recognized that the sets of homologous chromosomes in diploid cells would provide the physical basis for a double set of genes. At meiosis, each gamete receives only one of the sets of genes.

An important aspect of Mendelian theory is that the activity of a gene is independent of whether it was contributed to the zygote by sperm or ovum. Mendel found that for all the traits he studied, results obtained with the pollen-bearing plant as a parental type did not differ from those obtained with the seed-bearing plant. When a new zygote is formed, the genes appear to act without any "memory" of previous cytoplasmic environments.

An important step in the analysis of an inherited trait is the formulation of a hypothesis of the mode of heredity. If a trait is designated dominant or recessive, a definite prediction is made regarding the number and relationship of individuals with the trait. The validity of the hypothesis can be verified by an examination of the families of affected individuals. Should the results prove to be different from those predicted, then the hypothesis can be modified or discarded.

The 3:1 Ratio

With many plants and animals, it is a relatively simple matter to establish genetic ratios through controlled matings. An example may be taken from Mendel's studies of peas. He crossed two parental (P_1) varieties, one having round seeds and the other wrinkled seeds. The F_1 hybrid seeds were all round, indicating round to be dominant over wrinkled. When the plants that developed from the F_1 seeds were allowed to self-fertilize, both round and wrinkled seeds were recovered. Of the 7324 F_2 seeds observed, 5474 were round and 1850 were wrinkled, a ratio of 2.96 to 1. A diagrammatic representation of the study is given in Figure 2–1. The observed 2.96 to 1 satisfies the 3:1 prediction, and it is not necessary to postulate additional factors operating in the inheritance of this trait.

The 3:1 ratio among offspring of two heterozygous parents is perhaps the most important means of recognizing simple recessive inheritance. A trait may be suspected of being recessive if it appears among the offspring of parents neither of whom has the trait. But it can be accepted as a simple recessive only if it occurs in one fourth of the progeny of all appropriate matings. If a fraction other than one fourth is affected, then consideration must be given to environmental influences as well as more complex genetic relationships. Differential survival of gametes or zygotes also may alter the ratio and cause a deviation from one quarter.

The Backcross

A 3:1 ratio characterizes the dominant allele as well as the recessive in a mating of two heterozygotes. A more efficient means of demonstrating simple dominant inheritance is the *backcross*, or *test cross*, to the recessive parent. In experimental organisms, this consists in mating the F_1 generation to the parental stock that exhibits the apparently recessive phenotype. For example, in a cross between pigmented and albino mice, the F_1 is pigmented. If the F_1 is then crossed with the albino parental stock, and if pigment formation is a simple Mendelian trait with pigmentation dominant to albinism, both pigmented and albino offspring should occur in a ratio of 1:1. This can be symbolized as follows:

P_1	pigmented (CC) × albino (cc)
F_1	pigmented (Cc)
backcross	pigmented (Cc) × albino (cc)
progeny	½ pigmented (Cc) + ½ albino (cc)

MENDEL'S LAW OF INDEPENDENT ASSORTMENT

In the previous discussion, only one trait at a time was considered. When Mendel considered two or more traits together, he found that they were transmitted independently of each other. The inheritance of round instead of wrinkled seeds in the F_2 generation did not influence the probability of inheriting long versus short stems.

Consider a mating of parental types that breed true for two traits: This may be written $AABB \times A'A'B'B'$, without specifying which alleles are dominant or recessive. Such a mating of two loci is called a *dihybrid cross*. The F_1 generation would consist of $AA'BB'$ individuals. The gametes of the F_1 will consist half of A and half of A'; the same is true with respect to the B and B' alleles. If the two sets of alleles are independent, then half of the A gametes should be B and half should be B'. The same is true of the A' gametes. Thus, there would be four types of gametes in equal numbers: AB, $A'B$, AB', and $A'B'$.

Formation of the F_2 zygotes (Fig. 2–3) would result in nine genetically different types in the ratio $1AABB:2AABB':2AA'BB:4AA'BB':$
$1AAB'B':2AA'B'B':1A'A'BB:2A'A'BB':1A'A'B'B'$. All nine genotypes
could be recognized only in the event both AA' and BB' are distinguishable from their respective homozygotes. If alternate forms are clearly

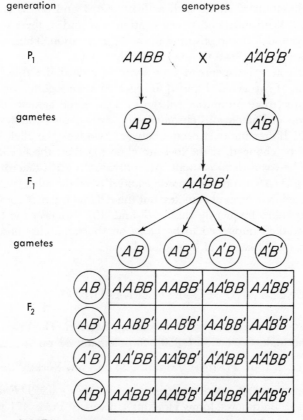

Figure 2–3. Diagram showing independent assortment of alleles at two loci
in a dihybrid cross. Each of the F_1 gametes comprises ¼ of the total; therefore, each
cell in the F_2 chart represents ¹⁄₁₆ of the total F_2 generation.

dominant or recessive, as in the traits studied by Mendel, only four types
of offspring can be recognized, in the ratio 9:3:3:1. For example, in a cross
of round-seeded, yellow cotyledon $\times$ wrinkled, green cotyledon, 556
seeds were obtained in the F_2. These consisted of 315 round and yellow,
101 wrinkled and yellow, 108 round and green, and 32 wrinkled and
green. Further breeding indicated, as predicted above, that nine geno-

types were present among these seeds. Thus, the assortment of genes into gametes appears to be entirely a random process.

Two loci may segregate independently and yet interact in the production of a single trait. For example, albinism in some plants may result from homozygosity for a recessive allele at any of several loci. In Figure 2–3, suppose that either $A'A'$ or $B'B'$ produces albinism and that any combination of alleles with at least one A and one B is normally pigmented. With independent segregation of A and B, there would be 9 pigmented and 7 albino offspring in the F_2 generation. Thus, more complex situations may lead to ratios other than 3:1.

Although independent assortment is indeed the rule, there are exceptions. If two genes A and B are located close together on the same chromosome, they ordinarily will go into the same gamete. Exchanges of segments of homologous chromosomes (*crossing over*) commonly occur at meiosis. If crossing over occurs between two loci, the allele combinations will be changed. If the loci are close together, the likelihood of a crossover between them is small. An individual who is heterozygous for two such loci (AB on one chromosome and $A'B'$ on the other) will produce the expected four types of gametes, but the AB and the $A'B'$ combinations will occur more frequently than AB' and $A'B$. None of the traits that Mendel studied happened to be *linked* on the same chromosome. The significance of linkage will be explored later.

REFERENCES AND SUGGESTED READING

The Birth of Genetics. English Translation. Mendel, De Vries, Correns, Tschermak. *Genetics* 35 (1950): Supplement, 47 pp.

GARDNER, E. J. 1964. *Principles of Genetics*, 2d ed. New York: Wiley, 386 pp.

GLASS, B., TEMKIN, O., and STRAUS, W. L., JR. (eds.). 1959. *Forerunners of Darwin.* Baltimore: Johns Hopkins University Press, 471 pp.

LEVINE, R. P. 1962. *Genetics.* New York: Holt, Rinehart and Winston, 180 pp.

MENDEL, G. 1865. Experiments in plant hybridization. [Translation of the original which appeared in *Verhandlungen naturforschender Verein in Brünn*, Abhand. 4, 1865.] Reprinted in Peters, J. A. (ed.), 1959, *Classic Papers in Genetics* (Englewood Cliffs, N. J.: Prentice-Hall, pp. 2–26) and in Sinnott, E. W., Dunn, L. C., and Dobzhansky, T., 1958, pp. 419–443.

SINNOTT, E. W., DUNN, L. C., and DOBZHANSKY, T. 1958. *Principles of Genetics,* 5th ed. New York: McGraw-Hill, 459 pp.

PROBLEMS

1. Define:

dominant	phenotype	backcross
recessive	genome	hybrid
segregation	homozygous	dihybrid cross
recombination	allele	heterozygous
genotype	genetic ratio	

2. Albinism is inherited as a recessive trait. If two normally pigmented parents produce an albino offspring, what ratio of albino to normal would be expected among subsequent offspring?

3. If a normal offspring of an albino marries an albino, what would be the expected ratio of normal and albino phenotypes among their offspring?

4. Deafness frequently is inherited in man, affected persons being homozygous for a recessive gene. Cases have been reported in which two deaf persons have married and produced only normal offspring. How can this be explained? If two such normal offspring marry, what are the expected phenotypes and genotypes among their offspring?

5. The ability to taste phenylthiocarbamide (PTC) is a dominant trait in man. In the Rh blood group system, Rh + is dominant to Rh −. Two parents, both of whom are Rh + and tasters, have an Rh − nontaster child. What are the genotypes of the persons in this family? What are the expected genotypes in subsequent children? In what ratio would these genotypes be expected?

Chapter Three

THE CHROMOSOMAL BASIS OF INHERITANCE

The cytologists of the late nineteenth century described in detail the events associated with cell division in many species of plants and animals. Among their observations was the elaborate process of nuclear division, a process that assures that each daughter cell receives an exact portion of the parental nuclear contents. When a cell is not dividing, the nucleus usually appears as a relatively homogeneous body. As cell division begins, the nucleus condenses into a series of elongated bodies, designated *chromosomes* because of their affinity for certain dyes. Both the number and types of chromosomes are characteristic of a given species.

The precision with which chromosomes are distributed in cell division is analogous to the manner in which inherited traits are transmitted, a fact that led W. S. Sutton and T. Boveri in 1902 to suggest that chromosomes are the physical structures which act as messengers of heredity. This hypothesis has been extensively verified.

The chromosomes of higher organisms, including man, occur in pairs. That is, the genetic information found in any one chromosome is duplicated in another chromosome ordinarily identical in size and shape. There appears to be considerable advantage in having genetic information present in duplicate, although in many cases a single copy is adequate for the direction of specific cellular activities.

A complement of unpaired chromosomes is called a *haploid* complement. In man, in whom there are 46 chromosomes, the haploid complement is 23 chromosomes. The double set of chromosomes is a *diploid* complement. Occasionally, there are aberrant *triploid* cells containing three chromosomes of each type. Higher degrees of *polyploidy* are observed in special situations.

The chromosomes of nondividing cells are not usually individually visible. It is thought that they are uncoiled into very long, narrow structures whose diameters are below the limits of resolution of ordinary light microscopes. This period during which no division occurs is designated *interphase*. It is probably during interphase that chromosomes carry out most of their chemical activities. It is also during interphase that the chemical replication of chromosomes occurs.

Although minor variations occur, nuclear division in most higher plants and animals is similar. Most organisms exhibit two kinds of cell division. *Mitosis* occurs in somatic cells, yielding two daughter cells identical in their chromosomal complement. *Meiosis* occurs in germinal cells, producing *gametes* (eggs and sperm) with half the full complement of chromosomes. Furthermore, each gamete has a unique assortment of parental chromosomes. A consideration of these two processes will provide a basis for understanding transmission of inherited variation.

MITOSIS

The earliest stage of cell division that is recognized is designated *prophase*. As shown in Figure 3–1, this is characterized by the appearance first of the chromosomes as long, thin threads. These gradually contract, becoming shorter and thicker and more readily visible. As prophase continues, each chromosome appears double along its longitudinal axis, and each half is termed a *chromatid*. Initially, the chromatids are coiled around each other, but as contraction of the chromatids continues, they separate, remaining attached to each other only at the *centromere* (also called *kinetochore*), which has not yet divided. The centromere is a region present in every chromosome, apparently free of genes but functioning in the distribution of chromosomes into daughter cells.

At the time of chromatid separation, other structures also undergo changes. The nuclear membrane disappears. The *centrioles,* two small bodies lying outside the nucleus, migrate to opposite poles of the cell and serve as centers for the formation of protein fibers. These fibers, issuing radially from the centrioles, join together in the center of the cell, giving rise to a continuous structure, the *spindle*. As the spindle is formed, the chromosomes align between the two poles of the spindle in a plane that is perpendicular to the spindle axis. This part of the cycle is designated *metaphase*. At this time, the chromosomes are maximally contracted and, therefore, most readily observable microscopically. The plane in which the chromosomes lie is known as the *equatorial plane* or *metaphase plate*.

At the conclusion of metaphase, the centromeres divide, completing the formation of two new chromosomes from each original chromosome. It also becomes apparent at this time that the centromeres are attached to spindle fibers. These fibers contract, pulling the chromosomes

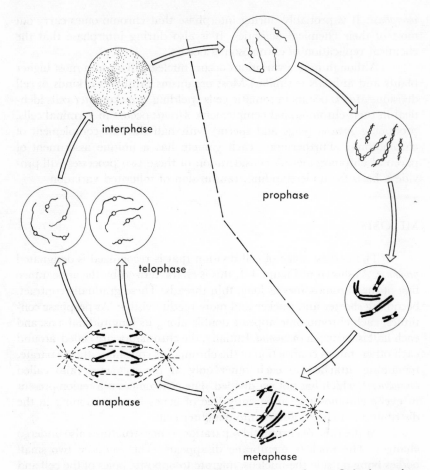

Figure 3–1. Mitosis. Two pairs of chromosomes are shown. Only the nucleus is represented. Following anaphase, new nuclear membranes are formed and the cell cleaves to give two daughter cells identical in genetic content to the parent cell.

toward the two poles of the spindle. The process is designated *anaphase*. During anaphase, each pair of newly formed chromosomes separates, the two migrating to opposite poles. The result is two identical and complete chromosome complements.

Following separation of the two sets of chromosomes, a new nuclear membrane is formed around each and the chromosomes become more extended, gradually losing their individual identity and forming a new interphase nucleus. This period of reorganization is known as *telophase*. With the formation of two nuclei, the cytoplasm divides, forming two complete cells.

MEIOSIS

Most organisms, both plant and animal, are characterizd by alternating cycles of haploid and diploid existence. In some, such as ferns, both haploid and diploid phases persist for appreciable periods of growth. In other organisms, one of the phases is transient. For example, in the mold *Neurospora,* diploid nuclei are present during one cycle of cell division only. In mammals, it is the haploid phase that persists only for one cell cycle. These haploid cells, the gametes, are incapable of mitotic division and must either fuse to form a diploid zygote or perish.

Meiosis is the process of cell division that yields haploid daughter cells from a diploid parent cell. In many ways, it is similar to mitosis, but there are very important differences. An outline of meiosis is given in Figure 3–2.

During late prophase, homologous chromosomes pair lengthwise, so that any given position on one chromosome is matched by the corresponding position on the homologous chromosome. This phenomenon is known as *synapsis*. Following synapsis, the homologous centromeres pull apart, a process designated *diakinesis*. At this stage the presence of one or more bridges joining together homologous points on the chromatids can be observed. A bridge, or *chiasma* (pl. *chiasmata*), may form between any two nonsister chromatids, and several chiasmata may be observed in any one *tetrad* involving any combination of pairs. They are the points at which *crossing over* occurs. In this process, homologous segments of chromosomes are exchanged among the four chromatids.

Diakinesis is followed by metaphase of the first of two divisions of meiosis. In metaphase I, the still paired chromosomes align in the equatorial plane. There is still a diploid number of centromeres and chromosomes, although each chromosome consists of two distinct chromatids. Metaphase I is followed by anaphase I, during which homologous chromosomes migrate to opposite poles of the spindle, resulting in two daughter cells, each with half the original number of chromosomes. The first meiotic division is sometimes referred to as a *reduction* division, each daughter cell having a reduced number of chromosomes as well as a reduced amount of genetic variation.

Following anaphase I, the chromosomes do not disappear as in mitosis. Rather, they immediately undergo a second meiotic division. In each of the daughter cells of the first division a new spindle is formed, and the chromosomes align in the new equatorial planes, forming metaphase II. The centromeres divide, and the newly formed pairs of homologous chromosomes separate, migrating to opposite poles during anaphase II.

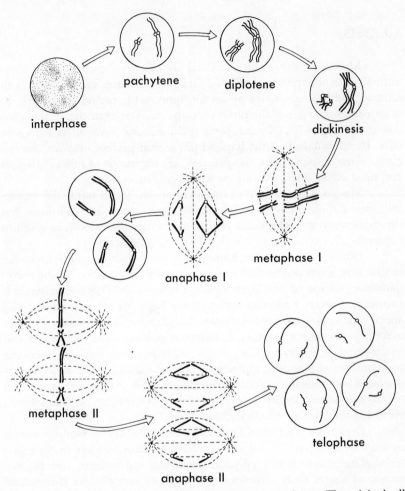

Figure 3–2. Meiosis. Two pairs of chromosomes are shown. The original cell gives rise to four haploid cells (gametes).

Since the second meiotic division produces cells having the same number of chromosomes (haploid) as the cell that is the product of the first division, this second division is sometimes referred to as an *equational* division.

The over-all result of meiosis is the formation from a diploid cell of four haploid cells. These meiotic products are then transformed into the functional gametes—spermatozoa and ova.

Crossing Over

One of the regular features of meiosis is crossing over. As stated earlier, this involves the exchange of chromatid segments preceding meta-

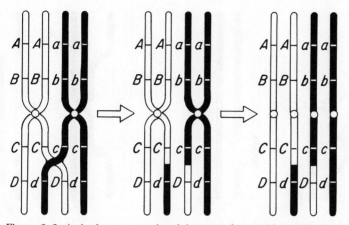

Figure 3–3. A single crossover involving two chromatid strands showing re-assortment to give four different combinations in the haploid products.

phase I. If a homologous pair of chromosomes is different for a series of genes, as in Figure 3–3, then the effect of crossing over is to produce four different chromosome combinations. Figure 3–3 illustrates the results of a single crossover involving two of the four chromatids of a chromosome pair. The existence of a crossover in one position does not prevent other crossovers occurring elsewhere among the chromatids, and multiple crossovers commonly are observed. Figure 3–4 shows some of the types that are possible.

Crossing over plays an important role in reassorting genes into new combinations. Were it not for crossing over, the combination of genes on a particular chromosome would remain together indefinitely except for an occasional mutation. Since most mutations are deleterious, chromosomes gradually would accumulate mutations, eventually becoming incompatible with normal life. Crossing over permits a continual reshuffling of genes, so that new and sometimes advantageous combinations can occur. The genetic consequences of crossing over are considered in more detail in Chapter 15.

FORMATION OF GAMETES AND ZYGOTES

Spermatogenesis

In most male animals, meiosis occurs in the testes. In vertebrates, testicular tissue consists of two types—seminiferous tubules and interstitial tissue. These are illustrated in Figure 3–5. Interstitial tissue functions in the synthesis of male hormones, which influence many activities of the body. Sperm are produced in the seminiferous tubules.

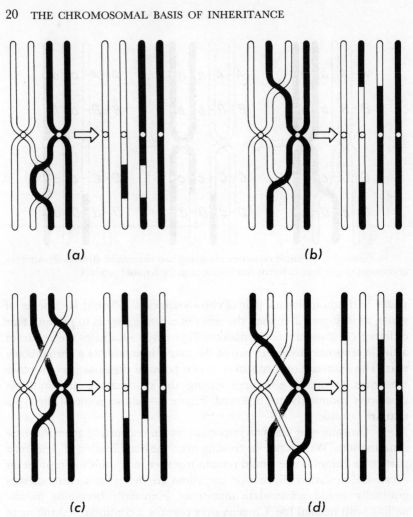

Figure 3–4. Some varieties of crossing over that have been observed. Other combinations, including triple or higher crossovers, may also occur. (*a*) Two-strand double crossover, both on same side of centromere. (*b*) Two-strand double crossover, involving different arms of chromosome. (*c*) Three-strand double crossover. (*d*) Four-strand double crossover.

The cells lining the tubules are known as *spermatogonia* and are the stem cells of the germinal tissue. They replicate mitotically, maintaining a supply of cells for the production of gametes. Half of the spermatogonia in each cell cycle undergo meiosis. Once on the pathway of meiosis, they are known as *spermatocytes*. At the completion of meiosis, the haploid products resemble other cells in possessing a nucleus surrounded by appreciable quantities of cytoplasm. At this stage they are known as *spermatids*. Transformation into *spermatozoa* involves loss of virtually

seminiferous tubule   spermatogonia

interstitial cells   spermatozoa

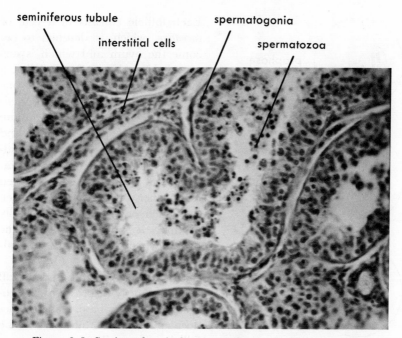

Figure 3–5. Section of testicular tissue, showing seminiferous tubules and interstitial tissue. (Furnished by Dr. C. de Chenar.)

all of the cytoplasm and formation of a long whiplike structure, the tail, which confers motility on the mature sperm.

The near absence of cytoplasm in a mature sperm has implications for the control of inherited variation. The nuclear contribution to an offspring is essentially equal for each parent. The cytoplasmic contribution from the father is very much less than that from the mother. For those traits which show equal contributions of the father and mother to the variation, it may be assumed that the control is transmitted by the nucleus.

Spermatogenesis is a quantitatively important process. An average ejaculate may contain 200,000,000 sperm. The rate of production is therefore very high. As the sperm mature, they pass from the seminiferous tubules into the epididymis, where they are stored until released into the semen by ejaculation.

Oögenesis

Gametogenesis in females occurs in the ovaries. During embryonic development of a human female, several hundred minute structures known as *ovarian follicles* or *Graafian follicles* are formed in the ovaries.

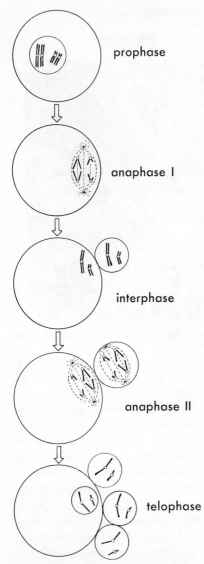

prophase

anaphase I

interphase

anaphase II

telophase

Figure 3–6. Oögenesis, showing unequal division of cytoplasm to give one ovum and three polar bodies.

Each follicle consists of a cell, or *oögonium,* which is destined to become the ovum and which is surrounded by a layer of cells. When a female reaches sexual maturity, one of these follicles matures approximately every month. The oögonium enlarges into a primary *oöcyte,* and the surrounding cells form a fluid-filled vesicle. The oöcyte is embedded in a corona of cells attached to the inner wall of the follicle. When the much enlarged follicle is fully mature, it bursts, releasing the ovum, which then enters the Fallopian tubes.

Meiosis is initiated in all oögonia shortly before birth. It proceeds to late prophase, then becomes dormant until maturation of the follicles. Thus, all oöcytes remain in prophase for at least twelve years, and many are dormant much longer, since normally only one follicle matures per month. With maturation, each oöcyte completes the first meiotic division to become a secondary oöcyte. These secondary oöcytes plus the corona of cells constitute the ova released from the follicle. The second meiotic division occurs immediately after fertilization. Without fertilization, it may not occur at all.

The nuclear aspects of meiosis are similar in males and females. There is a marked difference in the cytoplasmic aspects however, as indicated in Figure 3–6. In the female, following anaphase I, virtually all the cytoplasm stays with one of the two daughter nuclei, giving rise to one very large and one very small cell, the latter being designated a *polar body.* Both cells then undergo the second meiotic division, and again the cytoplasm of the large cell remains intact. The end products of oögenesis consist of a haploid cell with virtually all the original cytoplasm (the ovum) and three polar bodies, also haploid but with very little cytoplasm. Apparently, the polar bodies are by-products, not contributing further to oögenesis. The cytoplasm appears to function as a source of nourishment for the zygote prior to attachment to the uterine wall, somewhat analogous to the yolk of a hen's egg.

Fertilization

If sperm are present during the few days that an ovum is in the Fallopian tube, then one of the sperm may fuse with the ovum to form a zygote, a process called fertilization or *syngamy*. Penetration of the sperm through the corona of cells surrounding the ovum is accomplished in part by the enzyme hyaluronidase that is present in the sperm. When the head of the sperm reaches the cell wall of the ovum, fusion occurs. The ovum is then impenetrable to other sperm.

The nucleus of the sperm enters the cytoplasm of the ovum, and the two haploid nuclei are drawn to each other, fusing into a single diploid nucleus. The zygote then undergoes a series of mitotic divisions, leading to development of a fetus.

Two cases have been reported in which a person was a mosaic of cells derived from two different sperm. In one case, about half the cells had two X chromosomes and the remainder had one X and a Y. A number of other genetic markers also differed in the two cells, giving results that could only be explained by two separate haploid contributions from the patient's father. The patient was a hermaphrodite, having both an ovary and an ovotestis. The authors interpreted this patient as resulting from mitosis of a haploid egg followed by fertilization of each daughter cell by separate sperm. Other possibilities were not ruled out.

In the second case, only a small portion of cells were XX, the majority being XY. The patient was a male of normal phenotype. It was possible to show by blood group antigens that both father and mother each contributed two haploid complements to their offspring. These authors suggested that one sperm fertilized the regular egg nucleus, and the other fertilized a polar body. The resulting person is, in a sense, the product of two zygotes joined together.

The extreme rarity of these exceptional cases is indicative of the strict regularity of fertilization.

Parthenogenesis

The question sometimes arises as to whether an unfertilized ovum can develop into a functional organism. In some cases, this is known to happen. For example, if frog eggs are stimulated by various mechanical or chemical means, development is initiated and live tadpoles may hatch. Cases also have been recorded in which unfertilized turkey eggs have developed, yielding viable offspring. In both examples, the resulting individuals are haploid. In various species of Hymenoptera, males normally are haploid and are produced by development of unfertilized eggs, whereas fertilized eggs give rise to females.

The development of an unfertilized egg, called *parthenogenesis,* has been verified only in a very few species. Conceivably, individuals that develop parthenogenetically could be either haploid, as in the above examples, or diploid. In the latter case, the originally haploid chromosome complement of the egg might duplicate without cell division, producing a cell homozygous for all loci. Whatever the mechanisms visualized, all lead to one conclusion: Since all of the genetic material arises from the mother, it would be impossible for the offspring to possess genes not present in the mother. Thus, if the offspring has red cell antigens not present in the mother, this would be sufficient evidence that genetic material has been introduced from an individual other than the mother. In mammals, in which maleness depends on the presence of a Y chromosome, only females could arise by parthenogenesis, since ova do not contain a Y chromosome.

CYTOPLASMIC INHERITANCE

In addition to chromosomes, various other structures are transmitted through the egg and sperm to offspring. This is particularly true of the egg, which is a large cell containing a large amount of cytoplasm with mitochondria, ribosomes, Golgi apparatus, and other organelles. Is it possible that the characteristics of some of these are transmitted independent of nuclear control?

The usual procedure for testing for non-Mendelian (extranuclear, maternal, or cytoplasmic) inheritance is to compare the progeny from reciprocal crosses of two different strains. A prediction of chromosomal inheritance is that the offspring phenotype is independent of which parent serves as the maternal or paternal source of genes. Thus offspring from the cross $\male$ A × $\female$ B should be the same as offspring from $\male$ B × $\female$ A.

The exceptions to this prediction are very rare. Maternal inheritance was first demonstrated in certain crosses of plants where the plant size is dependent on the strain serving as female parent. Additional examples are known in other organisms. In *Neurospora,* some mitochondrial characteristics are transmitted by the maternal cytoplasm. *Chlamydomonas,* a genus of green algae, has also been shown to exhibit cytoplasmic inheritance.

The importance of cytoplasmic inheritance for man has not been fully ascertained. An important feature of cytoplasmic inheritance is that all offspring in a sibship resemble the mother. Thus, if segregation occurs, cytoplasmic inheritance can be ruled out. On the basis of this rule, it seems likely that little if any of the known human variation can be attributed to inheritance via cytoplasm.

REFERENCES AND SUGGESTED READINGS

BEATTY, R. A. 1957. *Parthenogenesis and Polyploidy in Mammalian Development.* New York: Cambridge, 132 pp.

GARTLER, S. M., WAXMAN, S. H., and GIBLETT, E. R. 1962. An XX/XY human hermaphrodite resulting from double fertilization. *Proc. Natl. Acad. Sci.* (U.S.) 48: 332–335.

OHNO, S., KLINGER, H. P., and ATKIN, N. G. 1962. Human oögenesis. *Cytogenetics* 1: 42–51.

SWANSON, C. P. 1957. *Cytology and Cytogenetics.* Englewood Cliffs, N. J.: Prentice-Hall, 596 pp.

WHITE, M. J. D. 1961. *The Chromosomes.* London: Methuen, 188 pp.

ZUELZER, W. W., BEATTIE, K. M., and REISMAN, L. E. 1964. Generalized unbalanced mosaicism attributable to dispermy and probable fertilization of a polar body. *Am. J. Human Genet.* 16: 38–51.

PROBLEMS

1. Define:

mitosis	gamete	synapsis
meiosis	zygote	chiasma
interphase	chromatid	crossing over
prophase	chromosome	polar body
metaphase	centromere	syngamy
anaphase	centriole	parthenogenesis
telophase	haploid	diploid
spermatogonium	spermatid	oöcyte
spermatocyte	oögonium	ovarian follicle

2. A diploid organism is heterozygous at three loci on the same chromosome (*ABC/abc*). With respect to these loci, what kinds of gametes could be formed by this organism? Indicate the number of crossovers necessary to produce each gamete. When does crossing over occur?

Chapter Four

THE NORMAL HUMAN CHROMOSOME COMPLEMENT

For many years it has been recognized that the numbers and kinds of chromosomes are highly characteristic for a given species. In some organisms (of which Drosophila is the outstanding example), it has been possible to map chromosomes both genetically by breeding experiments and cytologically by microscopic observation of chromosomes so that identification of minute structural deviations is possible. For most organisms—including man—direct examination of chromosomes has been a technically difficult procedure that for a long time gave rather unsatisfactory results.

One difficulty to be conquered was the procurement of satisfactory preparations of dividing cells at metaphase, for, in most organisms, chromosomes can be examined readily only during this limited part of the growth cycle. During interphase, chromosomes are not visible. In most tissues, only a very small portion of cells are in metaphase at any one time. The traditional solution to this problem was to examine testicular tissue, since the spermatogonia of mature males show a very high rate of proliferation. Such material is not readily available, however.

A second difficulty was that, even in the best preparations of metaphase chromosomes, the large number of chromosomes of man and many other species made accurate observation almost impossible. The clumping and overlapping of chromosomes always lent uncertainty to the results.

In spite of such technical difficulties, the estimates of several investigators came close to the correct number of chromosomes for man. The best preparations seemed to indicate the number 48, and for many years this was accepted. The chromosomal constitution (*karotype*) of human females was thought to be 46 + XX and that of males 46 + XY, the 46 representing 23 homologous pairs. The X and Y chromosomes are called *sex chromosomes;* the remainder are *autosomes*.

In the 1950s, several important technical advances were made that allowed the question of chromosome numbers and morphology to be reopened. The first of these was the development of techniques for culturing tissue *in vitro*. Although a few strains of cancer cells had been grown *in vitro* for some years, it was only after a systematic investigation of the fastidious nutritional requirements of mammalian cells that it became possible to culture a variety of normal tissues. At the present time, techniques for tissue culture have been so developed that it is possible to carry a portion of the white cells of blood through several divisions. This is an important advance, considering the relative ease of obtaining blood cells as compared to any other type of tissue. The rate of cell growth and division is much higher in cultured cells than in most tissues of a normal animal, thus providing many more opportunities for formation of metaphase figures.

A second technical development was the application to tissue cultures of the plant alkaloid colchicine or a derivative. For over 2000 years, this interesting compound has been the most effective treatment for gout. Although its action in gout is unknown, it does have the property of arresting cell division at the metaphase stage. Thus, if colchicine is present in a cell culture, division will proceed normally until formation of a metaphase plate. The arrested metaphase figures are sufficiently stable so that it is possible to accumulate many more of them than would exist at any one time without colchicine. This greatly increases the likelihood of finding cells suitable for examination.

A third development was the use of hypotonic treatment of cells prior to fixing on a slide. This treatment has the effect of spreading the chromosomes out over a much larger area, reducing the amount of clumping and overlapping. Treatment consists of suspending the cells briefly in a salt solution of concentration lower than that of the intracellular fluid. Water moves into the cell, causing expansion and separation of various structures, including chromosomes. These structures may then be examined with much greater reliability.

Adapting these techniques to cultured fibroblasts of human embryonic lung tissue, Tjio and Levan in 1956 found that earlier reports had erred slightly in reporting the number of chromosomes of man; they found only 46 rather than 48. The karyotype of females is 22 + XX; that of males is 22 + XY. These unexpected findings were quickly confirmed by other investigators. It was thought for a while that some normal persons might have 47 or 48 chromosomes. Additional studies, however, have consistently failed to yield a normal chromosome complement other than 46.

The total number of chromosomes is an inadequate characterization of karyotype and may hide abnormalities in chromosome structure. If a person is to be normal, the 46 chromosomes must be the correct 46. With

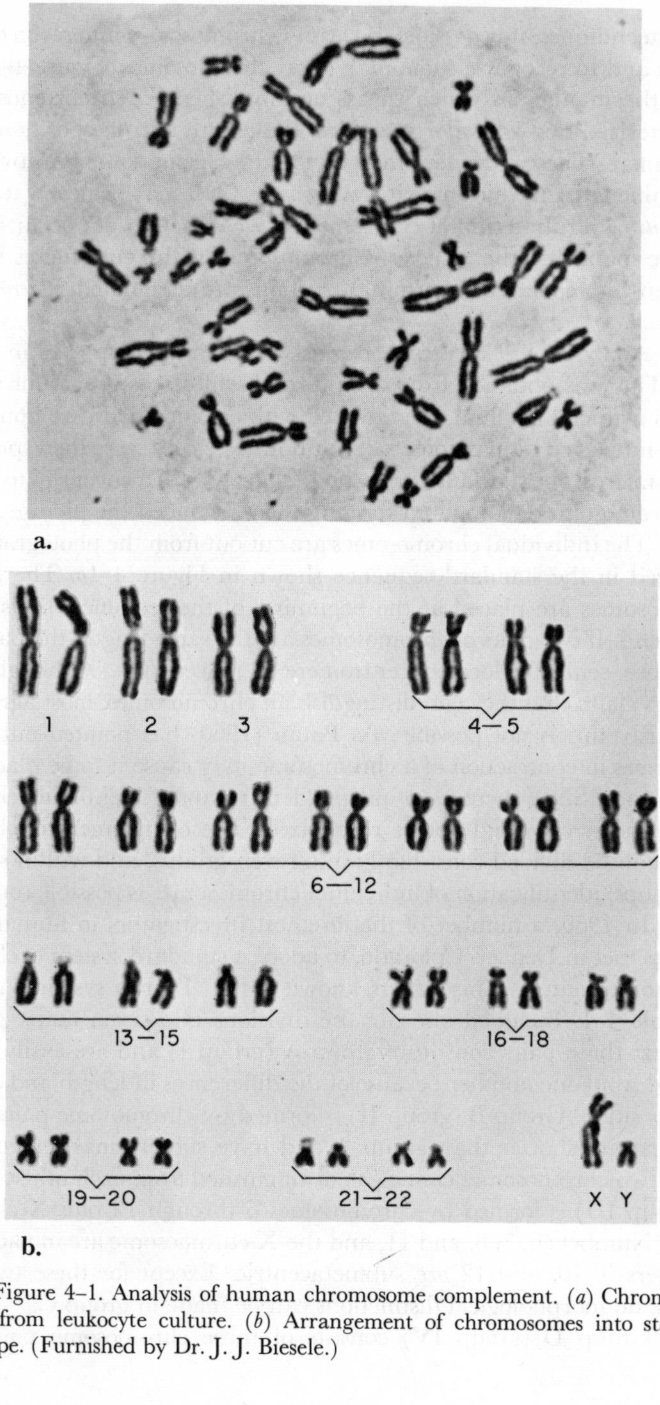

Figure 4–1. Analysis of human chromosome complement. (*a*) Chromosome spread from leukocyte culture. (*b*) Arrangement of chromosomes into standard karyotype. (Furnished by Dr. J. J. Biesele.)

newer techniques, it is possible to classify chromosomes into seven distinct groups and to recognize some individual chromosomes. Figure 4–1 illustrates the manner in which this is accomplished. Each chromosome is characterized by two major variables: the length and the position of the centromere. The centromere may divide the chromosome into two arms of equal length, in which case it is *metacentric*. Or it may be nearly terminal (*acrocentric*). Truly terminal centromeres (*telocentric*) do not occur in man but are found in other species. Chromosomes with centromeres located between the median and terminal positions are designated *subterminal* or *submedian*.

Analysis of a karyotype begins with a photograph, as in Figure 4–1*a*. This was obtained from a culture of white cells grown for several days in artificial medium, then treated with colchicine for two hours, and finally immersed in hypotonic salt solution. The cells were then spread on a glass microscope slide and "squashed" slightly with a cover slip to spread the chromosomes. Fixing and staining then produced the picture shown.

The individual chromosomes are cut out from the photograph and arranged in the standard sequence shown in Figure 4–1*b*. The longest chromosomes are placed at the beginning of the sequence, the shortest at the end. If two pairs of chromosomes are the same length, the pair with the more centrally located centromere is placed first. Although some workers claim that they can distinguish all chromosomes, most agree that ordinarily this is not possible. As Patau (1960) has pointed out, slight differences in contraction of a chromosome may cause it to be placed out of sequence. Since there is no independent means of identifying chromosomes, the error would not be recognized. The complement of chromosomes can be divided consistently into seven groups, and within some of the groups, identification of individual chromosomes is possible routinely.

In 1960, a number of the foremost investigators in human cytogenetics met in Denver, Colorado, to adopt a standard system of chromosome nomenclature. This system, known as the "Denver system," is given in Table 4–1. Included also are the divisions into seven major groups. The first three pairs constitute group A (group I) and are easily distinguished from one another because of the differences in length and centromere position. Group B (group II) is formed by chromosome pairs 4 and 5, which are shorter than group A and have subterminal centromeres. These two chromosomes cannot be distinguished from each other. Group C (group III) is formed by chromosomes 6 through 12 plus X chromosomes. Numbers 6, 7, 8, and 11, and the X chromosome are metacentric. Numbers 9, 10, and 12 are submetacentric. Except for these two subgroups, no morphological distinctions can be made in group C.

Group D (group IV) consists of three chromosome pairs that

TABLE 4–1

Nomenclature of Human Mitotic Chromosomes, Based on the System Devised by a Number of Cytologists Meeting at Denver in 1960. Values Are Averages of Those Published (Böök, *et al.*, 1960)

GROUP	CHROMOSOME NUMBER	RELATIVE LENGTH[a]	RATIO LONG ARM: SHORT ARM	RATIO SHORT ARM: TOTAL CHROMOSOME
A (I)	1	0.086	1.1	0.48
	2	0.081	1.6	0.39
	3	0.068	1.2	0.46
B (II)	4	0.062	2.7	0.27
	5	0.058	2.7	0.28
C (III)	X	0.055	2.0	0.36
	6	0.055	1.7	0.37
	7	0.050	1.7	0.37
	8	0.047	1.7	0.33
	9	0.046	2.0	0.36
	10	0.045	2.3	0.31
	11	0.044	2.1	0.35
	12	0.042	2.4	0.29
D (IV)	13	0.034	6.5	0.14
	14	0.034	6.1	0.15
	15	0.032	7.6	0.15
E (V)	16	0.030	1.5	0.38
	17	0.030	2.4	0.31
	18	0.026	3.2	0.25
F (VI)	19	0.024	1.4	0.41
	20	0.022	1.3	0.43
G (VII)	21	0.017	3.4	0.25
	22	0.016	3.4	0.25
	Y	0.018	2.9–∞	0–0.26

[a] Relative length = length of chromosome/length of haploid complement, including X.

cannot be distinguished. They are the same length, and all are acrocentric. Furthermore, each has a small appendage, called a *satellite*, attached to the terminal end of the short arm. These satellites are not always visible, but this seems to reflect technical difficulties rather than absence of the satellites.

Group E (group V) is formed by chromosomes 16, 17, and 18. In good preparations, number 16 usually can be recognized; numbers 17 and 18 usually cannot be distinguished. Group F (group VI) consists of numbers 19 and 20, which are not distinguishable.

Group G (group VII) has proved to be quite interesting. These small acrocentric chromosomes include numbers 21 and 22 and the Y chromosome. Numbers 21 and 22 both have satellites on the short arm and are not distinguishable. The Y chromosome is much more variable in appearance than other chromosomes, and frequently it is quite distinct from numbers 21 and 22.

This brief survey of human chromosome types gives some idea of our ability to detect deviations from the normal complement of chromosomes. It is a fairly simple matter to detect the presence of an extra chromosome or the absence of a normal chromosome. Moderate changes in morphology also can be recognized by an experienced observer. The absence of landmarks within the chromosomal arms makes it impossible to detect very small changes, since these would be indistinguishable from variations in the state of contraction of the chromosomes.

Chromosomes and Evolution

Since chromosomes are characteristic of a species, it is evident that during the course of evolution, karyotypes must occasionally have changed. Furthermore, it might be supposed that closely related species would resemble each other in their karyotypes more than would distantly related species.

Extensive comparative studies of karyotypes have been carried out in only a few groups, such as Drosophila. Some of the material available on Primates is summarized in Figure 4–2. It is apparent that numbers of chromosomes are not a useful index of relationship. Within the genus *Cercopithecus,* a prevalent group in Africa, three numbers are found—60, 66, and 72. Most of the other genera in the family Cercopithecidae have 42 chromosomes.

If the amount of chromosomal material is measured, either by analysis of DNA or by measuring total length of chromosomal arms, differences among the Primates disappear for the most part. The differences in chromosome numbers seem largely to represent differences in distribution of equivalent amounts of genetic material. The manner in which this arises is suggested by considering the genus *Cercopithecus.* The species with 72 chromosomes have nine pairs of acrocentrics, those with 66 have six pairs, and those with 60 have only three pairs. Translocation of a long arm of one acrocentric to a nonhomologous chromosome results in a single chromosome with virtually the total amount of genetic material

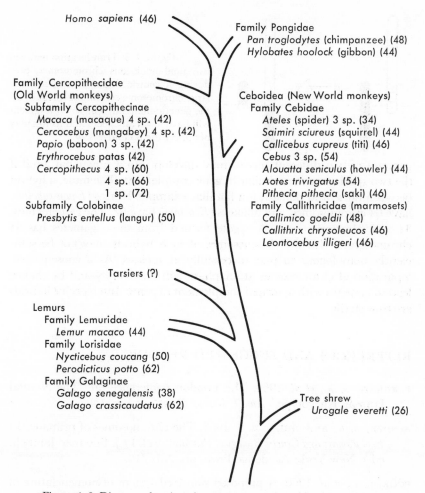

Figure 4–2. Diagram showing chromosome numbers found in various species of the order Primates. Many of the chromosome counts are based on a single animal. (Data from Chu and Bender, 1961.)

(Fig. 4–3). Individuals bearing translocations of this type are known in a variety of species, including man. They may be completely normal, except for the irregularity of chromosome pairing during meiosis with formation of abnormal gametes.

Formation of new combinations of chromosomes serves as an isolating mechanism in evolution. A zygote rarely is viable unless it possesses a balanced complement of genes. In diploid organisms, this usually means two of each genetic locus. A hybrid zygote formed from

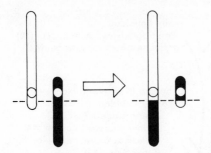

Figure 4–3. Translocation between two nonhomologous chromosomes, producing a centric fragment and a single large chromosome containing virtually all the genetic material. The small fragment will have few if any genes and its loss may not affect the host adversely.

gametes of two different species may develop into a functional adult if the two species are very similar in gene complement. The mule, a hybrid between horse and donkey, is a familiar example. Horses (*Equus caballus*) have 64 chromosomes, and donkeys (*E. asinus*) have 62. The gametes have 32 and 31, respectively. A zygote formed from these gametes has 63 chromosomes. But the chromosomes of such hybrids may not be sufficiently homologous to pair successfully at meiosis. As a consequence, separation of chromosomes at anaphase will only rarely and by chance lead to gametes with a normal complement of genes. Interspecific hybrids are thus sterile.

REFERENCES AND SUGGESTED READING

BARNICOT, N. A., *et al.* 1964. The London conference on "The Normal Human Karyotype." *Am. J. Human Genet.* 16: 156–158.

BENDER, M. A., and CHU, E. H. Y. 1963. The chromosomes of primates. In *Evolutionary and Genetic Biology of Primates,* Vol. 1 (J. Buettner-Janusch, ed.). New York: Academic Press, pp. 261–310.

BÖÖK, J. A., *et al.* 1960. A proposed standard system of nomenclature of human mitotic chromosomes. *Am. J. Human Genet.* 12: 384–388.

CHU, E. H. Y., and BENDER, M. A. 1961. Chromosome cytology and evolution in primates. *Science* 133: 1399–1405.

———, and GILES, N. H. 1959. Human chromosome complements in normal somatic cells in culture. *Am. J. Human Genet.* 11: 63–79.

FORD, C. E. 1962. Methods in human cytogenetics. In *Methodology in Human Genetics* (W. J. Burdette, ed.). San Francisco: Holden-Day, pp. 227–239.

PAINTER, T. S. 1923. Studies in mammalian spermatogenesis. II. The spermatogenesis of man. *J. Exptl. Zool.* 37: 291–335.

PATAU, K. 1960. The identification of individual chromosomes, especially in man. *Am. J. Human Genet.* 12: 250–276.

STERN, C. 1959. The chromosomes of man. *J. Med. Educ.* 34: 301–314.

TJIO, J. H., and LEVAN, A. 1956. The chromosome number of man. *Hereditas* 42: 1–6.

TRUJILLO, J. M. 1962. Chromosomes of the horse, the donkey, and the mule. *Chromosoma* 13: 243–248.

PROBLEMS

1. Define:

karyotype	metacentric	satellite
autosome	acrocentric	
sex chromosome	telocentric	

Chapter Five

HUMAN CHROMOSOMAL ABNORMALITIES

Deviations from normal chromosome complements can be grouped into those involving an abnormal number of normal chromosomes and those involving a structural change in one or more chromosomes. Either of these two types of deviation may on occasion lead to the same phenotypic result. However, the mechanisms by which they arise are different and will be considered separately.

ABNORMAL NUMBERS OF CHROMOSOMES

During normal cell division, each daughter cell receives an exact complement of chromosomes, either a copy of each chromosome (in mitosis) or one of each pair of chromosomes (in meiosis). Should an accident prevent normal functioning of the spindle apparatus, one or more chromosomes may fail to migrate properly during anaphase. As a result of this *nondisjunction,* one daughter cell receives extra chromosomes and the other daughter cell is deficient in these chromosomes. *Chromosome lag* during cell division also causes a chromosome not to be incorporated into the daughter nucleus on occasion. This leads to deficiency of the chromosome in one daughter cell.

Although somewhat rare, these phenomena have been observed in many species, including man. The effects of nondisjunction depend on the chromosomes involved and on the time during development when nondisjunction occurs. If it occurs late in the somatic development of an organism, then only the cells that are direct descendants of the defective mitosis are *aneuploid*. The individual is a *mosaic,* some tissues being *euploid* (with a normal diploid complement of chromosomes), some being *monosomic* (deficient in a chromosome), and some being *trisomic* (with an extra chromosome). If only a small portion of the total somatic tissue is aneuploid, there may be very little effect on the development of the individual, and the aneuploidy may go unrecognized. If nondisjunction occurs early in development, there may be very little euploid tissue present and the individual usually shows marked effects of the aneuploidy.

Although both monosomic and trisomic cells are produced by somatic nondisjunction, it should not be assumed that they are equally represented in the derived tissues. Generally, the two types of cells are not equally viable. Cells seem to tolerate presence of an extra chromosome more readily than absence of one. As a result, monosomic cells often do not survive.

If nondisjunction occurs during meiosis, the gametes are abnormal. If nondisjunction occurs at the first meiotic division, all four gametes are abnormal, two having an extra chromosome and two being deficient. With nondisjunction occurring at the second meiotic division, only the two gametes derived from that division are abnormal; the other two have a normal haploid complement of chromosomes (see Fig. 5–1). A zygote derived from an abnormal gamete is aneuploid, and all the cells of the organism derived from that zygote are aneuploid.

Examples of aneuploidy in organisms other than man have long been recognized. In *Datura stramonium,* the Jimson weed, there are 12 pairs of chromosomes. Plants trisomic for each of these chromosomes have been observed, each leading to characteristic morphological changes. In some organisms, such as Drosophila, trisomics are known for some chromosomes but are unviable in the case of the other chromosomes.

Trisomy of Autosomes

The first trisomics in man were discovered in 1959 by Lejeune and his associates. Their paper stands as one of the classics in human genetics, in that it opened the area of human cytogenetics to intensive investigation.

The condition known as *trisomy 21 syndrome* or mongolian idiocy (sometimes referred to as Down's syndrome) had long been an enigma. Approximately one in every 600 to 700 births is a child with trisomy 21 syndrome, and these comprise some 5 to 15 percent of institutionalized mental defectives. A variety of stigmata in addition to mental deficiency characterize the disease, including such features as short stature; short, broad fingers and toes; a round face with epicanthal folds and a long protruding tongue; and unusual finger and palm prints, including a single transverse palmar crease (simian crease). Most patients do not have all these features. Furthermore, the features occur occasionally in individuals who do not have mongolism. Nevertheless, an experienced observer can usually recognize a mongol rather easily because of the typical appearance of the patients (Fig. 5–2).

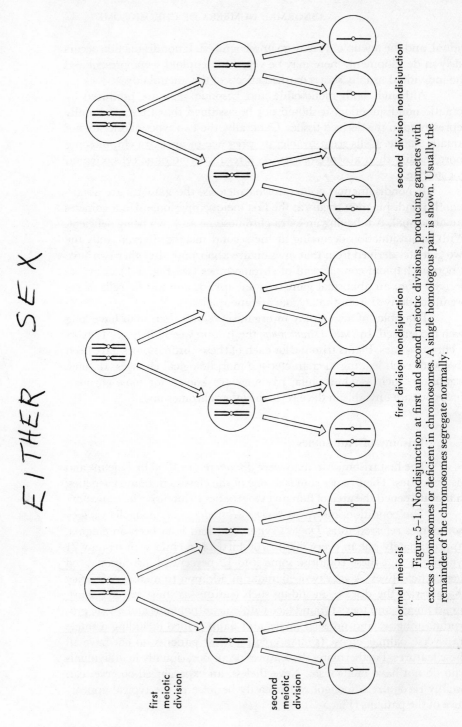

Figure 5–1. Nondisjunction at first and second meiotic divisions, producing gametes with excess chromosomes or deficient in chromosomes. A single homologous pair is shown. Usually the remainder of the chromosomes segregate normally.

EITHER SEX

first meiotic division

second meiotic division

normal meiosis

first division nondisjunction

second division nondisjunction

É. Séguin in 1844 was apparently the first to give a detailed description of the disease. Langdon Down in 1866 considered these patients to resemble members of the Mongolian race, and he interpreted the condition as an atavism toward a more primitive Mongoloid type of individual. The terms mongolism and mongolian idiocy were applied to the disease and are still widely used.

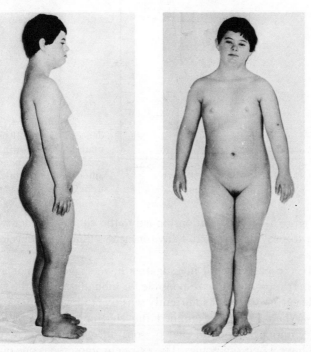

Figure 5–2. A patient with trisomy 21 syndrome (mongolian idiocy) showing many features typical of this condition. Note particularly the face. (Courtesy J. Lejeune.)

Many investigators attempted to discover the cause of mongolism, but with no success. Because it is congenital, a hereditary basis was suggested. Supporting a genetic etiology was the observation that identical twins (who have identical genetic make-up) are nearly always alike in being either both affected or both unaffected. On the other hand, non-identical twins are rarely both affected, and more than one affected person in a sibship is uncommon. This would rule out any simple genetic mechanism as a cause.

The risk of having a child with mongolism increases with age of the mother. The incidence of affected offspring is plotted against maternal

NORTHWEST MISSOURI
STATE COLLEGE LIBRARY

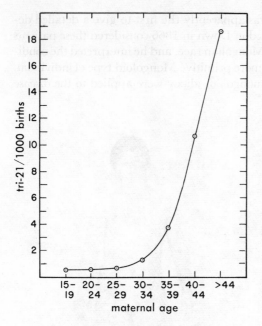

Figure 5–3. The incidence of trisomy 21 births versus maternal age, showing the much greater risk of nondisjunction among older mothers. (Data from Carter and Evans, 1961.)

age in Figure 5–3. This relationship led to the view that older women are less able to provide a prenatal environment suitable for development of embryos.

In the past, several investigators have suggested that a chromosomal aberration might be responsible for mongolism, but the techniques available earlier were not sufficiently sensitive to reveal a departure from normal. When Lejeune examined the chromosome complement with newer techniques, he found that persons affected with mongolism consistently have 47 chromosomes. The extra chromosome is one of the small acrocentrics in Group G (21 or 22). This observation was quickly confirmed in many other laboratories. Since it has not been possible to differentiate chromosomes 21 and 22, it is uncertain which is involved in the trisomy. Several early observations favored chromosome 21, hence the designation trisomy 21 syndrome for the condition. Figure 5–4 is a karyotype of such a patient.

The recognition that mongolism results from an autosomal trisomy has led to the understanding of many of the features of the disease. For example, identical twins would both be affected if the trisomy were present in the original zygote before it separated into two individuals. But since fraternal twins arise from entirely different zygotes, the likelihood of trisomy occurring independently in both zygotes is very small.

A person who is trisomic for an autosome should form two types of

ЯОЯТНWEST MISSOURI
STATE COLLEGE LIBRARY

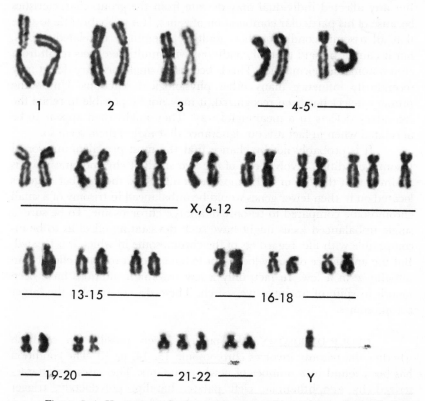

1   2   3   —— 4-5· ——

—————————— X, 6-12 ——————————

—— 13-15 ——————   —— 16-18 ——

—— 19-20 ——   — 21-22 —   Y

Figure 5–4. Karyotype of a boy with trisomy 21 syndrome. Instead of the usual five small acrocentric chromosomes (21, 22, and Y), there are six. The remainder of the complement is normal. (Courtesy J. J. Biesele.)

gametes—normal ones and those with an extra chromosome. Their offspring should therefore consist of both normal and trisomic individuals. In the case of trisomy 21 syndrome, fertility is greatly reduced and males appear to be completely infertile. A few females have produced offspring, however. These consisted of five affected and seven normal children, approximately a 1:1 ratio. A 1:1 ratio would be expected only if the abnormal gametes and zygotes were of normal viability.

A characteristic of trisomic conditions is the large number of tissues and organs that are affected. The normal chromosome complement is balanced, and an extra chromosome means that a large number of genes are present three times rather than the balanced two. Since the genes on a particular chromosome may be quite unrelated in their primary action, trisomy would disturb many apparently unrelated functions.

But any affected individual may deviate from the group characteristics because of his particular combination of genes. It is probably safe to state that all trisomic conditions show multiple, seemingly unrelated, effects, but it cannot be said that all conditions with multiple effects result from chromosomal abnormalities. This is because a single primary defect may secondarily influence many other physiological reactions. Unless the primary defect has been recognized, it may not be possible to relate the secondary defects in a meaningful way. They might then appear to be unrelated when in fact it is our ignorance that makes them seem so.

It is probably not by chance that the most prevalent autosomal trisomic condition involves one of the two smallest chromosomes. If it is assumed that the size of a chromosome is related to the number of genes located on it, then fewer genes would be unbalanced in trisomy of a small chromosome compared to trisomy of a large chromosome. To be sure, a single unbalanced locus might have such devastating effect as to be incompatible with life, regardless of the chromosome in which it is located. But the imbalance of many loci is apt to have more profound effects than imbalance in a few. In fact, only a few trisomic conditions have been found, in spite of an intensive search. These do not involve the larger chromosomes.

GROUP D TRISOMY. It has not been possible to establish whether the trisomy involves chromosome 13, 14, or 15. The condition has been found in a number of newborn infants. The cases are characterized by anophthalmia, cleft palate, harelip, polydactyly, trigger thumbs, hemangiomata, and congenital heart defects.

GROUP E TRISOMY. Chromosome 18 appears to be trisomic in this disease. It is characterized by ear deformities, spasticity due to a central nervous system defect, "rocker bottom" feet, flexion deformity of the fingers, micrognathia, umbilical hernia, congenital heart defects, and failure to thrive. A photograph of a patient is shown in Figure 5–5. This condition was thought originally to be very rare. However, with a full clinical description and chromosome analysis available, the disease is now recognized much more often. Good estimates are not available, but it may be almost as frequent as trisomy 21. The patients rarely survive more than a few months.

Abnormalities of Sex Chromosomes

Among the numerous congenital defects in which abnormal karyotypes might be expected are those involving aberrant sexual development.

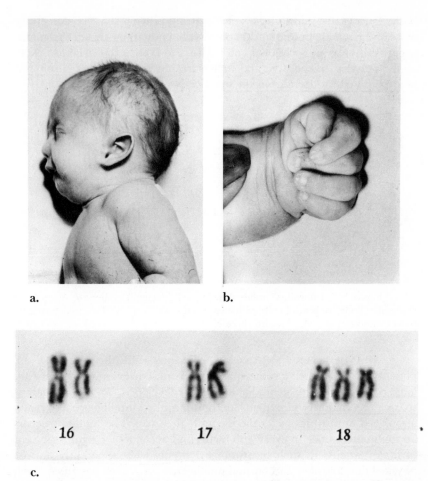

a.   b.

c.

Figure 5–5. Trisomy 18 syndrome. (*a*) A patient, showing characteristic facial structure and low-set ears. (*b*) Unusual hand position found in trisomy 18 syndrome. (*c*) Group E chromosomes, showing an extra number 18 chromosome. (Courtesy J. Lejeune.)

Of the various types of sexual abnormalities, two were outstanding as candidates for sex chromosome studies. These were Klinefelter's syndrome and Turner's syndrome. Both of these conditions are characterized by a *sex chromatin* status opposite to that of the external sex.

SEX CHROMATIN.   In 1949, Barr and Bertram reported a difference in the appearance of interphase nuclei, a difference that was found to be associated with sex. Most of the nuclei of females have a deeply staining body attached to the inside of the nuclear membrane (Fig. 5–6). The nuclei of males lack this body, known as the *sex chromatin* or Barr body. Persons are said to be sex chromatin positive if some 30 percent or more of their cells (buccal smear) possess the body; they are sex chromatin negative if only an occasional cell appears to possess the structure. Normally, females are positive and males are negative. The sex chromatin body is thought to form from the inactive X chromosome (p. 92).

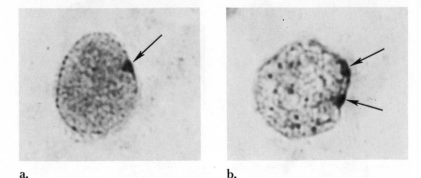

a.   b.

Figure 5-6. Interphase nuclei showing sex chromatin bodies. (*a*) A single sex chromatin body, typical of cells with two X chromosomes. (*b*) Two sex chromatin bodies, characteristic of cells with three X chromosomes. (Courtesy J. de Grouchy.)

KLINEFELTER'S SYNDROME.   Persons with this condition are phenotypic males, being somewhat eunuchoid, however. Their limbs are longer than average, genitalia are underdeveloped, and body hair is sparse. The majority of patients are of diminished intelligence and many are placed in institutions for the mentally defective. The condition occurs approximately once in every 400 births and accounts for some 1 percent of male patients in such institutions. Patients with apparently normal physical development and normal intelligence have been described. Such patients appear to have reduced fertility, however.

Most Klinefelter patients are sex chromatin positive, suggesting an XX constitution. In 1959, shortly after the first report on trisomy 21 syndrome, Jacobs and Strong published the observation that these patients have 47 chromosomes, including a normal Y chromosome. The extra chromosome has the same morphology as an X chromosome. It is now accepted that the patients are XXY. They have five small acrocentric chromosomes, typical of a normal male, but they also have a complement of group C chromosomes typical of a female (Fig. 5-7). The presence of sex chromatin suggests that two of these are X chromosomes.

TURNER'S SYNDROME.   Concurrent with the studies of Klinefelter patients were studies of patients with Turner's syndrome (Ford, *et al,*

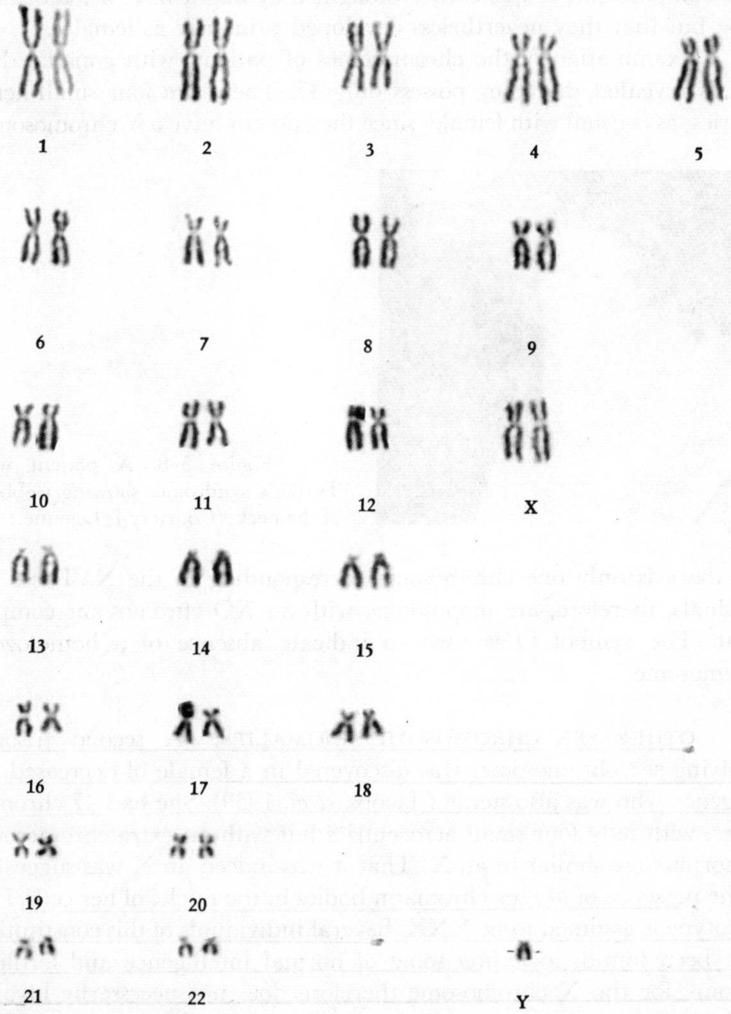

1	2	3	4	5

6	7	8	9

10	11	12	X

13	14	15

16	17	18

19	20		

21	22	Y

Figure 5–7. Karyotype of a patient with Klinefelter's syndrome, showing both a Y chromosome and 16 chromosomes in group C, two of which are thought to be X chromosomes. (Courtesy J. de Grouchy.)

1959). These persons are females phenotypically, but ovaries are not properly developed; hence the frequently used terms ovarian or gonadal dysgenesis. Individuals with this condition are characterized by short stature, pronounced webbing of the neck, and usually impaired intelligence. Figure 5–8 is a photograph of a patient with Turner's syndrome.

They are sex chromatin negative, suggesting an abnormal sex chromo-some complement. It was earlier thought they might have a male kary-otype but that they nevertheless developed primarily as females.

Examination of the chromosomes of patients with gonadal dys-genesis revealed that they possess only 45. There are four small acro-centrics, as is usual with females since they do not have a Y chromosome,

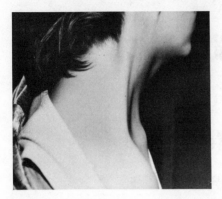

Figure 5–8. A patient with Turner's syndrome, showing webbing of the neck. (Courtesy J. Lejeune.)

but there is only one chromosome corresponding to the X. These in-dividuals, therefore, are monosomic, with an XO chromosome comple-ment. The symbol O is used to indicate absence of a homologous chromosome.

OTHER SEX CHROMOSOME ANOMALIES. A second trisomy involving sex chromosomes was discovered in a female of decreased in-telligence who was also sterile (Jacobs, et al, 1959). She had 47 chromo-somes, with only four small acrocentrics but with an extra chromosome of morphology similar to an X. That it was indeed an X was suggested by the presence of two sex chromatin bodies in the nuclei of her cells. Her karyotype is assumed to be XXX. Several individuals of this constitution have been found, including some of normal intelligence and fertility. Trisomy for the X chromosome therefore does not necessarily involve marked abnormality.

In Drosophila, trisomy for the X chromosome results in a fly that is morphologically normal but sterile. They are designated superfemales. The term has also been applied to human tri-X's, but Stern has argued in favor of the term metafemale. Practice is not uniform, but the triplo-X syndrome seems to be the most satisfactory designation.

Table 5–1 is a summary of abnormal complements of sex chromo-somes discovered in human beings up to the present time. Most of the types listed in the table have been observed only in a very few patients, but these rare cases are very useful in the elucidation of chromosome function. Knowledge of sex determination in human beings is based on consideration of abnormal persons of these types, as discussed in the following chapter.

TABLE 5–1

Combinations of Sex Chromosomes That Have Been
Observed in Human Beings

X CHROMOSOMES		Y CHROMOSOMES				
		O		Y		YY
O	OO:	not observed	OY:	not observed	OYY:	not observed
X	XO:	Turner's syndrome	XY:	normal male	XYY:	normal male
XX	XX:	normal female	XXY:	Klinefelter's syndrome	XXYY:	Klinefelter's syndrome
XXX	XXX:	Triplo-X syndrome	XXXY:	Klinefelter's syndrome	XXXYY:	Klinefelter's syndrome
XXXX	XXXX:	Tetra-X syndrome	XXXXY:	Klinefelter's syndrome		

There are features, such as dermatoglyphics and intelligence, which differ among the various chromosomal types of Klinefelter's syndrome. For this reason, these abnormalities are often designated by the specific chromosome defect, for example, XXXY syndrome, XXYY syndrome.

Compared to the sex chromosomes, for which a great variety of abnormal combinations is known, the autosomes do not occur in abnormal numbers except for the few cases listed earlier. For the majority of autosomes, no abnormalities in number or morphology have been detected, although one would expect them to occur occasionally. The greater tolerance of abnormalities in sex chromosomes is probably the result of selection for genes on the X chromosome, which can function properly whether one or two copies is present (p. 92). Such flexible genes may function more or less normally even when three or more copies are present. No such selection has taken place in the autosomes, since every normal individual has exactly two copies of each. Hence, some of the autosomal genes may not be as flexible.

Although most of the theoretically possible autosomal trisomics have not been detected, it is supposed that they do occur. Many of them may result in unviable zygotes that might not be detected. Others may lead to early embryonic death and abortion, which also might not be recognized. Only limited work has been done on the chromosomal status of spontaneously aborted embryos, although some aberrant karyotypes have been detected in them. These have all been types already discussed in this chapter. Since chromosomal imbalance is a consequence of the genes on the trisomic chromosomes, some trisomics might be viable provided certain mutant genes were also present but unviable if other genes were present.

Mosaicism

Postzygotic nondisjunction should lead to two cell lines, or *clones*, differing in chromosomal constitution in the same individual. Many examples of chromosomal mosaicism are known. A large portion of patients with Turner's syndrome have proved on detailed analysis to consist of some cells with XO constitution and others with normal XX. Their karyotype is symbolized XX/XO.

Nondisjunction may produce either two abnormal daughter cells, one deficient and the other with an extra chromosome, or only one abnormal daughter cell if a chromosome is lost because of anaphase lag. In the latter case, there should be only two cell lines, and the XX/XO karyotypes may arise primarily by this means. If two abnormal daughter cells are produced, there should be three cell lines. Examples of three cell line mosaics that have been observed include XX/XO/XXX and XXY/XX/XXYY. Two-line mosaics involving sex chromosomes include XO/XY, XO/XYY, XO/XXY, XO/XXXY, XY/XXY, XY/XXXY, XX/XY (p. 23), XX/XXX, and XXX/XXXX.

Mosaicism of autosomes can also occur. Several persons who are mosaic for normal and tri-21 cells have been observed. These persons characteristically show only mild expression of the stigmata of trisomy 21 syndrome. Without karyotype analysis, diagnosis would be very uncertain. It is possible that many persons are mosaic for trisomy 21 without expressing any significant clinical signs. Such persons might have only a small portion of their cells trisomic. If this small portion included gonadal tissue, the risk of producing a trisomic offspring could be high. A few families have been observed in which several trisomy 21 offspring were produced by seemingly normal parents. Whether these families have a high tendency to nondisjunction or whether one of the parents is mosaic for the trisomic condition has not been ascertained. The occurrence of *different* trisomic conditions (trisomy 21, XXY) in some families indicates that a tendency for nondisjunction is possible.

One of the most interesting examples of mosaicism has been observed in a small boy in Sweden. This child was first reported to be triploid (69 chromosomes). Subsequently, it was established that he is mosaic for diploid and triploid cell lines. Although most tissues of the body consist of both cell lines, the white cells are entirely diploid. This is thought to be because there is a high rate of replication in the blood cell-forming tissue, and the triploid line would be unable to replicate as fast as normal tissue. It would therefore fail to keep pace and would gradually be replaced by the diploid line. In other tissues, there is less diploid advantage.

Factors That Influence Nondisjunction

Nondisjunction has been shown in Drosophila to increase in eggs of older female flies. This effect apparently is valid also for mammals, the risk of tri-21 offspring being notably greater among offspring of older mothers. Although the cause has yet to be firmly established, it possibly is related to the prolonged meiotic prophase of females. All of the oöcytes enter prophase for the first meiotic division during late embryonic development. They remain dormant until the female reaches sexual maturity, at which time one oöcyte each month continues meiosis to yield a mature ovum. Should defects in the arrested meiotic process tend to accumulate with time, a 40-year-old woman would have twice as much time for such defects to occur compared to a 20-year-old woman. It is also possible that the physiological changes that accompany aging influence the rate of meiotic accidents. A recent report suggests that some virus infections may increase nondisjunction. That nondisjunction can be influenced by metabolic processes of the cell and in turn by genetic constitution of the cell is apparent from studies of experimental organisms and from the many reports of human families in which nondisjunction has occurred repeatedly more often than can be explained by chance.

ABNORMALITIES OF CHROMOSOME STRUCTURE

Chromosomes are considered to have a precise amount of genetic information arranged in a precise manner. Although this is usually true, variant forms have long been known in experimental organisms, and a number of variant chromosomes recently have been described in human beings. Most of these do not function as well as normal chromosomes and hence are designated aberrant. A few chromosomes have been found that are distinctive morphologically but that do appear to function normally.

The mechanism that leads to aberrant chromosomes is breakage followed by incorrect reunion. This may be part of the normal process of crossing over in meiosis, or it may result from an environmental factor such as radiation. Radiation effects are discussed in a later chapter.

Deletions and Duplications

During crossing over, homologous chromatids break and rejoin, sometimes having exchanged segments. Normally, breakage occurs at the same points on the chromatids, yielding new chromatids but with equivalent information. However, if the chromatids break at slightly different places, then recombination gives two new chromatids that are no longer equivalent to each other or to normal chromatids. This is illustrated in Figure 5–9. One chromatid will have a *deletion* of genetic material; the other will have a *duplication*. The segment involved may be any

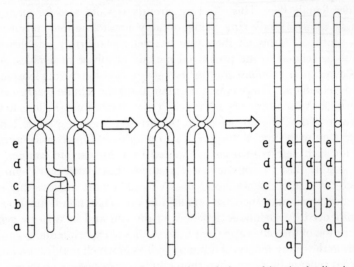

Figure 5–9. Unequal crossing over in meiosis, resulting in duplication of a chromosome segment in one product and deletion of a segment in another.

size. Terminal deletions also may occur as a consequence of a single chromosome break with failure to rejoin. This could occur at any phase of the cell cycle.

The effects of a deletion depend on the particular genes deleted. If only one or two genes are involved, a deletion may not be readily distinguishable from a single gene mutation. Indeed, many mutations in bacteria and bacteriophage have proved on detailed analysis to behave as small deletions, sometimes involving only a small portion of a single gene. In general, a chromosome with a major deletion will not function properly and will be eliminated by selection.

A rare example of a visible deletion in man was reported by de Grouchy and others in 1963. The patient was mentally defective and, in addition to various other disorders, possessed a number 18 chromosome that lacked its short arm. The best known example of a visible deletion in man was described by Lejeune and co-workers in 1963. This group reported studies of several cases in which severe mental deficiency and a "moon face" appearance were associated with deletion of a major portion of the short arm of a group B chromosome, believed to be number 5 (Fig. 5–10). An important feature of the condition is the very plaintive cry,

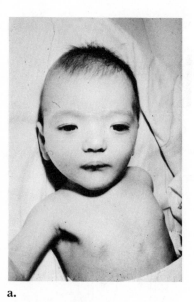

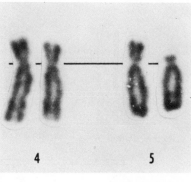

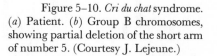

b.

Figure 5–10. *Cri du chat* syndrome. (*a*) Patient. (*b*) Group B chromosomes, showing partial deletion of the short arm of number 5. (Courtesy J. Lejeune.)

a.

described as similar to a cat's cry; hence, the name *cri du chat* syndrome. Although the condition has been described only recently, some twenty cases have already been recorded, and the syndrome does not appear to be exceedingly rare.

A chromosome with a small duplication is less apt to function abnormally than one with a deletion. No definite examples of duplications are known in man, although suggestions have been made by O. Smithies for very small duplications on the basis of chemical rather than cytological evidence. In Drosophila, the classical example of gene duplication is Bar Eye. The exact limits of the duplication can be observed in the salivary chromosomes. It is thought that one way in which new genes are added to a genome is by duplication of existing genes followed by mutation of one of these genes.

Translocation

Another chromosomal aberration is translocation. This occurs when two chromosomes break and then rejoin in the wrong combinations (see Fig. 5–11). Since the genetic information in a cell is still complete following translocation, there may be no cellular malfunction, and balanced function will be maintained through subsequent mitosis. But, at

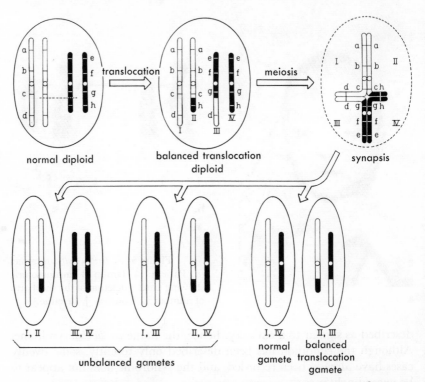

Figure 5–11. Translocation followed by meiosis to give six types of gametes, of which two carry a normal complement of genes.

meiosis, six types of gametes are possible, only two of which have a normal gene complement. The presence of a translocation can be recognized by the figure with four arms formed in the chromosome pairing of meiosis.

The best example of translocation in man is found in trisomy 21 syndrome. Although the great majority of such patients have 47 chromosomes and are trisomic for a group G chromosome, a small portion of them possess 46 chromosomes. Analysis of their karyotype gives the pattern shown in Figure 5–12. Although the number of chromosomes is normal, the morphology is not. A chromosome of the D group has been replaced by one with a long arm typical of this group but with a much larger short arm. Since these patients appear to have the information of chromosome 21 (or 22) present three times and show no additional effects that would suggest monosomy for one of the D group, the unusual chromosome is interpreted as resulting from translocation between a 21 and

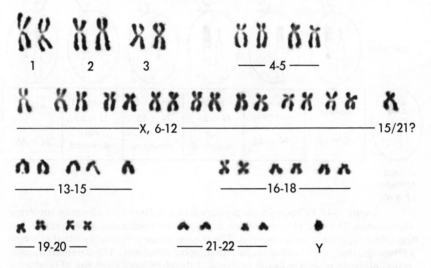

Figure 5–12. Karyotype of a translocation trisomy 21 syndrome. There are only 46 chromosomes, but there is an extra chromosome in group C (the translocation chromosome) and one missing from group D. (Courtesy J. J. Biesele.)

a D chromosome (see Fig. 5–13). The only abnormality in the amount of information lies in the extra segment of chromosome 21 and a possible small deficiency on the group D chromosome from the point of translocation. In some pedigrees, translocation involves another G chromosome rather than a D.

A most interesting feature of the translocation-type trisomy 21 syndrome is its transmission by apparently normal individuals. The meiotic products of a cell carrying the original translocation (or derived from the original cell by mitosis) would be six types of gametes, as shown in Figure 5–13. When combined with a normal gamete, these would produce six types of zygotes. Three of the zygotes appear to be unviable. Individuals derived from the second type of zygote would be identical to the parent in chromosomal constitution. The total genetic information is normal, so they would develop normally but would possess only 45 chromosomes. They would produce the same gametes as the parent

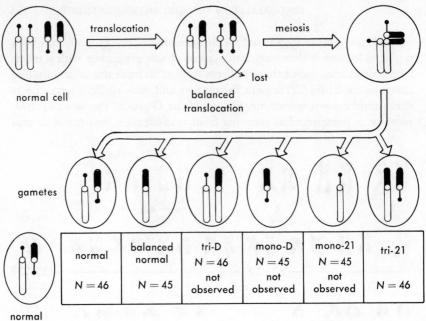

normal
gametes
of mate

Figure 5–13. Offspring from person who is a balanced translocation involving chromosome 21 and a D chromosome. Six types of offspring should be possible, but only three types have been observed. The remainder are presumably lethal at a very early stage, since they involve major chromosome imbalance. The balanced translocation offspring is similar to the parent and therefore has a high risk of producing trisomy 21 offspring.

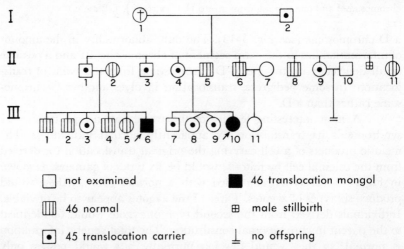

Figure 5–14. Pedigree showing transmission of trisomy 21 syndrome through persons who have balanced translocations of chromosomes 21 and 22. (Redrawn from M. W. Shaw, 1962, with permission of the author and publisher, S. Karger Basel/New York.)

with the original translocation and, hence, could produce children who are normal with 46 chromosomes, affected with 46 chromosomes, and carriers with 45 chromosomes. A pedigree of translocation-type trisomy 21 syndrome is given in Figure 5–14.

There are two important differences in the occurrence of translocation trisomy 21 and nondisjunction trisomy 21. In translocation families, there is frequent occurrence of affected persons. If the six types of gametes produced by a 45-chromosome parent were equally likely to be produced, one third of the viable offspring should show the trisomy 21 syndrome. As yet, it has not been established that the gametes occur with equal frequency. Studies of chromosomal anomalies in other organisms indicate that various gametic combinations are not equally probable. Analysis of the few families available suggests that the risk of an affected offspring is close to one third. This contrasts with nondisjunction trisomy 21, where risk of giving birth to an affected child is about 1/800 and increases only slightly for later children born to the same sibship.

A second difference between the two causes for trisomy 21 syndrome is the absence of a maternal age effect in translocation trisomy. Each trisomic patient may be considered the consequence of a new nondisjunction, an event that occurs much more frequently in older females. But an individual who has 45 chromosomes, including the translocation, may produce affected offspring in high frequency as soon as sexual maturity is attained.

No clinical distinction has been made between the two types of trisomy 21 syndrome, and therefore patients are treated alike regardless of their chromosomal status. However, it is useful to parents to know which of the types is present in a child. If it is the more common trisomy, the risk of another affected child is very low. There is evidence that nondisjunction tends to occur in certain individuals more than in others, but this slight increase in risk is negligible so far as counseling is concerned, and parents can be reassured with respect to additional children. Parents of a translocation patient, on the other hand, may wish to discontinue having children in the face of a high risk of recurrence.

Isochromosomes

Several examples of *isochromosomes* have been found in human beings. An isochromosome is a chromosome in which both arms are identical. It is thought to arise when a centromere divides in the wrong plane, yielding two daughter chromosomes, each of which carries the information of one arm only but present twice. This process is illustrated in Figure 5–15. Formation of isochromosomes presumably can occur either

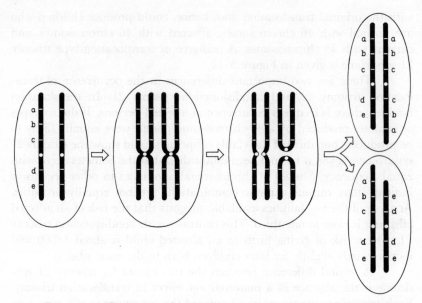

Figure 5–15. Formation of an isochromosome by division of the centromere in the wrong plane. The daughter cells will each be partial trisomic and partial monosomic.

during mitosis or meiosis. Fertilization of an isochromosome-bearing gamete by a normal gamete would lead to an unbalanced karyotype. The zygote would have the information of one arm present three times and that of the other arm only once. Thus, the individual developing from such a zygote would be partially trisomic and partially monosomic.

The patients thought to be examples of isochromosome formation are females with gonadal dysgenesis who show some evidence of possessing at least two X chromosomes (for example, they are sex chromatin positive). These patients have 46 chromosomes but only one normal X. There is present a chromosome larger than an X and characterized by the exactly central location of the centromere. The two arms are the same length as the longer arm of a normal X chromosome, and the condition has been interpreted as resulting from an x_I (iso-X) chromosome.

Ring Chromosomes

If a chromosome breaks on both sides of the centromere, occasionally the two proximal ends join to form a ring and the two distal fragments, being acentric, are lost (Fig. 5–16). The extent of the phenotype defect depends on the specific genes lost in the deleted fragments. Several patients have been found to have ring chromosomes, indicating that certain small deletions are compatible with life. Chromosome 18 seems to be most often involved, although other chromosomes—a group D, a group G, and an X chromosome—have also been reported. The number of patients observed with ring chromosomes is still very limited. The existence of ring chromosomes raises interesting questions regarding chromosome replication, most of which cannot be answered at present. The ring

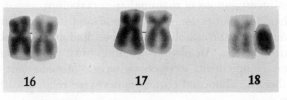

Figure 5–16. Group E chromosomes from a person possessing a ring chromosome instead of a normal number 18. Such a ring chromosome would have a deletion at the distal end of both arms. (Courtesy J. de Grouchy.)

chromosome does not appear to have a marked disadvantage with respect to replication. Ring chromosomes have been known in lower animals and plants for many years.

"Normal" Aberrations

There are several reports of normal persons whose karyotypes include a small but consistently recognizable aberration. In one such case, both a father and son possessed an abnormal group G. In addition to the Y chromosome, there were only three typical small acrocentrics. The unusual chromosome appeared to be the remaining member of group G, but with a distinct short arm rather than the normal satellite.

Another variation in chromosome morphology of normal people is enlarged satellites. The function of these usually minute structures is not known, but it is possible that they do not contain ordinary genes. Occasionally, a particular chromosome in a normal individual will have a satellite that is noticeably enlarged. This particular chromosome can be distinguished from its homologue in all the cells of that person.

It is difficult to make a distinction between minute chromosomal aberrations and mutations. Indeed, a mutation may be considered an aberration limited to one gene. Just as each person carries a variety of unexpressed mutant genes, many seemingly normal chromosomes may have very small aberrations not detectable by present cytological techniques. The effects of minute aberrations may not be expressed so long as the homologous chromosome can function properly.

Chromosomes and Cancer

Among the mammalian cells most readily cultivated *in vitro* are those derived from malignant tumors. Long before it was possible to cultivate normal tissues routinely, a number of viable cell lines had been established starting with tumor cells. Several of these cell lines have been maintained in the laboratory for a period of years and have proved invaluable in investigations of mammalian metabolism.

When techniques for chromosomal analysis were introduced, it was discovered that the established cell lines had grossly abnormal numbers of chromosomes. An obvious question was whether the abnormal chromosome complements were characteristic of malignant tissues and, if so, whether the abnormal chromosomes were related to the origin of the cancer.

Contrary to the idea of a direct relationship was the observation that different cell lines originally derived from a single source had acquired complements of chromosomes different from each other. Although this probably happened subsequent to laboratory culture, it seemed possible that an aberration originally might have been responsible for the malignancy. There was also the possibility that cancerous cells might be more prone to develop abnormal chromosomes.

Repeated examinations of newly explanted cancer cells have shown that deviations in number or morphology of chromosomes are not characteristic of tumors *in vivo*. With very few exceptions, cancer cells have a normal karyotype. The deviations observed in cultured lines thus appear to have arisen entirely as a result of variation following explantation. It is supposed that a variety of variations occur purely by chance both *in vivo* and *in vitro*. The "normal" karyotype is well adapted for balanced function and growth *in vivo*, and chance variations are unlikely to compete successfully. However, the very different *in vitro* environment and the competitive advantage of rapidly growing cells may favor a cell with an "abnormal" complement of chromosomes.

LEUKEMIA.   The one consistent association between a malignancy and aberrant chromosomes involves chronic granulocytic leukemia. Marrow cultures from approximately three fourths of patients with this uncommon type of leukemia are characterized by replacement of one of the small acrocentrics (21 or 22) with a smaller chromosome. A portion of the long arm of one of the acrocentrics appears to have been lost (Fig. 5–17). The resulting abnormal chromosome is known as a Philadelphia or Ph[1] chromosome. Individuals with Ph[1] chromosomes also have many cells with a normal complement of chromosomes, sug-

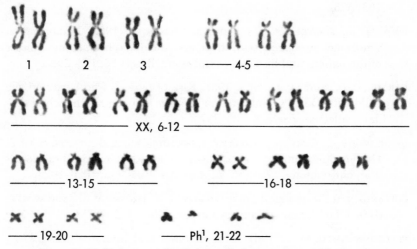

Figure 5–17. Karyotype of leukemic cells from a person with chronic granulocytic leukemia. The Philadelphia (Ph[1]) chromosome has shorter long arms than normal. (Courtesy J. J. Biesele.)

gesting that the Ph[1] chromosome arose from originally normal cells. Although rigorous proof is lacking, the abnormal chromosome is thought to play a role in the development of the leukemia in those cases where it is found.

A chromosomal anomaly involving deletion of the short arm of a group G chromosome has been reported in members of two families. Although most persons with this chromosome, designated Christchurch or Ch[1], were normal, several had developed chronic lymphocytic leukemia, ordinarily a very rare disorder. It seems likely that the Ch[1] chromosome greatly increases the risk of developing chronic lymphocytic leukemia, although most patients with this form of leukemia do not have a Ch[1] chromosome.

A more obscure relationship exists between trisomy 21 syndrome and leukemia. Among juvenile leukemics, the frequency of 21-trisomics is considerably increased, as is the frequency of leukemia among all individuals who are 21-trisomics. Various types of leukemia appear to be involved. The reason for the increased incidence has not been established.

REFERENCES AND SUGGESTED READING

BARR, M. L., and BERTRAM, E. G. 1949. A morphological distinction between neurones of the male and female, and the behaviour of the nucleolar satellite during accelerated nucleoprotein synthesis. *Nature* (Lond.) 163: 676.

BÖÖK, J. A., MASTERSON, J. G., and SANTESSON, B. 1962. Malformation syndrome associated with triploidy—further chromosome studies of the patient and his family. *Acta genet.* (Basel) 12: 193–201.

CARTER, C. O., and EVANS, K. A. 1961. Risk of parents who have had one child with Down's syndrome (mongolism) having another child similarly affected. *Lancet* 2: 785–787.

DE GROUCHY, J., LAMY, M., THIEFFRY, S., ARTHUIS, M., and SALMON, C. 1963. Dysmorphie complexe avec oligophrénie: délétion des bras courts d'un chromosome 17–18. *C. R. Acad. Sci. Paris* 256: 1028–1029.

EDWARDS, J. H., HARNDEN, D. G., CAMERON, A H., CROSSE, V. M., and WOLFF, O. H. 1960. A new trisomic syndrome. *Lancet* 1: 787–790.

FERGUSON-SMITH, M. A. 1961. Chromosomes and human disease. *Progr. Med. Genet.* 1: 292–334.

FORD, C. E., JONES, K. W., POLANI, P. E., DE ALMEIDA, J. C., and BRIGGS, J. H. 1959. A sex-chromosome anomaly in a case of gonadal dysgenesis (Turner's syndrome). *Lancet* 1: 711.

HARNDEN, D. G. 1961. The chromosomes. In *Recent Advances in Human Genetics* (L. S. Penrose and H. Lang Brown, eds.). London: J. and A. Churchill, pp. 19–38.

JACOBS, P. A., BAIKIE, A. G., COURT BROWN, W. M., MACGREGOR, T. N., MACLEAN, N., and HARNDEN, D. G., 1959. Evidence for the existence of the human "super female." *Lancet* 2: 423.

JACOBS, P. A., and STRONG, J. A. 1959. A case of human intersexuality having a possible XXY sex-determining mechanism. *Nature* (Lond.) 183: 302.

LEJEUNE, J. 1964. The 21 trisomy—current stage of chromosomal research. *Progr. Med. Genet.* 3: 144–177.

———, GAUTIER, M., and TURPIN, R. 1959. Étude des chromosomes somatiques de neuf enfants mongoliens. *C. R. Acad. Sci. Paris* 248: 1721–1722.

———, et al. 1963. Trois cas de délétion du bras court d'un chromosome 5. *C. R. Acad. Sci. Paris* 257: 3098–3102.

PENROSE, L. S., ELLIS, J. R., and DELHANTY, J. D. A. 1960. Chromosomal translocation in mongolism and in normal relatives. *Lancet* 2: 409–410.

POLANI, P. E., BRIGGS, J. H., FORD, C. E., CLARKE, C. M., and BERG, J. M. 1960. A mongol girl with 46 chromosomes. *Lancet* 1: 721–724.

RUSSELL, L. B. 1962. Chromosome aberrations in experimental mammals. *Progr. Med. Genet.* 2: 230–294.

SHAW, M. W., 1962. Familial mongolism. *Cytogenetics* 1: 141–179.

SMITH, D. W., PATAU, K., THERMAN, E., and INHORN, S. L. 1960. A new autosomal trisomy syndrome: Multiple congenital anomalies caused by an extra chromosome. *J. Pediat.* 57: 338–345.

WANG, H. -C., MELNYK, J., MCDONALD, L. T., UCHIDA, I. A., CARR, D. H., and GOLDBERG, B. 1962. Ring chromosomes in human beings. *Nature* (Lond.) 195: 733–734.

PROBLEMS

1. Define:

euploid	mosaic	deletion
aneuploid	nondisjunction	isochromosome
monosomy	sex chromatin	ring chromosome
trisomy	translocation	acentric fragment

2. Assume the following to be fertile. What are their karyotypes? What types of gametes would they produce? If these gametes united with a normal gamete, what would be the karyotypes of the zygotes?
    a. Klinefelter's syndrome
    b. Turner's syndrome
    c. metafemale
    d. mongol (nondisjunctional)
    e. mongol (D-translocational)
    f. carrier of D-translocational mongolism
    g. Xx_I (long arm)

Chapter Six

DETERMINATION OF SEX

Reproductive mechanisms are divided into two major categories—sexual and asexual. In asexual reproduction, an organism gives rise to one or more daughter organisms identical in genetic content to the parent. In sexual reproduction, daughter cells receive a genetic contribution from more than one parent. Many organisms can reproduce either sexually or asexually. Most organisms that rely primarily on asexual mechanisms in reproduction undergo sexual reproduction on occasion.

The universal occurrence of sexual reproduction among higher plants and animals suggests that the system is biologically beneficial. This benefit would seem to be the greatly increased opportunity to experiment with new combinations of genes. In asexual reproduction, new genetic combinations arise only by mutation of genes. Evolution by the accumulation of mutations is at best a slow process, since favorable new complexes of mutant genes must arise by stepwise accumulation of individual mutations. Unless these mutations are individually favorable, they are not likely to persist.

By contrast, in sexual reproduction, mutations arising in different organisms have a chance to reassort and come together into the same genome. Such assortment permits evolution to proceed at a much faster rate than is possible by sequential mutation, thus providing the population with greater flexibility to respond to environmental changes.

The mechanisms of sexual reproduction are quite varied. Probably the simplest occurs among viruses. In bacteriophage, for example, if two related but genetically distinguishable virus particles both infect the same bacterial cell, many of the new virus particles produced will carry genes from both parents. There is no basic difference in the sexual and asexual processes in viruses, the only distinction being whether the progeny DNA has more than one parental template from which to copy. Furthermore, there are no "sexes," since there are no restrictions involving combinations of parental particles and there are no functional differences among various particles.

62

A slightly more complex system is found in the few bacteria in which sexual processes can be observed. In certain strains of *Escherichia coli,* conjugation and transfer of genetic material depend on the presence in one of the cells of tiny DNA particles that may be in the cytoplasm or attached to the chromosome. These F (fertility) particles promote conjugation and lead to the transfer of genes from F-infected (F+) cells to non-infected cells. The recipient cell is then comparable to a zygote, although it may have received only a portion of the genome of the F+ cell. This partially diploid state may be maintained through several divisions, but eventually a haploid state is restored. The new haploid cell may exhibit genetic traits characteristic of both of the original parental cells.

Two other sexual processes are observed in bacteria in the laboratory and may also occur in nature. These are *transformation* and *transduction.* In transformation, the genetic material (DNA) from one bacterial cell is present in solution in the environment of another related cell. This intact cell absorbs the DNA, and after cell division the progeny have acquired some of their genes from the absorbed DNA. Transduction is a similar process except that viruses serve as vectors in transporting DNA from one cell to another. The virus must be temperate; that is, it must be able to infect without destroying the host cell.

In these organisms, sexual reproduction is the exception rather than the rule. As evolution led to more complex organisms, selection favored those groups in which sexual reproduction became an integral part of the life cycle. This assured that each generation was a new complex of genes and hence a new experiment in survival advantage. Along with the acquisition of sexual reproduction, most species developed special structures for transmitting nuclear and cytoplasmic material to offspring. These generally can be classified as "male" or "female," the distinction being that the male contributes only nuclear material while the female contributes both nuclear and cytoplasmic material to the progeny. In many organisms, particularly in plants, both types of organ are found in the same individual, and self-fertilization may occur. In others, an individual is either male or female. In some plants, special genes prevent fertilization of the ova by pollen of the same plant, thus assuring greater variety of genes in the offspring.

SEX DETERMINATION IN NONMAMMALS

Although sexual dimorphism is characteristic of a very large segment of the biological world, the mechanism by which sexual distinction occurs is remarkably variable in different species. An example has already been given of primitive sex determination of some bacteria due to presence or absence of viruslike particles. A "female" cell lacking particles can be transformed into a "male" cell by becoming infected with the particles.

Environmental control of sex is found in the marine worm *Bonellia viridis*. Larvae that develop on the proboscis of a female become males, while those that develop away from females become females. Presumably, some chemical secretion of the females influences the direction of development.

Genetic control of sex is common, although the precise mechanisms vary. In *Hymenoptera*, fertilized eggs have a diploid complement of chromosomes and become females. Unfertilized eggs can develop, however, and always yield haploid males. Thus, diploidy versus haploidy appears to be the feature responsible for sex determination.

A simpler genetic mechanism is found in organisms such as the mold *Neurospora*. Although this mold commonly reproduces asexually, it can undergo meiosis and sexual reproduction. There are two sexes, exactly equivalent and designated *A* and *a*. Mating occurs only between gametes of unlike sex. The mating type, *A* or *a*, is determined by a pair of autosomal alleles and follows simple Mendelian inheritance.

A chromosomal basis for sex determination is found in mammals, birds, Drosophila, and many other animals. In mammals and Drosophila, sex determination is of the XY type. Females have two X chromosomes and are said to be *homogametic;* that is, all of the gametes produced by females have an X chromosome and are therefore equivalent with respect to sex determination. Males are *heterogametic* in that they have only one X chromosome plus one Y chromosome. Gametes may carry either an X or a Y chromosome. As indicated in Chapter 4, human X chromosomes are fairly large, while Y chromosomes are in the smallest group.

Birds have a similar mechanism of sex determination, except that females are the heterogametic sex. To avoid confusion with the XY mechanism, the symbols WZ are used, males being ZZ and females ZW. A third type of chromosomal mechanism is the XO type found in some fishes. Absence of a chromosome is designated O, and in these species the females are XX, the males XO. Thus, the males have one fewer chromosomes than the females.

The statement that human or Drosophila females are XX and males are XY leaves unanswered an interesting question regarding sex determination. What attribute of the chromosomal constitution actually is responsible for maleness or femaleness? This question is legitimate because at least four parameters are different in the XX and XY karyotypes: (1) the number of X chromosomes, (2) the number of Y chromosomes,

(3) the ratio of X chromosomes to autosomes, and (4) the ratio of Y chromosomes to autosomes. It is difficult to separate these variables in normal individuals, but consideration of chromosomally abnormal individuals can answer these questions, as suggested in the previous chapter.

Sex Determination in Drosophila

A variety of aneuploid states involving the sex chromosomes are known in Drosophila. In 1922, Bridges analyzed some of these to arrive at a theory of sex determination. Flies that were polyploid were normal females, provided the number of X chromosomes and the number of sets of autosomes were equal. Flies with three X chromosomes but the normal number of autosomes (2n) were sterile "superfemales." In the presence of three sets of autosomes, two X chromosomes produced a sterile intersex and one X chromosome produced a sterile "supermale." These results are tabulated in Table 6-1.

The number of Y chromosomes does not seem to play an important role in sex determination in Drosophila. Bridges concluded that the critical factor seemed to be the ratio of X chromosomes to sets of autosomes. The autosomes appear to have genes for maleness, whereas the X chromosome has genes for femaleness. In an XX diploid fly, the balance is correct to produce a functional female; in an XY diploid, the balance is right for a functional male. Any deviation from this ratio produces a sexually nonfunctional fly.

TABLE 6-1

Sex Determination in Drosophila (Bridges, 1925)

PHENOTYPIC SEX	X CHROMOSOMES	SETS OF AUTOSOMES	RATIO X/AUTOSOMES
superfemale (sterile)	3	2	1.5
normal female (tetraploid)	4	4	1.0
normal female (triploid)	3	3	1.0
normal female (diploid)	2	2	1.0
intersex (sterile)	2	3	0.67
normal male	1	2	0.5
supermale (sterile)	1	3	0.33

SEX DETERMINATION IN HUMAN BEINGS

Since Drosophila and mammals both have an XX-XY type of sex determination, it might be supposed that the mechanism in each case is the same. However, the evolutionary distance between them is so large as to necessitate independent verification. The analysis used in mammals is the same as in Drosophila.

A discussion of human aneuploidy involving sex chromosomes was given in Chapter 5. A variety of aneuploid conditions is known, all of which follow the rule that presence of a Y chromosome results in a male phenotype. Absence of a Y chromosome results in a female. The number of X chromosomes is important, but the effects are small compared to the effects of Y chromosomes. For example, persons with Klinefelter's syndrome, XXY, are clearly males, although with greatly reduced fertility. Whether an XXY person can be fertile at all is yet to be ascertained.

The contrast between sex determination in man and Drosophila is shown in Table 6–2. Sex determination in house mice resembles that in human beings, although the abnormal complements produce somewhat different phenotypes.

TABLE 6–2

Sex and Chromosome Status in Three Organisms with XX-XY Sex Determination

SEX CHROMOSOME STATUS	HUMAN PHENOTYPE	MOUSE PHENOTYPE	DROSOPHILA PHENOTYPE
XO	sterile female	fertile female	sterile male
XX	normal female	normal female	normal female
XXX	fertile female[a]	unknown	sterile female
XY	normal male	normal male	normal male
XXY	sterile male	semilethal male	fertile female

[a] Fertility is probably reduced

The manner in which the Y chromosome exerts its effects is unknown. No genes have been shown to occur on the Y chromosome unequivocally. Yet it is difficult to imagine a type of chromosomal action that does not involve genes or structures similar to genes. The activity of the Y chromosome may be primarily the suppression of specific female-determining genes elsewhere in the genome. In any event, the Y chromosome is not genetically inert.

Testicular Feminization

The readiness with which sex can be genetically influenced is illustrated by the rare condition known as testicular feminization. Persons with this condition have an apparently normal XY karyotype. Yet, externally they appear to be normal females. They are reared as females and have typical feminine attitudes and identification. In many cases, they have come to medical attention because of infertility in marriage. Internally, they lack ovaries and associated structures typical of normal females. The uterus ends blindly, and the gonads are testes.

Testicular feminization is inherited as a simple trait, although the mode of heredity has yet to be established with certainty. A pedigree is shown in Figure 6–1. Typically, affected persons occur in more than one generation. Since the condition is rare, a single copy of the gene must

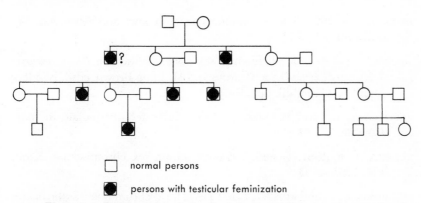

| | normal persons |
| persons with testicular feminization |

Figure 6–1. Pedigree of testicular feminization. Affected persons are females externally but have testes and an XY karyotype. They are related to each other through normal female carriers. This pattern of heredity is compatible either with a sex-linked recessive gene or an autosomal dominant gene with expression limited to males. (Redrawn from Pettersson and Bonnier, 1937.)

be adequate to provoke abnormal development. A combination of several genes seems unlikely because of the high frequency of affected persons in sibships where it occurs. Whether the gene occurs on the X chromosome or an autosome has not been established. This distinction, usually simple to make, is difficult here because affected persons of XY karyotype are sterile. Normal females, of XX constitution, do not show effects of the gene, although they may transmit it to their offspring. Pedigrees show typical X chromosome inheritance, but the condition itself prohibits fertile matings that would provide the evidence of father to son transmission necessary to eliminate the X chromosome as the site of the gene.

Nothing is known of the action of the gene for testicular feminization. Indeed, it has not been established that a gene of the traditional type is involved. Conceivably, a regulator region of some unknown type might have mutated so that it could no longer control the functions of a series of other genes. Or possibly there exists a region which normally is inhibited by a product of the Y chromosome but which has mutated so that it no longer can be inhibited. Whatever the explanation proves to be, this condition illustrates the dependence of normal sexual differentiation on a normal complement of genes as well as chromosomes, and it demonstrates the marked departure from normal development that may result from changes in one of the genes.

REFERENCES AND SUGGESTED READING

BRIDGES, C. B. 1925. Sex in relation to chromosomes and genes. *Am. Naturalist* 59: 127–137.

MILLER, O. J. 1961. Developmental sex abnormalities. In *Recent Advances in Human Genetics* (L. S. Penrose and H. Lang Brown, eds.). London: J. and A. Churchill, pp. 39–55.

PETTERSSON, G., and BONNIER, G. 1937. Inherited sex-mosaic in man. *Hereditas* 23: 49–69.

RUSSELL, L. B. 1961. Genetics of mammalian sex chromosomes. *Science* 133: 1795–1803.

WELSHONS, W. J., and RUSSELL, L. B. 1959. The Y-chromosome as the bearer of male determining factors in the mouse. *Proc. Natl. Acad. Sci.* (U.S.) 45: 560–566.

Chapter Seven

THE CHEMICAL NATURE
OF GENES

The action of all genes in the control of body processes is chemical. In order to understand the manner in which genes exert their influence, it is necessary to consider the chemical nature of the genes themselves. Analyses of isolated chromosomes reveal two major constituents, deoxyribonucleic acid (DNA) and histone (a basic protein). These two substances, in roughly equal amounts, comprise approximately 90 percent of the mass of most chromosomes. The remaining 10 percent is nonhistone protein, with a small proportion of ribonucleic acid (RNA).

Although both DNA and histone undoubtedly play essential roles in chromosome function, evidence favors DNA as the substance that stores genetic information. The distribution of DNA in various cells is consistent with a genetic function. For example, except for rather special circumstances, DNA is found only in nuclei. Also, and more important, the amount of DNA per cell corresponds to the degree of ploidy (Table 7–1). Diploid cells contain twice as much DNA as do haploid cells of the same species. The diploid amount of DNA is constant within a species but may vary among species.

TABLE 7–1

DNA Content of Various Cells, in Grams $\times$ 10^{-12} per cell (from Vendrely, 1955; Leuchtenberger, *et al.*, 1954)

ORGANISM	KIDNEY	LIVER	ERYTHROCYTES	SPERM
chicken	2.4	2.5	2.5	1.3
bovine	6.4	6.4	—	3.3
carp	—	3.0	3.3	1.6
human	5.6	5.6+[a]	—	2.5

[a] In addition to the usual diploid cells, liver has many tetraploid cells. This causes the mean DNA per cell to be higher than the diploid amount. If individual cells are studied (Leuchtenberger, *et al.*, 1954) the DNA content corresponds either to the diploid amount or to a multiple of the diploid amount.

69

DNA is present in every living organism except for some viruses. In these viruses, RNA is present and is believed to perform the genetic function. Unlike DNA, the amount of histone in each cell of an organism is not constant, being absent in many cells and in DNA and RNA viruses.

Storage of genetic information by DNA is proved by studies of *transformation* in bacteria. Microorganisms manifest heritable differences as do higher organisms. From a culture of bacteria derived from a single cell it is possible occasionally to isolate deviant cells that have acquired a trait different from the parental type. These traits, arising by gene mutation, are heritable, being transmitted to the progeny of the deviant cell.

Among the heritable differences of pneumococci are the types of polysaccharide capsules surrounding the cells. The capsular type is recognized by immunological techniques, and a type I cell produces only type I progeny, a type II cell only type II progeny, etc. Griffith observed, in 1928, that simultaneous injection of killed type I and living type II cells into mice enabled him to recover living type I cells. Apparently, the type I capsule genotype was transferred to living type II cells.

The nature of this transformation was established in 1944 by Avery, MacLeod, and McCarty, who found that conversion of one type to another could be effected by pure DNA extracts *in vitro*. Thus, DNA extracted from type I cells added to living type II cells yields a few living cells with type I capsule. The phenomenon has been observed with a variety of genetic traits such as penicillin resistance versus sensitivity, and in a variety of microorganisms.

Although the transformation experiments, along with other evidence, establish clearly that DNA is the usual transmitter of genetic information, RNA also can perform this role under certain circumstances. A number of viruses consist only of RNA and protein; in these viruses, RNA apparently functions as does DNA in other viruses and all other living matter. Tobacco mosaic virus is an RNA virus that has been extensively investigated. It is possible to extract from this virus pure RNA that is capable of causing tobacco mosaic infection usually associated with intact virus. Furthermore, the infective RNA leads to the production of new virus particles complete with protein coats and infectivity characteristic of the strain from which the RNA was extracted.

THE STRUCTURE OF NUCLEIC ACIDS

An understanding of the storage of genetic information is dependent on some knowledge of the structure of nucleic acids. DNA and RNA are similar in many respects. They are both large polymers. The molecular weights of some types of RNA are in the range 30,000 to 50,000; others commonly have molecular weights of about two million. DNA generally is larger, with some types of approximately two million molecular weight but most ten million or larger.

Both DNA and RNA are composed of similar types of chemical units. The differences are shown in Table 7–2. The primary (covalent) structure of each is a long chain of nucleotides. Each nucleotide consists of an organic base, a 5-carbon sugar, and phosphate (Fig. 7–1). The bases are of two types—purines and pyrimidines. The purines are either adenine or guanine (Fig. 7–2). The pyrimidines of DNA are cytosine and thymine; in RNA, they are cytosine and uracil. DNA from a few species has such bases as 5-methylcytosine, but these appear to be functionally equivalent to cytosine. Most RNA contains only the four bases given in Table 7–2, although some special types of RNA contain other pyrimidine derivatives as well. DNA contains D-2-deoxyribose as the sugar moiety, while RNA contains D-ribose. This difference is responsible for the difference in names—deoxyribonucleic acid and ribonucleic acid. Both contain phosphoric acid.

In nucleic acids, nucleotides are polymerized into long chains. This is accomplished by the phosphate of one nucleotide forming a bond with the 3'-hydroxyl of the adjacent nucleotide, resulting in a long chain with a "backbone" composed of alternating sugar and phosphate groups. A purine or pyrimidine base is attached to each sugar (Fig. 7–3). There is no theoretical limit to the number of nucleotides that can enter into such a chain; in nucleic acids, the chains may consist of many thousands of

TABLE 7–2

The Constituents of DNA and RNA

	DNA	RNA
bases	adenine	adenine
	guanine	guanine
	cytosine	cytosine
	thymine	*uracil*
	5-methylcytosine[a]	
	5-hydroxymethylcytosine[b]	
sugars	D-2-deoxyribose	D-ribose
	D-glucose[c]	
acid	phosphoric	phosphoric

[a] Replaces part of cytosine in some species.
[b] Replaces cytosine entirely in some bacterial viruses.
[c] Conjugated with 5-hydroxymethylcytosine in those bacterial viruses that contain the latter.

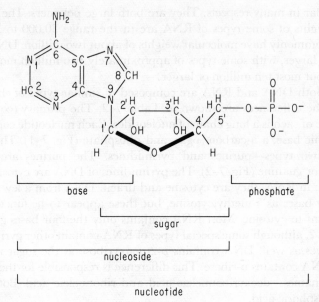

base | phosphate

sugar

nucleoside

nucleotide

Figure 7–1. The structure of adenosine-5'-phosphate (adenylic acid). Other nucleotides have different bases attached to the ribose. Deoxyribonucleotides have deoxyribose as the sugar.

PURINES:

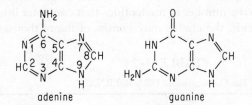

adenine   guanine

PYRIMIDINES:

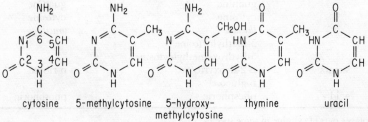

cytosine   5-methylcytosine   5-hydroxy-   thymine   uracil
                                methylcytosine

Figure 7–2. The purine and pyrimidine bases that occur commonly in nucleic acids.

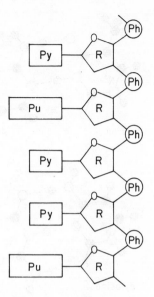

Figure 7–3. Diagram of the structure of a polynucleotide chain. A free phosphate bond is indicated at top and a free 3'-hydroxyl at the bottom. Note that the chain has polarity because of the asymmetry of the sugar units.

nucleotides. At one end there will always be a phosphoric acid group and at the other end an unbound 3'-hydroxyl on the sugar.

The aspect of the structure in which every element is attached by covalent bonds is known as the *primary* structure. A single chain such as that pictured in Figure 7–3 would be quite flexible and resemble a tangled mass of string. The DNA of cells is normally a somewhat rigid rodlike structure. This property is conferred by interaction between DNA chains of forces other than covalent bonds. These noncovalent forces are responsible for the *secondary* structure of DNA.

Native DNA consists of two nucleotide chains coiled about each other to form a double-strand helix. In the structure proposed by J. D. Watson and F. H. C. Crick, the two strands of the double helix are held together by hydrogen bonds between pairs of bases. Hydrogen bonds are weak bonds formed when a hydrogen atom covalently bound to one organic grouping also has an affinity for another grouping to which it is not covalently bound. For example, a hydrogen bound to an oxygen or nitrogen may form a weak bond with other oxygen or nitrogen atoms having unshared electrons. The groups must be precisely oriented spatially in order for bond formation to occur. The purines and pyrimidines found in nucleic acids can combine in several ways to form hydrogen-bonded structures. The distance between the sugar-phosphate backbones, however, is such that only a purine-pyrimidine combination can fit properly. Two purines would be too large and two pyrimidines too small. Only two combinations meet all the physical and chemical requirements

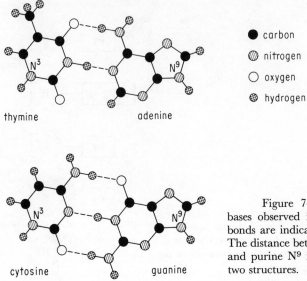

● carbon

◍ nitrogen

○ oxygen

⊕ hydrogen

Figure 7–4. The pairing of bases observed in DNA. Hydrogen bonds are indicated by dotted lines. The distance between pyrimidine N^3 and purine N^9 is the same in these two structures.

of the DNA structure—adenine bonded to thymine and cytosine bonded to guanine (Fig. 7–4). In these two paired structures, the distances between pyrimidine N^3 and purine N^9 are the same and correspond to the distance between the sugar-phosphate backbones.

One consequence of this specific pairing is that the amount of thymine in a particular source of DNA should always be equal to the amount of adenine, and the amount of cytosine should equal the amount of guanine. These relationships have been widely verified. A segment of a DNA molecule is illustrated in Figure 7–5.

The sequences of bases is an important feature of the molecule. At any one position, any of the four bases may be present. Thus, for any one chain, any sequence of bases is possible. However, the sequence in one chain requires a specific reciprocal sequence in the other. If adenine is present at a given position in one chain, thymine must be present at the corresponding position in the other. The sequence AATCGGC (using initial letters as symbols for the bases) in one chain must be matched by the sequence TTAGCCG in the other.

Since any one of the four bases may be present at any one of the nucleotide positions, an enormous number of DNA forms is possible. The number is 4^n, where n is the number of nucleotide positions. For only two positions—a dinucleotide—sixteen structures could exist: AA, AT, AC, AG, TA, TT, etc. For three positions, the number is 64, and for $n = 10$, the number is 1,048,576. Therefore, DNA can exist in the many forms necessary to store the information of a vast number of different genes.

The Structure of RNA

The primary structure of RNA is similar to that of DNA (Table 7–2). RNA normally is found to be a single-strand structure, in contrast to the double helix of DNA. Certain types of RNA show hydrogen bonding between bases, probably resulting from twisting of a single RNA strand—in the same way that a suspended rope that is twisted will coil to form a double helix.

Three types of RNA have been observed. The largest type has a molecular weight of approximately two million and is a component of *ribosome* particles. Ribosome particles are complexes of RNA and protein found primarily in cytoplasm but also to some extent in nuclei. Next in size is *messenger RNA,* which is synthesized in nuclei and migrates to the cytoplasm. This RNA is thought to carry genetic information from the DNA of chromosomes to ribosomes, where protein is synthesized. The third type is *transfer RNA* (molecular weight 30,000 to 50,000), sometimes

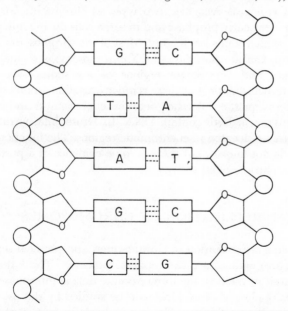

Figure 7–5. Diagram of a segment of a double-stranded DNA molecule. In the crystalline form and under many biological conditions, the two strands are twisted around each other to form a helix.

referred to as soluble RNA because it does not precipitate in acid as do other nucleic acids. It functions in the transfer of amino acids in protein synthesis. The functions of the three types of RNA will be discussed in more detail in the next chapter.

THE STRUCTURE OF CHROMOSOMES

DNA and histone are present throughout the length of a chromosome, although the distribution is not uniform. Their relationship has yet to be established. The amount of DNA in a chromosome is too great to be compatible with a straight, unfolded structure. For example, the DNA in the smallest human chromosomes (21 and 22) has a total molecular weight of 2×10^{10} and a length of 1 cm. The lengths of the chromosomes are only 1.5 μ during metaphase, and, though they may be much longer during interphase, they could not accommodate 1 cm of DNA unless it were coiled or made more compact.

Chromosomes readily pick up a variety of cytological stains. Because of their high affinity for dyes, they sometimes are said to consist of *chromatin*. Cytologists recognize two types of chromatin: *heterochromatin*, stainable in very early prophase and in some cells during interphase, and *euchromatin*, which stains less readily. Most of the chromosomal material is euchromatin. Certain portions—the Y chromosome, a segment of the X chromosome, and centromere regions of autosomes—are characteristically heterochromatic, but there is much variation among species. The chemical basis for the difference between euchromatin and heterochromatin is unknown. Both contain DNA. In Drosophila, virtually all the known genes are located in euchromatic regions. The function of heterochromatin is not known, but there is some evidence of a possible role as regulator of chromosomal activity.

CHEMICAL REPLICATION OF CHROMOSOMES

Chemical replication of chromosomes and physical separation of daughter chromosomes are two separate processes. The latter occurs as part of mitosis or meiosis; the former occurs during interphase. The time of synthesis of chromosomal DNA can be studied by the use of tritium-labeled thymidine. (Tritium, H^3, is a radioactive isomer of hydrogen.) This nucleoside of thymine is incorporated only into DNA. If a pulse of labeled thymidine is added to growing cells, chromosomes that have completed their replication will not acquire the label. However, chromosomes that have not completed replication will become radioactive. In cultures of human cells, DNA synthesis occurs approximately three hours before prophase.

DNA has two important functions as the carrier of genetic information: a *heterocatalytic* function concerned with the direction of cellular activities of other kinds of chemical components, and an *autocatalytic* function concerned with the direction of synthesis of a copy of itself. The double helix of the Watson-Crick structure suggested to its discoverers a means of replication that preserves the base sequences. As previously stated, the two strands of a DNA double helix have sequences of complementary bases. If the two strands are separated, each could serve as a template to direct a copy of its complementary strand (Fig. 7–6). The result would be two complete DNA molecules, each consisting of a strand of the original molecule and a strand of newly synthesized material.

The chemical reactions involved in DNA synthesis have been extensively studied by Kornberg and his associates. The following reaction has been established:

$$A—dR—P—P—P + G—dR—P—P—P \xrightarrow[\text{primer}]{\text{enzyme, Mg}^{2+}}$$

$$A—dR—P—dR—P—P—P + P—P$$
$$\overset{|}{G}$$

This equation illustrates formation of a dinucleotide from the triphosphates of adenine deoxyriboside and guanine deoxyriboside. An enzyme is required, as is Mg^{2+} and a "primer." The primer is preformed DNA. All four deoxyribonucleosides must ordinarily be present if large polymers are to be formed. Newly formed DNA is similar to whatever primer may have been used, indicating that the primer serves as a template for the condensation of bases in a specific sequence.

Although the chemical reactions of DNA synthesis are largely understood, it has not been satisfactorily established that DNA unwinds during synthesis in the manner suggested by Watson and Crick. Several lines of evidence favor the hypothesis, however. Of particular significance is the observation that single-stranded DNA, obtained from the unusual virus ϕX174 or by heating double-stranded DNA, is superior to double-stranded DNA in the promotion of DNA synthesis *in vitro*. On infection of a cell, the single-stranded virus directs synthesis of a reciprocal strand, the double-stranded structure serving as the replicating form inside the cell.

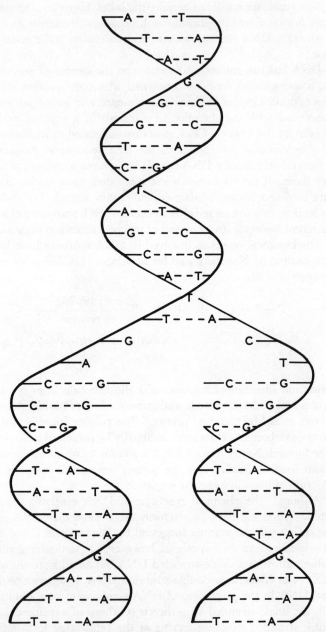

Figure 7–6. Proposed replication of DNA. As the double-stranded parent DNA unwinds, the separated strands serve as templates for the alignment of nucleotides, which combine to form new strands complementary to the parental strands.

REFERENCES AND SUGGESTED READING

AVERY, O. T., MACLEOD, C. M., and MCCARTY, M. 1944. Studies on the chemical nature of the substance inducing transformation of pneumococcal types. *J. Exptl. Med.* 79: 137–158.

DAVERN, C. I., and MESELSON, M. 1960. The molecular conservation of ribonucleic acid during bacterial growth. *J. Mol. Biol.* 2: 153–160.

GRIFFITH, F. 1928. The significance of pneumococcal types. *J. Hyg.* 27: 113–159.

KORNBERG, A. 1957. Pathways of enzymatic synthesis of nucleotides and polynucleotides. In *The Chemical Basis of Heredity* (W. D. McElroy and B. Glass, eds.). Baltimore: The Johns Hopkins Press, pp. 579–608.

LEUCHTENBERGER, C., LEUCHTENBERGER, R., and DAVIS, A. M. 1954. A microspectrophotometric study of the desoxyribose nucleic acid (DNA) content in cells of normal and malignant tissues. *Am. J. Pathol.* 30: 65–85.

SWANSON, C. P. 1957. *Cytology and Cytogenetics.* Englewood Cliffs, N. J.: Prentice-Hall, 596 pp.

VENDRELY, R. 1955. The deoxyribonucleic acid content of the nucleus. In *The Nucleic Acids,* Vol. II (E. Chargaff and J. Davidson, eds.). New York: Academic Press, pp. 181–198.

WATSON, J. D. 1963. Involvement of RNA in the synthesis of proteins. *Science* 140: 17–26.

————, and CRICK, F. H. C. 1953a. A structure for deoxyribose nucleic acid. *Nature* 171: 737–738.

————, and CRICK, F. H. C. 1953b. Genetical implications of the structure of deoxyribonucleic acid. *Nature* 171: 964–967.

WILKINS, M. H. F. 1963. Molecular configuration of nucleic acids. *Science* 140: 941–950.

PROBLEMS

1. Define:

    deoxyribonucleic acid   messenger RNA
    ribonucleic acid   transfer RNA

histone   euchromatin
transformation   heterochromatin
nucleotide   heterocatalysis
Watson-Crick structure of DNA   autocatalysis
hydrogen bond   DNA primer
ribosome

Chapter Eight

CHEMICAL ACTIVITY
OF GENES

Genes exert their influence on cells by altering the reaction rates of metabolic processes. This occurs through their influence on the kinds and amount of enzymes and other proteins. Consideration of the changes in proteins that result from genetic changes should lead to understanding of the manner in which genes control cellular activities.

GENETIC CONTROL OF PROTEIN STRUCTURE

The Chemical Nature of Proteins

Proteins are large organic molecules that occur in a variety of sizes, shapes, and functions. Molecular weights vary from 6000 for insulin and 13,500 for ribonuclease to 500,000 or higher. Proteins are composed of one or more chains of amino acids, folded and coiled into a three-dimensional structure. Twenty amino acids occur commonly in proteins (Table 8–1). The rare instances of other amino acids in proteins are thought to happen by conversion of one of the twenty to a related structure. Chemically, amino acids are compounds of the type structure $H_2N-CH(R)-COOH$, where R denotes a variety of organic groupings. Only proline and hydroxyproline deviate from this general structure.

In proteins, amino acids are linked by peptide bonds. This involves elimination of a hydroxyl from the carboxyl group of one amino acid and a hydrogen from the amino group of another:

$$H_2N-\overset{R'}{\underset{|}{C}H}-\overset{O}{\underset{||}{C}}-OH + H\overset{H}{\underset{|}{N}}-\overset{R''}{\underset{|}{C}H}-\overset{O}{\underset{||}{C}}-OH \longrightarrow$$

$$H_2N-\overset{R'}{\underset{|}{C}H}-\overset{O}{\underset{||}{C}}-\overset{H}{\underset{|}{N}}-\overset{R''}{\underset{|}{C}H}-COOH + HOH$$

TABLE 8-1

The Amino Acids Found in Proteins
All of the Amino Acids Are of the L Configuration

AMINO ACID	ABBREVIATION	AMINO ACID	ABBREVIATION
1. alanine	ala	11. leucine	leu
2. arginine	arg	12. lysine	lys
3. aspartic acid	asp	13. methionine	met
4. asparagine	asp(NH₂) or asn	14. phenylalanine	phe
5. cysteine	cys	15. proline	pro
6. glutamic acid	glu	16. serine	ser
7. glutamine	glu(NH₂) or gln	17. threonine	thr
8. glycine	gly	18. tryptophan	try
9. histidine	his	19. tyrosine	tyr
10. isoleucine	ileu	20. valine	val

The reaction is conveniently written as the elimination of water, but it is very much more complex than indicated. There remains a free amino group, conventionally written on the left, and a carboxyl group, written on the right. These are capable of reacting with other amino acids to form long *polypeptide chains*. Theoretically, there is no limit to the length of a polypeptide chain; many are known to consist of 200 or more amino acids. At one end there is always an amino group (the N-terminal end) and at the other a carboxyl group (the C-terminal end). In some proteins, the amino group is acetylated so that it cannot react as a free amino group, but this is uncommon.

The sequence of amino acids in a polypeptide chain is known as its *primary structure*. Two additional levels of structure are distinguished in proteins: *secondary structure,* in which sections of polypeptide chains are coiled into a helix stabilized by hydrogen bonds between consecutive turns of the coil, and *tertiary structure,* in which polypeptide chains, including helical segments, are oriented three dimensionally. Proper three-dimensional structure is necessary to provide a surface that functions biologically. The tertiary structure is stabilized by various chemical forces between functional groups of the amino acid side chains. Of particular significance in most proteins is the amino acid cysteine. The side chain of cysteine contains a sulfhydryl group; two sulfhydryl groups can react to form a disulfide, producing thereby a covalent bond between adjacent polypeptide chains (or segments of a chain). Heating and various other treatments disrupt the tertiary structure, destroying the biological activity of the molecule. This is called *denaturation*. In some cases, following the denaturation process, the active tertiary structure will re-form spontaneously after the denaturing agent is removed, demonstrating that the secondary and tertiary structures are largely, and perhaps entirely, a consequence of the primary structure.

Heredity and Primary Structure of Proteins

The manner in which protein structure is influenced by genes has been elucidated through studies of abnormal proteins. Human hemoglobin was the protein first found to exist in an abnormal form as a result of genetic change.

Hemoglobin is a globular protein of molecular weight 66,200. It contains four heme groups, each attached to a separate polypeptide chain. The four polypeptide chains of hemoglobin are of two types: one with the N-terminal sequence val-leu-, arbitrarily designated the alpha chain; the other with the N-terminal sequence val-his-leu-, designated the beta chain. Each chain is present twice in a hemoglobin molecule, and thus it can be symbolized $\alpha_2\beta_2$. The alpha chains consist of 141 amino acids, the beta chains of 146 amino acids. The exact sequence of amino acids in these chains has been established.

For several decades, the disease sickle cell anemia has been recognized. It is an inherited condition in which affected persons suffer from anemia due to excessive destruction of red cells in the circulatory system. In the presence of oxygen, the red cells are essentially normal. If oxygen pressure is low, as happens in many tissues, the red cells become distorted, in some instances resembling sickles (Fig. 8–1). Formation of sickle-shaped

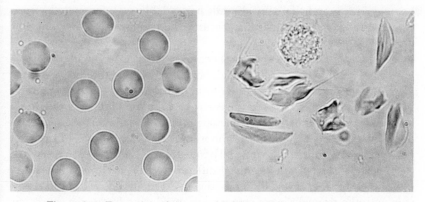

Figure 8–1. Formation of abnormal "sickle cells" under low oxygen pressure by red cells from persons homozygous for the sickle cell gene. On the left are normal red cells. On the right are sickle cells. (Courtesy W. C. Levin.)

cells in capillaries impedes circulation, leading to greater oxygen deficit and hence to more sickling. Interference with circulation leads to a variety of pathological consequences, depending on the tissues involved. Persons with the disease ordinarily do not survive to adulthood.

In addition to the severe form of the disease, there is a mild form in which red cells, although they do not sickle *in vivo,* can be induced to sickle *in vitro* in the presence of reducing agents. This form of the disease is known as sickle cell trait. In 1949, Neel demonstrated that sickle cell disease is inherited as a simple Mendelian recessive condition. Persons with the severe disease are homozygous for the gene, and those with the trait are heterozygous.

The chemical nature of sickle cell anemia also was discovered in 1949 by Pauling, Itano, Singer, and Wells. Proteins carry electrical charges because of the ionization of amino, carboxyl, and other functional groups. These charges cause migration toward cathode or anode when proteins are placed in an electrical field. The speed of migration of a particular protein is influenced by several factors, including electrical charge of the molecule, shape of the molecule, and so on. The charge that a protein carries depends also on the pH of the surrounding solvent.

When hemoglobin from a normal person is examined for electrophoretic mobility, virtually all of the hemoglobin migrates as a single entity (Fig. 8–2). Persons heterozygous for sickle cell disease possess two types of hemoglobin—normal hemoglobin and a slower moving variety. Persons homozygous for the sickle cell gene possess only the slower moving variety. Pauling and co-workers suggested that the altered mobility of sickle cell hemoglobin reflects a change in molecular structure due to the effects of the sickle cell gene. The abnormal hemoglobin was designated hemoglobin S, and the normal adult hemoglobin was designated hemoglobin A. Sickle cell anemia thus became the first established example of "molecular disease."

In addition to the abnormal hemoglobin associated with sickle cell anemia, a number of other hemoglobins have been detected. Nearly all were recognized because they differ from hemoglobin A in electrophoretic mobility. The remainder were detected because they influence the equilibrium between reduced (Fe^{2+}) hemoglobin and methemoglobin (Fe^{3+}). Some of these hemoglobins are abnormal, usually resulting in anemia; others appear to function as normal hemoglobin.

The nature of the chemical difference characteristic of Hb S was established by Ingram in 1956. He digested the large hemoglobin molecule with the proteolytic enzyme trypsin, producing fragments consisting of short sequences of amino acids. Both Hb A and Hb S produced the same array of small peptide fragments, with a single exception. One of the peptides of Hb S differed slightly from the homologous peptide of Hb A.

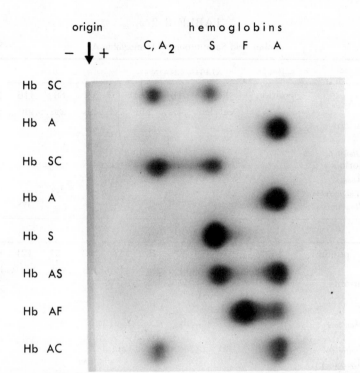

Figure 8–2. Electrophoretic mobility of hemoglobins from persons homozygous for Hb A, homozygous for Hb S, heterozygous for Hb's A and S, heterozygous for Hb's A and C, and heterozygous for Hb's S and C. The sample designated Hb AF is from umbilical cord blood, showing a high concentration of fetal hemoglobin. Hb A_2 is a normal hemoglobin present in small amounts (about 2 percent) in most persons. Mobilities of Hb C and Hb A_2 are similar under the conditions used. A slower mobility toward the anode at alkaline pH indicates a smaller negative charge. (Furnished by Rose G. Schneider.)

Detailed analysis of the amino acid sequences in these peptides gave the following results:

Hb A: val-his-leu-thr-pro-glu-glu-lys

Hb S: val-his-leu-thr-pro-val-glu-lys

These two peptides are identical except for the amino acid in position 6, which is glutamic acid in the case of Hb A and valine in the case of Hb S. Thus the effect of the Hb S mutation is to cause the substitution of a single amino acid out of a sequence of 146 amino acids in the β chain.

These observations have been extended to many other hemoglobin variants as well as to other proteins found in microorganisms. A summary of amino acid substitutions in those hemoglobins which have been analyzed is given in Table 8–2. The substitutions are found in both α and β chains in various positions along the chains.

TABLE 8–2

Amino Acid Substitutions of Hemoglobin A

	ALPHA CHAIN									
position	1	2	16	30	57	58	68	116	141	
	val .	leu ...	lys ...	glu ...	gly .	his ...	asn ...	glu ...	arg	
Hb variant										
I			asp							
G$_{Honolulu}$				gln						
Norfolk					asp					
M$_{Boston}$						tyr				
G$_{Philadelphia}$							lys			
O$_{Indonesia}$								lys		

	BETA CHAIN										
position	1	2	3	6	7	26	43	63	67	121	146
	val .	his .	leu ...	glu .	glu ...	glu ...	glu ...	his ...	val ...	glu ...	his
Hb variant											
S				val							
C				lys							
G$_{San Jose}$					gly						
E						lys					
G$_{Galveston}$							ala				
M$_{Saskatoon}$								tyr			
Zurich								arg			
M$_{Milwaukee-1}$									glu		
D$_{Punjab}$										gln	
O$_{Arabia}$										lys	

Of the variety of proteins that are structurally altered as a consequence of gene mutation, all have proved to be altered in their primary structure. Studies of denaturation and renaturation of proteins also have indicated that secondary and tertiary structure are determined by the sequence of amino acids. It seems likely then that the role of genes in controlling protein function is in determining the primary structure only. Changes in molecular shape would arise as a secondary consequence of changes in amino acid sequences.

Biosynthesis of Proteins

Proteins are synthesized in all cells, primarily in the cytoplasm but to some extent also in the nucleus. The sites of synthesis are ribosomes, minute bodies consisting of RNA and proteins. Cells whose special function is secretion of protein (for example, salivary glands) are especially rich in ribosomes.

The principal features of protein synthesis have been established, although many details are lacking. Three kinds of RNA are involved— messenger RNA, transfer RNA, and ribosomal RNA. Messenger RNA, the transmitter of genetic information from DNA to cytoplasm, is synthesized in the nucleus and then passes into the cytoplasm. In the cytoplasm, it combines with ribosomes. Transfer RNA combines with activated amino acids and aligns them in the proper sequence for the protein to be synthesized. It is the smallest of the RNA molecules, with molecular weights in the range 30,000 to 50,000.

Figure 8–3 is a diagram of the major aspects of protein synthesis. Free amino acids react with adenosine triphosphate (ATP), forming amino acyl adenylates. An enzyme specific for each amino acid is necessary to catalyze these reactions. Without dissociating from the surface of the enzyme, the amino acyl adenylate reacts with transfer RNA, each amino acid requiring a specific RNA. These amino acid–RNA com-

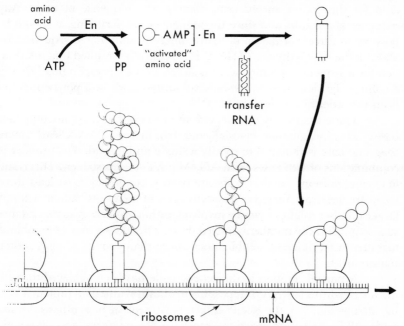

Figure 8–3. Diagram of protein synthesis showing activation and reaction of amino acids with transfer RNA, followed by alignment on messenger RNA and formation of polypeptide. The ribosomes, mRNA, tRNA, and amino acids are not drawn to scale.

pounds then align on a template formed by messenger RNA and ribosomes. The nature of the protein synthesized depends entirely on the source of messenger RNA, not on the source of ribosomes. It is thought therefore that messenger RNA forms the essential part of the template. With the amino acid–RNA compounds in the correct sequence, the amino acids are joined together by peptide bonds to form a polypeptide chain, which in turn separates from the RNA template. The free polypeptide chain can fold into a biologically active tertiary structure, although the proximity of microsomal elements may facilitate the folding.

The Genetic Code

The studies of hemoglobin demonstrate that DNA stores information specifying the precise sequence of amino acids. From biochemical studies of protein synthesis, it is also apparent that this information is transferred to RNA and that RNA directs the alignment of amino acids. In the structure of DNA, there is one attribute that is an obvious candidate for the coding mechanism, namely, the sequence of bases. Any sequence is possible, and since the sequences are very long, it should be possible to direct formation of many different amino acid sequences by altering the base sequence of DNA. It is generally assumed that information for a sequence of amino acids is stored in the corresponding DNA in a colinear fashion; that is, the order of amino acids in a polypeptide reflects the order of coding units in DNA.

There are twenty amino acids in proteins, but there are only four bases—adenine, guanine, cytosine, and thymine—in DNA. Clearly, more than one base is required to specify a single amino acid. The number of combinations of two bases (AA, AG, AC, AT, . . .) is sixteen. This is still four combinations too few to specify twenty amino acids. At least three bases are necessary therefore to specify each of the twenty amino acids. A larger number might in fact be involved, although there is some evidence suggesting that the number is indeed three. Three bases may be combined together in 64 different combinations, more than enough to meet coding requirements.

A partial solution to the genetic code has been achieved through the use of synthetic RNA. It is possible to obtain synthesis of protein *in vitro* by mixing together the essential factors in protein biosynthesis: amino acids, ATP, activating enzymes, transfer RNA mixtures, and ribosomes. The ribosomes must have messenger RNA bound to them in order to function. Nirenberg and Matthaei found that synthetic RNA can replace natural messenger RNA. Instead of directing the synthesis of a biologically active protein, a "nonsense" protein is made.

In their first studies, they used synthetic RNA consisting entirely of uridylic acid units, so-called polyuridylic acid or poly-U. The polypeptide chain that was synthesized contained only phenylalanine, although the other amino acids were present in the reaction mixture and could have been incorporated, had the RNA message so specified. It was concluded that a sequence consisting only of uridylic acids codes for phenylalanine. If exactly three bases are required, then the coding unit (*code word* or *codon*) for phenylalanine is UUU. It should be remembered that this is the RNA code. The mechanism for transferring information from DNA to RNA has not been fully clarified. It is thought that RNA must have a reciprocal relationship to one of the DNA strands. If so, then UUU would be the "transcription" of AAA, since U in RNA is homologous to T in DNA.

Of the 64 possible sequences of three bases, some 50 have been shown to code for specific amino acids. The remainder had not been tested when this was written. It seems likely then that every sequence codes for one particular amino acid, but some amino acids may be coded in more than one way.

QUANTITATIVE ASPECTS OF PROTEIN SYNTHESIS

In the previous sections, the qualitative effects of genes were considered. It is known, however, that genes do not function at all times. Many proteins that play an important role in an adult animal are not synthesized during embryonic development, and probably very few are synthesized during early development of the zygote. Other proteins may be synthesized primarily during embryonic development but not during adulthood. It is necessary then to consider what factors may influence the quantitative aspects of gene action.

Control Genes

Most knowledge concerning control of gene action comes from bacterial studies. In bacteria, and in higher organisms as well, enzymes are known that are produced only in special environmental situations. An example in the bacterium *Escherichia coli* is the enzyme β-galactosidase. This enzyme splits the sugar lactose into galactose and glucose, which then can be metabolized for energy. If lactose is not present in culture media, *E. coli* does not produce galactosidase. If lactose (or certain other galactosides) are present in the media, then large quantities of the enzyme are manufactured. This responsiveness to environmental conditions is designated *induced* enzyme formation.

Mutant forms of *E. coli* have been isolated that cannot be induced. Instead, they are *constitutive,* manufacturing the enzyme continually whether or not galactosides are present. The enzyme produced is apparently normal enzyme, but a mutation has given rise to a defect in the control system for enzyme synthesis. It is possible to show by genetic means that the mutations which lead to constitutive enzyme production are located at definite positions on the chromosome, some adjacent to the locus that determines structure of β-galactosidase and others separated from this locus. Such genes might be considered *control genes* as opposed to *structural genes.*

Two types of control genes have been detected in the *E. coli* galactosidase system. Mutations of either may cause constitutive enzyme production. One of the control genes is located separate from the structural gene. It appears to act by means of a diffusible chemical substance rather than by direct physical effects. The nature of the diffusible substance has not been established. The function of the diffusible substance is to repress enzyme synthesis by the structural gene. It is therefore called *repressor,* and the gene that directs its synthesis is known as a *regulator gene.*

The precise mode of action of repressor substance is unknown, although it appears to form a complex with a control region that is located adjacent to or is part of the structural gene. When repressor is present, the structural gene does not function; when it is absent, the structural gene acts in the production of its specific protein. The control region that forms complexes with repressor and that appears to turn the structural gene "on" and "off" is designated an *operator.* An operator and the one or more structural genes associated with it are called an *operon.*

Current ideas on the relationships of the three types of genes are summarized in Figure 8–4. The environment acts through its influence on repressor-operator complexes. In the galactosidase example, galactosides presumably interfere with complex formation, permitting the operator to remain in the "on" position. In the absence of galactosides, the repressor forms complexes with the operator, leading to inhibition of enzyme formation.

A mutation of the regulator gene could lead to abnormal repressor, which might show either of two effects. First, the repressor might be unable to form a complex with the operator, in which case enzyme synthesis would occur at the maximum rate. Or second, the repressor might no longer be sensitive to inhibition by inducer from the environment and would form complexes with operator regardless of presence of inducer.

Since the product of regulator genes is diffusible, the repressor

substance from a single regulator gene may influence both the operators
on homologous chromosomes of a diploid cell (Fig. 8–4). A defect in one
of the two homologous regulator genes would not necessarily lead therefore to abnormal gene function, since the remaining regulator gene could
synthesize sufficient repressor to inhibit both operators. Such a constitutive mutation would be recessive.

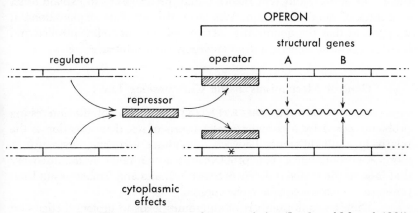

Figure 8–4. The operon theory of gene regulation (Jacob and Monod, 1961).
Regulator genes are responsible for synthesis of a repressor substance which can form
complexes with specific operators. Presence of a repressor causes genes in the same
operon not to synthesize mRNA. Mutation of an operator, indicated in the figure by
an asterisk, could lead to loss of ability to form complexes with repressors, with continued synthesis of mRNA by that operon. Cytoplasmic factors can either enhance or
diminish the activity of repressors. The mRNA is shown as a single molecule carrying
the information of two structural genes. Recent studies of microbial systems suggest
that all the structural genes in one operon give rise to one mRNA molecule. Each
polypeptide is synthesized in turn as a specific ribosome moves along the mRNA.

Mutations in operators might also lead to various effects. If operators are considered as "off" and "on" switches for structural genes, then
mutation of an operator conceivably could lead to continuous function of
the structural gene or to the permanent lack of function, regardless of
the presence of inducer. In the latter case, this could occur by alteration
to a form that is unable to form a complex with repressor or to a form that
complexes but nevertheless permits function of the structural gene. There
is no diffusible substance involved in the action of the operator on the
structural gene; therefore, the effects are limited to structural genes in
the same operon.

Although a logical distinction can be made between some of the
above types of mutants, it is not always possible to distinguish them experimentally. For example, a defect in a structural gene leading to lack

of enzyme synthesis is functionally indistinguishable from mutation of the operator gene to a form that does not permit the structural gene to function.

The operon theory explains very well observations made on several bacterial systems. Whether it is the explanation for all cases of gene regulation is yet to be determined. Possibly, modifications of the operon theory, or entirely different theories, may be necessary to explain other examples of gene regulation. Whatever the ultimate explanations, it is apparent that the quantitative activity of genes is well controlled and is subject both to genetic and to environmental influences.

Control Mechanisms at the Chromosome Level

X-CHROMOSOME DIFFERENTIATION.   One of the interesting problems posed by a chromosomal pattern of sex determination is the relatively small difference between individuals with one versus two or more X chromosomes. This problem was accentuated by the discovery that most of the sexual differences between males and females result from presence of or absence of a Y chromosome.

Differences in numbers of autosomes leads to profound effects on function. The only essentially viable autosomal trisomy is trisomy 21 syndrome, involving one of the smallest chromosomes. But, males and females differ by an X chromosome, one of the larger chromosomes known to carry many genes. How is it that genic imbalance does not occur with the X chromosome? Indeed, persons with four X chromosomes are little different from those with two.

The operon theory, which accounts for regulation of individual loci, would not seem a satisfactory explanation for an entire chromosome. It is possible that natural selection has favored location on the X chromosome of those genes which can readily be controlled. An alternate hypothesis of X-chromosome inactivation has been advanced and is supported by several lines of evidence. The hypothesis states that in any one mammalian cell, only one X chromosome is active. In males, the single X chromosome is always active; in females, one of the two X chromosomes becomes inactive at an early stage of development. In any given cell, the choice of which X chromosome is to become inactive is entirely a matter of chance. Once inactivated, a chromosome continues to replicate at mitosis but remains inactive through subsequent cell cycles. This hypothesis has been most fully stated by Mary F. Lyon and is known as the Lyon hypothesis.

Several lines of evidence support the hypothesis. B. M. Cattanach's observations on coat color in mice initially provided support. He found that certain color genes in mice behave abnormally when translocated to X chromosomes. Instead of the usual dominant and recessive relationship of alleles characteristic of autosomal position, a variegated phenotype was produced. In an animal heterozygous for two color alleles, some parts of the skin showed the effect of the dominant allele, other parts expressed the recessive allele. In these latter areas, the dominant allele does not function, although it always is expressed if the alleles are in their normal autosomal location.

A second line of evidence is cytological. During prophase, the two X chromosomes are not precisely equivalent. Comparison of nuclei at various stages of mitosis indicates that one X chromosome behaves similarly to the autosomes. If more than one X is present, as in an XX female, the second X is somewhat more condensed at some stages and appears to participate in formation of the sex chromatin body.

Radioautographic studies of replicating chromosomes clearly show that in females one of the X chromosomes replicates later than the other chromosome. The chromosomes of human cells in culture replicate approximately three hours before mitosis. If tritium-labeled thymidine is added prior to mitosis, then DNA synthesized after the addition is radioactive. If the thymidine is added early enough, all the chromosomes will be labeled. If it is added late in the replication period, then only those portions of chromosomes which are still replicating will be labeled. Although there are small consistent differences in the time of DNA synthesis in various chromosomes, the most pronounced difference is observed with X chromosomes. In males, the single X chromosome replicates at the same time as the autosomes. In females, one of the X chromosomes replicates with the autosomes and one somewhat later. If tritium-labeled thymidine is added just before the late X begins replication, most of the label incorporated will be in that chromosome. Figure 8–5 is a radioautograph showing one of the X chromosomes highly labeled, with the remainder of the chromosomes bearing only a small label.

The most impressive evidence illustrating X-chromosome inactivation involves the enzyme glucose-6-phosphate dehydrogenase (G6PD). This enzyme is found in virtually all forms of life, including man. It occurs in essentially all tissues, including red blood cells, where it acts to maintain the proper balance of reduced glutathione. Variant forms of the enzyme occur in man and are transmitted genetically by a gene on the X chromosome. Electrophoresis of G6PD reveals mobility differences among some of the variants. Males never have more than one form of G6PD, but females can be heterozygous and frequently have two forms.

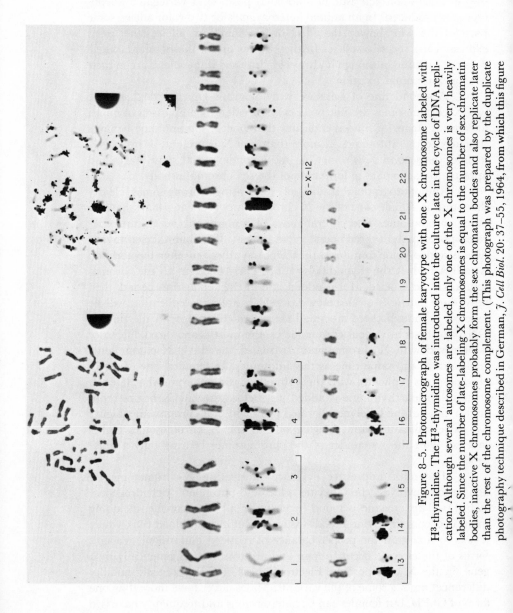

Figure 8–5. Photomicrograph of female karyotype with one X chromosome labeled with H³-thymidine. The H³-thymidine was introduced into the culture late in the cycle of DNA replication. Although several autosomes are labeled, only one of the X chromosomes is very heavily labeled. Since the number of late-labeling X chromosomes is equal to the number of sex chromatin bodies, inactive X chromosomes probably form the sex chromatin bodies and also replicate later than the rest of the chromosome complement. (This photograph was prepared by the duplicate photography technique described in German, *J. Cell Biol.* 20: 37–55, 1964, from which this figure

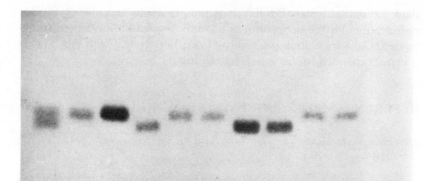

Figure 8–6. Electrophoretic separation of glucose-6-phosphate dehydrogenase variants from a woman heterozygous for types A (fast) and B (slow). On the left is an extract from a skin culture, showing both forms of the enzyme. The remaining preparations were extracted from clones derived from *single* cells of the skin culture. In individual cells, only one X chromosome is active and only one form of the enzyme is produced. Once an X chromosome becomes inactive, it remains so through subsequent cell divisions, even though it replicates. (From Davidson, Nitowsky, and Childs, *Proc. Natl. Acad. Sci.* (U.S.) 50: 481–485, 1963, with permission.)

Beutler, Yeh, and Fairbanks obtained evidence from studies of enzyme activities that red cells of heterozygotes are a mixture of two types of cells, each containing only one of the two forms of G6PD. Davidson, Nitowski, and Childs cultured cells from a woman heterozygous for two forms of G6PD. Electrophoresis of enzyme prepared from a mixture of cells showed both forms to be present (Fig. 8–6). However, if single cells were isolated and permitted to replicate to form a clone of cells adequate for extraction, quite different results were obtained. In this case, each clone (or culture) contained only one form of G6PD. It might be either the fast or slow form but not both.

While the fact of X-chromosome differentiation can now be accepted, there are many aspects that are not well understood. There is no evidence on the nature of the process. The exact period in development when it occurs is unknown. Whether it occurs simultaneously in all tissues and whether it extends to all tissues are unknown. Since both X chromosomes in a zygote have full potential, inactivation must be reversed by meiosis or may not occur in germinal tissue. L. B. Russell has demonstrated in mice that inactivation does not extend over the entire X chromosome. The limits are still poorly described and are not known in other organisms.

X-chromosome inactivation is an example of a means of regulating gene activity. It is concerned with segments of chromosomes rather than individual genes. Possibly it is unique among regulatory mechanisms, although the opportunities to study regulation have been rather limited. Gene regulation is a topic of great importance, and much effort is being expended in the search for additional systems.

REFERENCES AND SUGGESTED READING

ANFINSEN, C. B. 1959. *The Molecular Basis of Evolution.* New York: Wiley, 228 pp.

BAGLIONI, C. 1963. Correlations between genetics and chemistry of human hemoglobins. In *Molecular Biology,* Part I (J. H. Taylor, ed.). New York: Academic Press, pp. 405–475.

BEUTLER, E., YEH, M., and FAIRBANKS, V. F. 1962. The normal human female as a mosaic of X-chromosome activity: Studies using the gene for G-6-PD-deficiency as a marker. *Proc. Natl. Acad. Sci.* (U.S.) 48: 9–16.

CRICK, F. H. C., BARNETT, L., BRENNER, S., and WATTS-TOBIN, R. J. 1961. General nature of the genetic code for proteins. *Nature* 192: 1227–1232.

DAVIDSON, R. G., NITOWSKI, H. M., and CHILDS, B. 1963. Demonstration of two populations of cells in the human female heterozygous for glucose-6-phosphate dehydrogenase variants. *Proc. Natl. Acad. Sci.* (U.S.) 50: 481–485.

DINTZIS, H. M. 1961. Assembly of the peptide chains of hemoglobin. *Proc. Natl. Acad. Sci.* (U.S.) 47: 247–261.

GERMAN, J. 1964. The pattern of DNA synthesis in the chromosomes of human blood cells. *J. Cell Biol.* 20: 37–55.

INGRAM, V. M. 1956. A specific chemical difference between the globins of normal human and sickle-cell anaemia haemoglobin. *Nature* 178: 792–794.

JACOB, F., and MONOD, J. 1961. Genetic regulatory mechanisms in the synthesis of proteins. *J. Mol. Biol.* 3: 318–356.

JONES, O. W., and NIRENBERG, M. W. 1962. Qualitative survey of RNA codewords. *Proc. Natl. Acad. Sci.* (U.S.) 48: 2115.

LYON, M. F. 1962. Sex chromatin and gene action in the mammalian X-chromosome. *Am. J. Human Genet.* 14: 135–148.

NEEL, J. V. 1949. The inheritance of sickle-cell anemia. *Science* 110: 64–66.

NIRENBERG, M. W., and MATTHAEI, J. H. 1961. The dependence of cell-free protein synthesis in *E. coli* upon naturally occurring or synthetic polyribonucleotides. *Proc. Natl. Acad. Sci.* (U.S.) 47: 1588–1602.

PAULING, L., ITANO, H. A., SINGER, S. J., and WELLS, I. C. 1949. Sickle-cell anemia, a molecular disease. *Science* 110: 543–548.

SUTTON, H. E. 1964. Genes and protein synthesis. In *Second International Conference on Congenital Malformations*. New York: International Medical Congress, Ltd., pp. 113–124.

WARNER, J. R., KNOPF, P. M., and RICH, A. 1963. A multiple ribosomal structure in protein synthesis. *Proc. Natl. Acad. Sci.* (U.S.) 49: 122–129.

ZUBAY, G. 1963. Molecular model for protein synthesis. *Science* 140: 1092–1095.

PROBLEMS

1. Define:

amino acid	induced enzyme
protein	constitutive enzyme
peptide	control gene
denaturation	structural gene
N-terminal	regulator gene
C-terminal	repressor
sickle cell anemia	operator
electrophoresis	operon
ribosome	X-chromosome inactivation
codon	clone

Chapter Nine

PHENOTYPIC EXPRESSION OF GENES

In the preceding chapters, consideration has been given to the manner in which genes act. Any organism, whether a single cell or a human being, is the product of its genes, or *genotype,* acting in a specific environment. The resulting *phenotype* is a complex expression of both genotype and environment. The distinction between genotype and phenotype should be kept clearly in mind. The phenotype is the observable organism. The genotype is the complex of genes, which, with the environment, gives rise to the phenotype. The existence of the genotype can be inferred only through its effect on the phenotype of the individual organism or through studies of his family.

To understand clearly the relationship of genes to phenotype requires consideration of the chemical events that result from gene action. This will require also a discussion of the consequences of gene malfunction, since the expression of abnormal gene effects is a major source of the information gained concerning normal gene function.

GENES AND METABOLISM

The first suggestion that genes act by controlling metabolism was made by Garrod in the first decade of this century. This British physician believed that inherited diseases could be explained in terms of the new science of genetics, and he reported his investigations of four diseases—alkaptonuria, cystinuria, pentosuria, and albinism—as examples of Mendelian inheritance. From his studies of alkaptonuria, he concluded that persons homozygous for this rare gene lack a specific enzyme necessary for the complete metabolism of homogentisic acid.

Garrod's remarkable perception was largely unrecognized. Even though his ideas are known to have been familiar to many biochemists and geneticists, very little was known then about enzymes and their

98

function. Garrod's ideas could not be effectively tested, and by the time biochemistry had made the necessary advances, they had been forgotten.

Modern understanding of gene action began with the studies of G. W. Beadle, E. L. Tatum, B. Ephrussi, and others in the 1930s. Their experimental approach to the questions began with transplantation in Drosophila larvae. Parts destined to become eyes can be transplanted from one larva to the abdominal region of another, where a fully developed eye will appear in the adult. The many mutations of eye color known in Drosophila provide a rich field for the study of host-donor interactions. From these studies came the suggestion that each gene is associated with a single step in the metabolic sequence leading to eye pigment. However, the complexity of eye pigment metabolism made it difficult to pinpoint gene action effectively. To accomplish this, Beadle and Tatum began their now famous studies of biochemical mutants in the mold *Neurospora*.

For biochemical studies, *Neurospora* has many advantages over Drosophila. It is morphologically much simpler than Drosophila, so that many problems of tissue differentiation are avoided. It undergoes meiosis, but, unlike the situation in Drosophila and many other organisms, the four meiotic products of a single gametocyte remain together in a single spore sac (Fig. 9–1). *Neurospora* is a haploid organism, and therefore

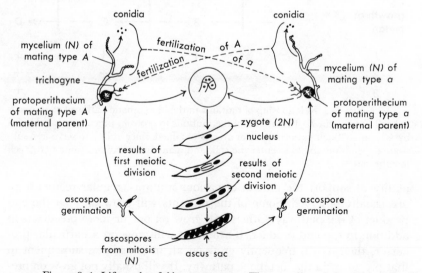

Figure 9–1. Life cycle of *Neurospora crassa*. The mycelium is haploid and reproduces asexually. If both mating types are present, the sexual cycle may occur as indicated. (From R. P. Wagner and H. K. Mitchell *Genetics and Metabolism,* 2d ed. New York: Wiley, 1964, by permission.)

mutations which might be recessive in a diploid organism are fully expressed. The diploid state exists in *Neurospora* but only transiently as a prelude to meiosis. Finally, and of particular importance to the type of study undertaken by Beadle and Tatum, the nutritional requirements of *Neurospora* are simple and were well known. They consist of inorganic salts, a source of energy (glucose), and biotin. Mutations that lead to additional nutritional requirements have provided a rich area for the study of gene action.

A large number of induced or spontaneous mutations have been obtained in *Neurospora*. Many of these are characterized by their inability to grow on the minimal media that is satisfactory for wild type. However, a large number of them grow very well if supplied with various additional nutrients. The mutants can be classified according to the nutritional elements that will support their growth. For example, some of the mutants will grow if minimal media is supplemented with the amino acid arginine; they are unable to manufacture their own arginine and are referred to as "arginineless".

Such mutants have been a powerful tool both in our gaining knowledge of the pathways by which substances such as arginine are synthesized and in our understanding how genes operate in these pathways. If the precursors in the biosynthetic pathway are studied for their

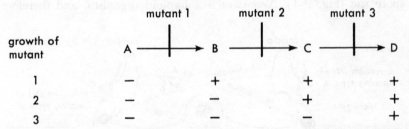

Figure 9–2. Relationship of mutants in the biosynthetic pathway of an essential cell constituent *D*. The ability of the mutants to grow on precursors is indicated by + and −. Such patterns are not always obtained, since ability to serve as a substrate depends on ability to enter the cell, and many intermediates cannot cross cell membranes.

ability to support the growth of various mutants, regular relationships are usually observed. Some of the mutants will grow only on the end product of the pathway. Others will grow on one or more precursors in addition to the end product. If a mutant will grow on a particular precursor, then it will frequently grow on all intermediates subsequent to that precursor in the metabolic pathway. It will usually not grow on precursors that fall earlier in the pathway. This is illustrated in Figure 9–2.

The simplest interpretation of these observations is that each mutant organism lacks a single enzyme necessary for the conversion of one chemical substance to another. Such a defect is referred to as an enzyme block, or a metabolic block, since the mutant can carry out steps in the metabolic pathway only up to the missing enzyme. If a substance normally formed subsequent to the block is supplied, then the block is bypassed and the organism can grow. Supplying intermediates prior to the block is of no value.

On the basis of such studies, Beadle and Tatum were able to show that mutations can be related to loss of single specific enzymes. From this they postulated that the normal function of a gene is to direct the synthesis of a specific enzyme. This concept has become widely known as the one gene–one enzyme theory.

It is now known that the one gene–one enzyme theory is not strictly correct. For example, there are two kinds of polypeptide chains in each hemoglobin molecule, and each kind of chain is under control of a separate structural gene. Furthermore, as was stated in Chapter 8, there are genes whose function is the quantitative regulation of other structural genes. Nevertheless, the work of Beadle and Tatum changed the concept of gene action, since it proved a simple and direct relationship between genes and specific enzymes. The experimental approach used so successfully in *Neurospora* has been extended to many other organisms and has been shown to be valid throughout the biological world.

Metabolic Blocks

Mutations, such as those in *Neurospora,* that lead to lack of enzyme activity have come to be known as metabolic blocks. The relationship of genes to protein structure was discussed in Chapter 8. Mutations may lead either to altered proteins or to absence of a protein. An altered protein may or may not have enzyme activity. Some altered proteins are not distinguishable from normal protein on the basis of enzyme activity. However, most will probably have diminished enzyme activity. In this case, the metabolic block may be only partial.

The effects of a metabolic block depend on a variety of factors in addition to the blocked enzymatic step. Some of the possibilities are illustrated in Figure 9–3. Consider the conversion of substrate S to product P catalyzed by enzyme E. If the gene controlling E mutates, then the conversion of S to P is blocked. If S is supplied continuously from other metabolic steps or from the environment, then it will accumulate or be excreted or converted into other products. These possibilities are not mutually exclusive. If S accumulates to abnormally high levels, it may interfere with other metabolic steps. The product of the blocked reaction,

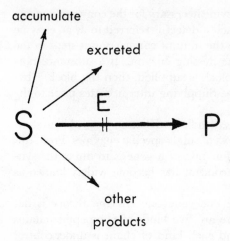

Figure 9–3. Some of the consequences when the gene(s) which control synthesis of enzyme E mutate, so that conversion of substrate S to product P is no longer possible.

P, will also be deficient. If P is an essential constituent of the organism, then the organism cannot develop normally without an alternate source of P. However, if P is a waste product, deficiency of P will not be deleterious.

A single blocked reaction may initiate a network of metabolic changes. It is useful therefore to distinguish between primary blocks—blocked reactions due directly to mutant enzyme—and secondary blocks—reactions blocked because of inhibition by abnormal amounts of metabolites.

Several metabolic blocks are known in the metabolism of phenylalanine in man (Fig. 9–4). In persons affected with alkaptonuria, one of the four diseases studied by Garrod, the enzyme homogentisic acid oxidase is missing. Consequently, homogentisic acid cannot be converted to its oxidation product, maleylacetoacetic acid. Homogentisic acid accumulates as a consequence, but it is not reabsorbed by the kidney from the glomerular filtrate and, therefore, cannot reach very high levels in the tissues and blood. Large amounts of homogentisic acid appear in the urine and upon excretion undergo further oxidation spontaneously, forming a black pigment. The condition is present from birth and can be recognized because of the dark color appearing on wet diapers.

Alkaptonuria is a relatively benign disease. The amino acids phenylalanine and tyrosine are normal dietary constituents. However, the diet supplies much more than the body can use as such, and the excess is metabolized via homogentisic acid. No essential metabolites are formed subsequent to homogentisic acid. The fact that the kidney cannot retain excess homogentisic acid prevents major deviation from normal metabolism. The only pathological consequence of alkaptonuria is a

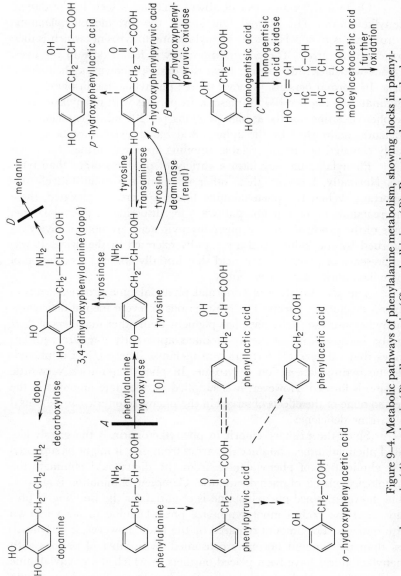

Figure 9–4. Metabolic pathways of phenylalanine metabolism, showing blocks in phenyl-ketonuria (*A*), tyrosinosis (*B*), alkaptonuria (*C*), and albinism (*D*). Reactions shown by broken arrows are quantitatively unimportant in normal persons but become important in phenyl-ketonuria.

slow deposition of pigment in some of the joints, leading ultimately to a form of arthritis.

Quite a different effect of absent enzyme is seen in the disease phenylketonuria. The normal function of the enzyme phenylalanine hydroxylase is to convert excess phenylalanine to tyrosine, which is then further metabolized. The enzyme normally is found only in the liver. Persons who lack this enzyme have the disease known as phenylketonuria. In normal persons, the level of free phenylalanine in blood is approximately 1 mg per 100 ml plasma. In persons with phenylketonuria, the phenylalanine may be as high as 50 mg per 100 ml. Phenylalanine is efficiently reabsorbed by the kidney, and blood levels must be considerably elevated before appreciable amounts appear in urine.

Phenylalanine may form a variety of products other than tyrosine. Normally, however, these other reactions are quantitatively unimportant. When the phenylalanine levels are greatly elevated, these side reactions become major pathways for disposing of phenylalanine. Some of the products, such as phenylpyruvic acid, are not effectively reabsorbed by the kidney and are rapidly excreted in the urine. It was the presence of phenylpyruvic acid that initially enabled recognition of phenylketonuria as a disease entity.

The accumulation of abnormal phenylalanine products leads to various deleterious effects. The most serious is severe mental deficiency. Phenylketonurics usually have less pigment than other members of their family, because some of the by-products apparently interfere with enzymes that catalyze the formation of melanin. The product of phenylalanine hydroxylase action is tyrosine. In phenylketonurics, very little tyrosine is formed. However, it is supplied in adequate amounts in the diet, so none of the effects observed in the phenylketonuric can be traced to tyrosine deficiency.

Since the primary culprit in phenylketonuria is the grossly elevated phenylalanine, and since this arises from diet, it might be supposed that elimination of phenylalanine from the diet would eliminate the pathological effects of phenylketonuria. Complete elimination is not possible, however, since phenylalanine is essential for the building of proteins, and the body cannot synthesize phenylalanine to meet its own requirements. The amount required by the body, however, is very much less than the amount normally consumed. A number of persons with phenylketonuria have been placed on diets in which the phenylalanine level is very low, and, in some cases, great benefit has been derived from such diets. If the disease is detected within the first few months of life, administration of low phenylalanine diets prevents development of the neurological defect that leads to mental deficiency. If diet control is delayed, the deleterious effects may not be avoided. Initiation of diet control as late as the third or fourth year generally will have little beneficial effect. The timing of diet control is related to maturation of the central nervous system. Infants who are homozygous for the phenylketonuria gene do not show any abnormality at the time of birth, since the mother's metabolism can take care of excess phenylalanine. Once the child is on his own, the accumulation of phenylalanine leads to irreversible changes in the central nervous system.

Phenylketonuria also illustrates the difference between primary and secondary metabolic blocks. The block in conversion of phenylalanine to tyrosine is a primary block associated with lack of the enzyme. The deleterious effects, however, are due to secondary blocks, resulting from inhibition of enzymes by the abnormal by-products of phenylalanine. The inhibition is particularly demonstrated in pigment formation. The enzymes responsible for pigment formation are normal in phenylketonurics, but because of inhibition by phenylalanine metabolites, less pigment is formed. When phenylketonurics are placed on a low phenylalanine diet, the inhibitors are no longer present, and normal pigmentation results.

Defects in Transport Systems

Virtually all the many steps of metabolism take place inside cells. Supplies of nutrients and other substrates therefore must cross the cell membrane in order to participate in metabolism. In many instances, simple diffusion provides sufficient material to satisfy cell requirements; in other instances, however, diffusion is not adequate, and there are mechanisms for transporting substances across the cell membrane against a concentration gradient.

The means by which small molecules are actively transported across membranes are not so well understood as are the steps of intermediary metabolism. This is in part due to the fact that structures responsible for transport exist as part of the insoluble structure of the cell membrane. Furthermore, the substrate and ultimate product are the same. It is their location that changes rather than their constitution. Nevertheless, transport appears to be mediated by enzymes that are highly specific in their activity.

That these enzymes are also under genetic control is illustrated by the occurrence of mutant forms which are unable to transport specific substrates properly. A well-studied example in man is found in the condition known as cystinuria. Cysteine, being one of the essential amino acids, is efficiently reabsorbed by the renal tubule. Persons homozygous for the cystinuria gene are unable to reabsorb cysteine from the glomerular filtrate. Absorption in this case involves transport back into the blood stream rather than just to the cell interior. The defect also involves three other amino acids—lysine, arginine, and ornithine. At least one step of the reabsorption process is shared by these four amino acids, and this function is defective in cystinuria. The condition was named cystinuria because the inability to reabsorb cysteine was the first abnormality detected. Cystine (formed from cysteine) is relatively insoluble at the pH of urine. As a consequence, crystals of cystine are formed that coalesce into "stones." Apparently, this is the only pathological consequence. The excess excretion of lysine, arginine, and ornithine leads to no difficulty, since these amino acids are readily soluble.

The enzymic basis for cystinuria is unknown. The condition serves as an example of a type of enzyme block that cannot be detected as a block in intermediary metabolism. Blocks that do not permit the substrate to come into contact with the appropriate enzymes may be just as deleterious as, and indeed may superficially resemble, blocks in which the enzyme itself is defective.

THE TIMING OF GENE ACTION

All of the cell nuclei of a complex organism such as man appear to contain a full complement of chromosomes. It is assumed, although it has not proved possible to test, that each of the chromosomes contains its full normal complement of genes. However, many of the genes in a particular cell are inactive. This can be observed easily in hemoglobin synthesis. Normally, hemoglobin is synthesized only in cells destined to mature into erythrocytes and not in other body tissues. Yet the genes that specify hemoglobin structure are almost certainly present in all cells of the body.

The selective activity of a specific pattern of genes is the basis for differentiation of single cell zygotes into complex multicellular organisms with many types of tissue. The factors that determine the regular pattern of gene activation during differentiation are very poorly understood. Some examples will illustrate the fine degree to which gene action is controlled.

The prevalent hemoglobin in the human fetus is fetal hemoglobin or hemoglobin F. It is composed of two types of polypeptide chains, α and γ chains. At about the time of birth, the synthesis of hemoglobin F diminishes and the synthesis of hemoglobin A becomes predominant. Since hemoglobin A is composed of α and β chains, the switch to hemoglobin-A production is actually a change from γ-chain to β-chain production. These two polypeptide chains are each under the control of entirely separate structural genes. Chemically, the polypeptide chains are somewhat similar, there being many sequences of amino acids that are identical. It is thought that originally there was only one kind of hemoglobin tetramer, composed of two α chains and two chains that were precursors to the present β and γ chains. Through gene duplication and subsequent mutation, the β and γ chains no longer produce identical products.

Presumably, fetal hemoglobin provides some special need of fetal life more efficiently than hemoglobin A. As a consequence, evolution has favored the high production of γ chains during fetal life but the high production of β chains subsequent to birth. The dramatic nature of this switch-over is illustrated in Figure 9–5. The factor that causes the switch-over has not been identified. It does not appear to be the birth event itself, since switch-over precedes birth and is independent of whether a child is premature. In most persons, the γ-chain gene continues to function at a very low level throughout the life of the individual, producing less than 1 percent fetal hemoglobin. In certain exceptional persons, there is a

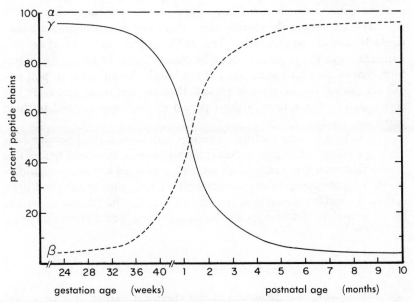

Figure 9–5. Production of hemoglobins A and F during late fetal and neonatal period. Total hemoglobin is taken as 100 percent. Since α chains are present in both Hbs A and F, the synthesis of α chains is constant during the switch-over from γ-chain to β-chain synthesis. (Redrawn from C. Baglioni, 1963, *Medical Genetics*, Part I. New York: Academic Press, pp. 405–475, by permission.)

genetic defect that causes continued synthesis of γ chains. Possibly, this defect is in the switch-over mechanism. The inhibition of various structural genes is presumably by means of repressors, as discussed in the previous chapter. But, as indicated, the environmental factors that cause repressors to inhibit structural genes, or not to inhibit the genes, are unknown.

Another example of ordered gene action is found in the appearance of chromosomal puffs. In certain tissues of *Diptera*, chromosomes multiply manyfold to give very thick *polytene* chromosomes. Such cells will not undergo further duplications, and therefore this unusual behavior on the part of the chromosomes represents a terminal pathway of development. Polytene chromosomes are characterized by darkly staining cross-striations known as chromosome bands. The position and size of a particular band is highly characteristic and the pattern of bands has been used effectively to characterize regions of a chromosome through cytological examination. The bands are rich in DNA and appear to be areas of high gene content.

During larval development, certain of the bands expand into puffs. These puffed regions appear to be regions of high nucleic acid and protein synthesis. Although the relationship of the chemical activity of puffs to gene action is not known precisely, it is thought that a puff represents an area of the chromosome where one or more genes are particularly active synthetically. The puffs appear in a very definite sequence, and the sequences of puffs characteristic of one tissue differs from that of another tissue. Most of the bands do not undergo puff formation during the observable period. Presumably, these genes are not active during this relatively short period of development and in these particular tissues.

Although other examples can be cited, these should provide convincing evidence that gene action is not random in time and space. The factors that turn genes on and off are well organized but not well understood. In attempting to detect metabolic defects that result from gene action, it must be understood that the defect may be limited to certain tissues or may be detectable only during a certain period of development.

DOMINANCE, PENETRANCE, AND EXPRESSIVITY

Following the discussion of the chemical nature of gene action and production of phenotypes, a review of some definitions of words used frequently in genetics should be useful. The terms *dominant* and *recessive* were first used by Mendel and are part of our everyday vocabulary. A dominant gene may be defined as one that is expressed when present in a single copy, whereas a recessive gene is detectable only when present on both chromosomes. By now it should be clear that such definitions are related to methods of observation rather than to properties of DNA. For example, some of the "abnormal" hemoglobins function very well in the transport of oxygen but are not synthesized efficiently. If the only measure of gene variation were the presence of anemia, then these hemoglobins would be classified as recessive. By other means of observation, such as migration in an electric field, differences can be detected, even though the mutant gene is present only a single time. By this criterion, then, the abnormal hemoglobin would be codominant; that is, it is expressed independently of the allele on the other chromosome. The terms dominant and recessive are of limited usefulness in a discussion of the physiological consequences of gene action. Many so-called recessive genes have been shown to be detectable in heterozygous combination if methods of observation are sufficiently discriminating. On the other hand, it is convenient to use the terms dominant and recessive as a means of predicting the pattern of inheritance in families (Chapter 13). Like many other terms, they are very useful when applied with discretion and understanding.

The term *penetrance* is another commonly used word that is frequently misunderstood. It may be defined as the probability of detecting a particular combination of genes when they are present. Most often, one makes use of a particular means of observation. As the means of observation changes, the level of penetrance may change also. Thus, it is not strictly a function of the gene in question. Genes at other loci may also influence penetrance. For example, detection of gene A may be possible only when it is in combination with M. When A occurs in combination with m it would be considered nonpenetrant. Unless we recognize the variation at the M locus, it may be very difficult to decide why A sometimes is expressed and other times is not. To say that a gene has less than 100 percent penetrance is purely a probability statement regarding the likelihood of detecting the presence of the gene. As such, it is a useful term for predicting the likelihood of showing genetic effects given a certain genotype.

The term *expressivity* refers to the variety of ways in which a particular gene manifests its presence. A classical example of variation in expression is found in the condition osteogenesis imperfecta. The three principal features of this disease are blue irises, very fragile bones, and deafness. The condition is inherited as a dominant with nearly 100 percent penetrance. However, the expressivity varies greatly. A person with the gene may have any one or any combination of these three traits.

The bone fragility may be a minor defect or it may be a major problem, the patient having dozens of fractures during his lifetime. Given that a person has the gene for osteogenesis imperfecta, there is no way to predict what combination of traits he will have and how severe they will be. As with penetrance, expressivity undoubtedly depends upon interactions with many environmental and genetic factors. In medical genetics, it is important to recognize that a given gene may vary widely in its expression.

The terms penetrance and expressivity should not be confused. Penetrance refers to the presence or absence of any effect of the gene. Expressivity refers to the type of manifestation.

Occasionally in experimental organisms, manipulation of the environment leads to production of a phenotype that mimics a particular genetic trait, even though the gene ordinarily responsible for the trait is known not to be present. The nongenetic form of the trait is said to be a *phenocopy*. Although phenocopies may cause little difficulty in the usual genetic analysis of human traits, they may be troublesome in the analysis of very rare events, such as mutation. This is particularly true if the trait cannot be investigated at the chemical level. Good examples of human phenocopies are not known, but some of the congenital malformations may prove to be genetic in some cases and environmental in others, the latter therefore qualifying for designation as phenocopies.

GENE INTERACTION AND EPISTASIS

Most of the examples of genetic variation discussed have been traits related in a simple manner to the variant genes. Since observations of gene action are many steps removed from the primary gene action, it is to be expected that a given trait will sometimes reflect variation at several loci.

Several levels of gene interaction may occur. Interaction at the chromosome level has already been discussed (Chapter 8). There is also interaction at the level of protein-synthesizing mechanisms, although examples of genetic variation in these mechanisms are not known. More commonly, interaction occurs at the metabolic level. The effects of metabolic interaction vary with the systems of interest and may be very complex. It will not be possible to consider all modes of interaction, but apparent departures from simple inheritance frequently are the result of such interaction.

Certain designations have arisen to describe types of gene interaction. A locus is said to be *epistatic* to another if variation at the first obscures variation at the second. An example of epistasis in mice is the masking of genes for variations in hair color by the gene for albinism. Mice that are homozygous for the recessive albino allele may have genes for a variety of coat patterns at other loci, but only the albino condition is expressed. The albino allele is thus epistatic to the other loci.

An example of epistasis in man occurs in the ABO blood group types. These red cell antigens usually are a function of the genotype at the ABO locus. Very rare persons exist whose cells react neither with anti-A or anti-B reagents, although it can be shown by pedigree analysis that they possess one or the other of these alleles. These persons are apparently homozygous for a recessive allele at another locus that prevents formation of the A or B substances or of the H substance, the "non-reactive" substance present in type O persons. The first such persons were located in India, and they are said to have Bombay type blood. The action of the normal Bombay allele H seems to be to direct synthesis of H substance, which in turn serves as a precursor for A and B substances. Homozygous hh persons cannot synthesize H substance. The h allele is therefore epistatic to the alleles at the ABO locus.

The term *suppressor mutation* was coined to describe mutations that restore or counteract the aberrant effects of a mutation at a different locus. In *Neurospora,* a number of mutants are known that lead to defects in the enzyme tryptophan synthetase. These mutants involve changes in the structural gene for the enzyme. There are also a number of mutants at other loci that, in combination with the structural mutants, permit *Neurospora* to grow without added tryptophan. The defective gene is still present, but its action has been suppressed. In terms of their primary action, suppressor genes appear to work in a variety of ways. In every case, their action is compensation for the defect rather than restoration of the original enzyme.

In addition to the use given here, the term suppressor gene has been applied to situations in which activity of a normal gene is suppressed. These cases might better be covered by the concept of epistasis. A suppressor gene, strictly speaking, should restore the wild-type phenotype.

REFERENCES AND SUGGESTED READING

BAGLIONI, C. 1963. Correlations between genetics and chemistry of human hemoglobins. In *Molecular Genetics,* Part I (J. H. Taylor, ed.). New York: Academic Press, pp. 405–475.

BEADLE, G. W. 1945. Biochemical genetics. *Chem. Rev.* 37: 15–96.

BEERMANN, W. 1956. Nuclear differentiation and functional morphology of chromosomes. *Cold Spring Harbor Symp. Quant. Biol.* 21: 217–232.

GARROD, A. E. 1909. *Inborn Errors of Metabolism.* (Reprinted with a supplement by H. Harris, 1963.) London: Oxford University Press, 207 pp.

HARRIS, H., MITTWOCH, U., ROBSON, E. B., and WARREN, F. L. 1955. Phenotypes and genotypes in cystinuria. *Ann. Human Genet.* 20: 57–91.

SUTTON, H. E. 1961. *Genes, Enzymes, and Inherited Diseases.* New York: Holt, Rinehart and Winston, 120 pp.

WAGNER, R. P., and MITCHELL, H. K. 1964. *Genetics and Metabolism,* 2d ed. New York: Wiley, 673 pp.

PROBLEMS

1. Define:

    enzyme   epistasis
    metabolic block   polytene chromosome
    codominance   penetrance
    suppressor gene   expressivity
    phenocopy

Chapter Ten

MUTATIONS

A mutation is defined as a heritable change. As observed in the human time scale, mutations are sudden. No transition from one form to another can be demonstrated, although radiation-induced mutations in some organisms do appear to have a transition state during which the gene may "repair" or change to a different form.

A key part of the definition of mutation is the word *heritable*. A new variation must be transmitted to offspring before it can be accepted as a mutation. A dominant mutation that causes loss of fertility cannot be shown to be heritable and can as well be attributed to an environmental factor. In rare instances, somatic mutation can be demonstrated. Mutation in a somatic cell gives rise to a clone of cells that differ from surrounding cells. The difference only rarely is detectable, usually only when visible features such as pigmentation or external morphological characteristics are altered. Without the possibility of transmission to offspring, it is difficult to establish the genetic nature of somatic mutations.

Most mutations, involving a change from function to nonfunction, are recessive. These can thus be observed only when they combine with a similar mutant allele, possibly many generations removed from the time of the original mutational event. In contrast, dominant mutations can be observed within one generation. Mutations on the X chromosome can be observed as soon as the mutant allele is transmitted to a male. One of the famous examples of a mutation whose occurrence can be pinpointed with some certainty is given in Figure 10–1.

THE CHEMISTRY OF MUTATION

Any change in the structure of genetic material is a mutation. Changes may involve substitution of a DNA base, deletion of one or more bases, or insertion of a new base. Alterations of chromosomes, either in

113

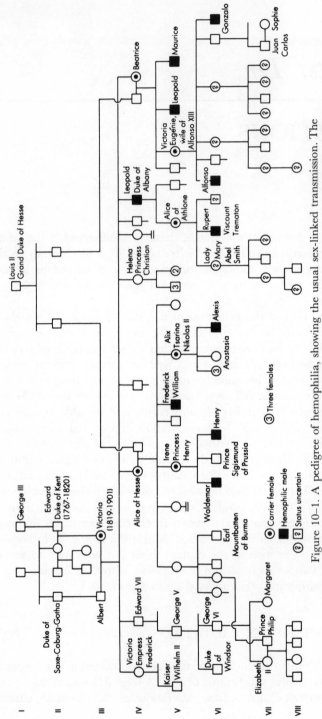

Figure 10-1. A pedigree of hemophilia, showing the usual sex-linked transmission. The mutation presumably occurred in one of the parents of Queen Victoria, since she appears to have been heterozygous. (From V. A. McKusick, *Human Genetics*, Englewood Cliffs, N.J.: Prentice-Hall, 1964, by permission.)

114

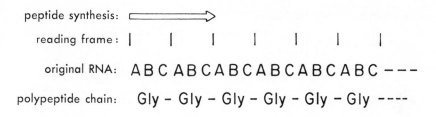

peptide synthesis:

reading frame:

original RNA: A B C A B C A B C A B C A B C A B C – – –

polypeptide chain: Gly – Gly – Gly – Gly – Gly – Gly – – – –

mutant RNA: A B C A C C A B C A B C A B C A B C – – –

polypeptide chain: Gly – Leu – Gly – Gly – Gly – Gly – – – –

Figure 10–2. Substitution of one nucleotide for another, giving rise to a single amino acid substitution in the polypeptide product. The original nucleotide substitution would occur in DNA and be transcribed to messenger RNA. An arbitrary code has been used in this figure.

number or structure, may be considered mutations, although other terms are generally more useful in describing these changes. Rearrangements of DNA sequences, such as inversions, change the genetic information. It is rarely possible to be certain that a mutation involves a single nucleotide pair (point mutation) or a larger segment such as a small chromosomal deletion. Either may be lethal.

The immediate chemical effects of mutation can be related to the function of genes. A structural gene determines the structure of a particular messenger RNA (mRNA), which in turn determines the structure of a specific polypeptide chain. Any alteration in a structural gene would lead either to altered mRNA or to failure to synthesize mRNA. The effects of altered mRNA on polypeptide synthesis depend on the type of change. If a base is substituted but the total number of bases remains the same, then a different amino acid code (codon) has been introduced (Fig. 10–2). Some amino acids have more than one code, but chances are that the new codon corresponds to a different amino acid. This would lead to an amino acid substitution in the polypeptide chain, such as apparently happened in many of the mutations of hemoglobin. For example, Hb S differs from Hb A by possessing valine rather than glutamic acid in position 6 of the β chain.

If a base pair is deleted in the DNA, a corresponding base would be deleted in mRNA. The effect of this would be to shift the reading frame for amino acid codons (Fig. 10–3) so that each base to the "right" of the deletion shifts its position in its codon one space to the left. The first base in a codon would become the last base of the previous codon. Amino acids between the deletion and the C-terminal end of the polypeptide

peptide synthesis: ⊏========⟹

reading frame: | | | | | | |

original RNA: A B C A B C A B C A B C A B C A B C A――

polypeptide chain: Gly – Gly – Gly – Gly – Gly – Gly ――――

mutant RNA: A B C A B C B C A B C A B C A B C A―――

polypeptide chain: Gly – Gly – Ala – Ala – Ala – Ala ――――

Figure 10–3. Deletion of one nucleotide, causing a shift in reading frame of the RNA. The seventh nucleotide has been eliminated, and all codons to the right have shifted to the left by one nucleotide.

chain would be altered. If the deletion were very close to the part of the gene corresponding to the C-terminal end, the polypeptide chain might have only a few amino acids altered. If the deletion were close to the N-terminal end, where polypeptide synthesis begins, most of the codons of the chain would be displaced and the polypeptide chain would be largely nonsense. Insertion of an extra base in the structural gene would have the same effect as deletion, except that the reading frame would be shifted to the "left" rather than to the "right."

Crick and his associates, using bacterial viruses, have confirmed these ideas by demonstrating that one insertion and one deletion very close together in a gene tend to counteract each other. If the two changes are far apart, they do not. Presumably, the shift in reading frame caused by a deletion (or insertion) is restored by an insertion (or deletion). If only a few amino acids are altered between the two mutations, then the polypeptide may function. If many are altered, the polypeptide is largely nonsense. Insertion or deletion of three nucleotides would correspond exactly to one codon. If the changes are very close together, then only a small portion of the polypeptide chain would be affected and it might be able to carry out its biological function, although possibly with decreased activity compared to the original polypeptide chain.

Many mutations, especially those induced by radiation, involve more than single base changes. The effects on phenotype are likely to be correspondingly greater. Deletions of more than a few nucleotides lead to loss of amino acids from the polypeptide chain. This is unlikely to be compatible with biological function. Furthermore, the quantitative regulation of protein synthesis may be seriously impaired, although little is known on this subject at present.

In spite of our limited knowledge of the chemistry of mutation, some generalizations can be made concerning the effects of various changes. Major chromosome alterations will result in failure to produce a functional peptide. Minor chromosome changes, such as very small deletions or insertions, may produce altered but functional mRNA if the change is in a position corresponding to the few amino acids at the C-terminal end of the polypeptide chain. Small deletions or insertions in other parts of the structural gene ordinarily produce greatly altered protein. Substitution of a nucleotide will lead to a slightly altered protein, whose function may or may not be different from normal.

THE MEASUREMENT OF MUTATION RATE

In view of the earlier discussion on the effects of mutation, it should be apparent that recognition of a mutation depends on the criteria used. If it were possible to survey amino acid sequences in proteins on a mass-screening basis, virtually any change in DNA sequence would be detected as a mutation. Where protein function is the indicator, many mutations are missed, since mutant proteins sometimes are functional. If a mutation must be lethal in order to be detected, many nonlethal mutations will be missed. Similarly, so-called "visible" mutations include only those mutations compatible with life but causing externally visible changes. In discussions of mutation rate, it is necessary to keep in mind that the findings with one set of specific endpoints may differ from findings based on different endpoints.

Mutation rate is usually expressed as the number of mutations per gamete per locus. Sometimes rather than measuring the mutations per locus, the lethal mutations per X chromosome are measured. Or other portions of the chromosome complement may be studied and classes of mutations other than lethals (for example, visible morphological variants) may be counted. The particular kinds of mutations counted depend on the experimental material available and on the interests of the observer.

Mutation Rates in Experimental Organisms

Muller, in demonstrating the induction of mutations by X rays, tested for the presence of X-chromosome lethals in Drosophila. The X chromosome is of particular value in this respect, since recessive lethals are expressed in males but can be carried in heterozygous form in females. A lethal at any locus on the X chromosome will be counted. An example

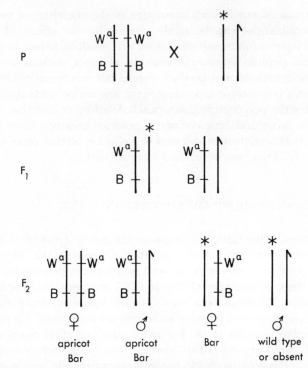

Figure 10–4. Diagram of the Muller-5 test for recessive lethals induced in the X chromosome. The Muller-5 chromosome carries the recessive gene w^a (apricot) and the dominant Bar-eyed (B) duplication. There are also inversions that prevent crossing over in the F_1 females. If the X chromosome of the irradiated male, indicated with an asterisk, has acquired a recessive lethal mutation at any locus, wild-type males in the F_2 will be absent.

of the Muller-5 test, one of the tests commonly used for mutation studies in Drosophila, is given in Figure 10–4.

Specific locus mutations also have been widely studied. In bacteria, where enormous numbers of cells can be examined by screening methods, very rare mutational events can be observed. Many of the bacterial mutations are nutritional. Through loss of function of a gene controlling synthesis of an enzyme on the biosynthetic pathway of a required substance, a bacterium mutates from nutritional independence (prototrophy) to a state in which there is a requirement for some specific vitamin, amino acid, or other substance (auxotrophy). The mutant bacteria cannot grow in the absence of the nutritional factor. Several methods of screening are possible. The penicillin method takes advantage of the fact that *growing* cells are killed by penicillin, although nongrowing cells

are not. If a culture of bacteria is suspended in medium containing penicillin but no growth factors other than those required by the nonmutant
cells, then the nonmutant cells will grow and be killed. Mutant cells that
require additional factors cannot grow and are not killed. The cell sus-
pension can then be transferred to agar plates containing additional
growth factors but no penicillin. Any mutants whose requirements are
met by the additional factors can grow and be counted or further studied.
The choice of additional nutritional factors permits the investigator to
select the classes of mutants in which he is interested. From the number
of organisms originally present and the number of mutants recovered,
the mutation rate can be calculated.

Mutations at specific loci have been investigated in mice, particularly at Oak Ridge in the United States and at Harwell in England, in
an effort to measure the mutational effects of radiation. W. L. Russell at
Oak Ridge has developed a test stock of mice homozygous for recessive
genes at seven loci that influence various externally visible features, such
as coat color. Males with normal chromosomes are irradiated and mated
to the test females (Fig. 10–5). In the absence of newly induced mutations,
offspring will have a normal phenotype. If a mutation has been induced
at one of the seven loci, the offspring receiving that gene will show the
mutant phenotype characteristic for the locus. Enormous numbers of
mice have been tested in order to measure the frequency of mutation in
the presence of low levels of radiation.

Measurement of Human Mutation Rates

DOMINANT MUTATIONS.   In man, the only mutations whose
rate is known with some certainty are those which are readily observed
in heterozygous combination. Furthermore, the resulting condition must
be such as to come to medical attention with high probability; it must not
be lethal at an early age, otherwise it could not be proved to be genetic;
and the frequency of phenocopies must be very low, preferably nonexistent. From a practical point of view, the condition must be uncommon
so that new mutations will comprise an appreciable portion of cases.
Otherwise, the investigator would have to examine hundreds, perhaps
thousands, of cases in order to locate several mutant cases.

Some of the conditions that meet these requirements are listed in
Table 10–1. Aniridia will serve as an example of the procedure by which
a mutation rate is established. Aniridia (absence of iris of eyes) is inherited
as a simple dominant trait. Persons heterozygous for the gene appear
always to express the trait. Because these persons are blind, or nearly so,

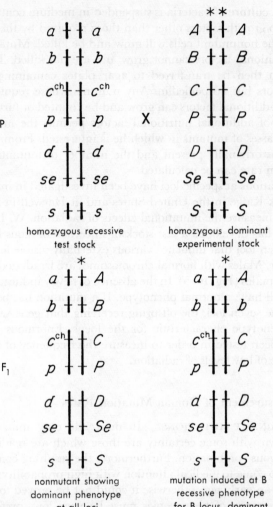

Figure 10–5. Diagram of Russell test stock for induced mutations in mice. The gene complements marked by asterisks are subjected to radiation. *C* and *P* are on one chromosome, as are *D* and *Se*. However, this is not relevant to this part of the experiment. (From Russell, 1951.)

they come to the attention of ophthalmologists and of various agencies concerned with the blind. Nearly complete location of patients can be made through these sources.

In the state of Michigan in the period 1919 to 1959, 4,664,799 persons were reported born, of which approximately 41 are estimated by

M. W. Shaw to have been aniridic offspring with normal parents. (Twenty-eight were actually located; because of the methods of locating patients, an additional 13 were estimated to have been missed.) If these 41 persons are considered to represent new mutations, all at a single locus, then the mutation rate would be $41/(2 \times 4,664,799) = 4.4 \times 10^{-6}$ mutations per gamete per locus.

TABLE 10-1

Some Estimates of Mutation Rates of Autosomal Genes in Man.
The Mutant Allele Is Dominant to the Normal Alleles.

TRAIT	MUTATION RATE PER GAMETE	INVESTIGATOR
Huntington's chorea	0.5×10^{-5}	Reed and Neel (1959)
retinoblastoma	$0.6 - 0.7 \times 10^{-5}$	Vogel (1957)
neurofibromatosis	10×10^{-5}	Crowe, Schull, and Neel (1956)
multiple polyposis of the colon	$1 - 3 \times 10^{-5}$	Reed and Neel (1955)
Marfan's syndrome	$0.4 - 0.6 \times 10^{-5}$	Lynas (1958)
aniridia	0.4×10^{-5}	Shaw, Falls, and Neel (1960)

Although the procedures used in measuring mutation rate of dominant genes are simple conceptually, there are few diseases that satisfy all the conditions stated initially. It is rare that all the cases of a disease in a prescribed population can be ascertained. Few dominantly inherited conditions are completely penetrant and yet without phenocopies; and few are so readily diagnosed and referred to special agencies.

The conditions that do satisfy these requirements are consistent in their results. All have rates near 1×10^{-5} mutations per gamete per locus. Some are consistently less and others consistently more. This probably reflects inherent differences in stability of the respective genes. It may also be that, for some diseases, mutations at any of several loci are counted and the rate is therefore the sum of two or more separate rates.

RECESSIVE MUTATIONS. Most mutations are from function to nonfunction or decreased function. For the most part, such mutations are recessive and are not evident unless they happen to be combined with another recessive allele. In human beings, it is not possible to know that a person who is homozygous for a recessive gene has a newly mutated gene. Direct counting of mutant genes is therefore impossible.

Estimates of mutation rates of recessives have been made on the assumption that, for a population in equilibrium, the number of recessive alleles removed from the population because of lack of fitness equals the number of recessive alleles added by mutation. If μ is the mutation rate and N the number of persons in a prescribed population, the number of new mutant genes is $2N\mu$. For autosomal genes, the number of genes removed because of lack of fitness is $2Nx(1 - f)$, where f is the fitness of homozygous recessives (Chapter 18), and x is the frequency of homozygous recessives. Equating these two quantities:

$$2N\mu = 2Nx(1 - f)$$
$$\mu = x(1 - f)$$

For conditions with a genetic fitness of zero, the mutation rate equals the frequency of the condition. The frequency in turn is equal to q^2, where q is the gene frequency (Chapter 16)

$$\therefore \mu = q^2$$

This procedure assumes that persons heterozygous for the mutant alleles are exactly equal in fitness to persons homozygous for the normal alleles. It is increasingly apparent that this requirement is rarely met. Furthermore, a very slight increase in fitness of heterozygotes will lead to grossly erroneous results in the calculated value of μ. This method therefore has been largely abandoned. Not satisfactory method for measuring mutation rates of recessive genes has been developed.

Detection of Sex-Linked Lethals

As in Drosophila, it is possible in man to detect classes of mutations without identifying specific loci. If a woman is exposed to a mutagenic agent, such as high energy radiation, mutations will be induced at random throughout the genome. For the most part, the mutations will be recessive and expressed only in the rare event that a similar mutant allele comes from the father of the woman's offspring. Dominant mutations, although expressed in the offspring, will be very rare. Many mutations, both dominant and recessive, exert their deleterious effect early in gestation or at prezygotic stages so that direct observation is impossible.

If mutations are induced on the X chromosome, they will be expressed in sons of the woman. Many of the mutations will be lethal prior to birth, but these can be recognized by their influence on the sex ratio. A deficiency of males among the offspring of women exposed to potential mutagenic agents can be accepted as evidence that such mutations were induced (Fig. 10–6). Irradiation of males would give rise to female offspring with one irradiated and one untreated X chromosome. To the

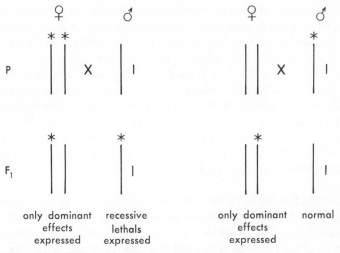

Figure 10–6. Effects of irradiation of maternal and paternal X chromosomes. If the mothers are irradiated (indicated by asterisks), there may be a small decrease in daughters due to dominant effects, but sons would show a greater effect, causing the sex ratio to decrease. If the fathers are irradiated, the sex ratio should increase slightly.

extent that induced mutations are dominant and deleterious, there should be a loss of female offspring, so that the sex ratio would increase.

A number of studies of human beings exposed to radiation have used changes in the sex ratio as a means of detecting an increase in mutation rate. The most extensive of these was carried out in Japan in Hiroshima and Nagasaki following the use of the atomic bombs. Other studies have been on offspring of X-ray technicians and radiologists and of patients treated with radiation for various disorders. The effects of radiation on the mutation rate have been so small that no single study shows a convincing change in sex ratio. However, most studies do show a small decrease in the proportion of males from irradiated mothers, and, taken together, the studies support the idea that radiation has been a cause of mutations in man. This has been assumed since the early demonstration of mutagenicity of X rays, but quantitative data were lacking. The data still are very poor, but they indicate that man probably is not notably more prone to radiation-induced mutation than are mice.

Some Consequences of Human Mutation Rates

THE FREQUENCY OF MUTATIONS.   From the average mutation rate and the total number of genetic loci, it should be possible to calculate the average number of new mutations per gamete. The figure 1×10^{-5} mutations per locus per gamete can be used as a rough approximation of the mutation rate. The number of loci is not known, however. From several lines of reasoning, all somewhat questionable, the number of loci in man has been estimated to be between 10,000 and 50,000. If the value 25,000 is arbitrarily selected, the mutations per gamete would be $(2.5 \times 10^4) \times (1 \times 10^{-5}) = 0.25$. Each zygote would contain twice this value, or 0.5 mutations per zygote. The very crude nature of this calculation should be appreciated, but it is sufficiently accurate to indicate that mutations occur with some frequency. Each person has about a 1/2 chance of having arisen from a zygote bearing a new mutation. Regardless of whether this probability should be multiplied by 10 or divided by 10, many persons, perhaps most, carry *new* mutations.

SOMATIC MUTATIONS AND MOSAICISM.   It is not possible to distinguish between mutations occurring during meiosis and mitosis. A new mutation that appears in a gamete could have arisen either during meiosis or during mitosis of the cell line that gave rise to the oöcytes or spermatocytes. That the latter may occur on occasion is suggested by rare pedigrees in which two or more mutant offspring have been produced by nonmutant parents. This is most readily explained by assuming that a single mutation occurred early enough in one parent to give rise to a clone of mutant cells in the germinal tissue. The person would thus be a mosaic.

If the mutation rate for mitosis is similar to the rate measured for gametes, then many mutations would occur during the development of a human being from a zygote. Some of these mutations might cause the daughter cell to be unviable; others might not cause obvious disadvantage. Few would be detectable by present means of observation. It is probable, therefore, that every person is a mosaic for a large number of mutant genes and that the phenotype is the expression of the majority genotype, present in the zygote.

FACTORS AFFECTING MUTATION RATE

Mutations occur spontaneously at a very low frequency. The frequency can be increased by many factors in experimental organisms and, presumably, in man. In spite of much research, little is known of the actual steps involved in mutation.

Radiation

The first induced mutations were reported in 1927 by H. J. Muller. He found that irradiation of Drosophila with X rays greatly increases the mutation rate. His studies have been greatly extended not only with Drosophila but also with many other organisms. Irradiation with ultraviolet light or with any ionizing radiation—for example, X rays, α particles, neutrons—produces mutations. The effectiveness is lowest for ultraviolet, since it must act entirely through excitation of the molecules. The most effective wavelength is about 260 mμ, which is the wavelength of maximum absorption of nucleic acids. Ultraviolet has no mutagenic effect for human beings, since it is absorbed in the outer layer of skin and does not reach the gonads. Some somatic mutations might be induced by ultraviolet in the skin.

Ionizing radiation can be highly penetrating and therefore is capable of causing mutations in man. Effects are produced in part by direct action on chromosomes but in part also by induced chemical changes in the chromosome environment. For example, sterile irradiated culture media can be mutagenic for bacteria subsequently introduced. When an ionizing particle or photon passes near a chromosome, the large amount of energy released is adequate to break the chromosome. Irradiated cells frequently have fragments of chromosomes broken off from the main body.

Breaks occasionally repair, restoring the intact chromosome, possibly with a mutation at the point of the break. If two breaks occur in the same cell, the broken ends can mismatch to give a chromosome rearrangement. All of the structural aberrations discussed in Chapter 5 can arise in this manner. A characteristic of these double-break rearrangements is the dose response. Single breaks respond linearly to dose, but double breaks increase with a higher power of the dose.

The two major sources of radiation to man are background and medical X rays. It is estimated that background radiation, from rocks, cosmic rays, and other natural sources, amounts to about four roentgens per 30 years. (A roentgen [r] is the quantity of radiation that will produce ions carrying one electrostatic unit of charge in one ml of air at 0° C and 760 mm Hg. The 30-year period is chosen because it is approximately equal to the generation time of human beings in the United States or in similar cultures.) Medical X rays account for about 3 r/30 years. In addition, there is a small exposure to radiation from fallout from atomic explosions, amounting at present to a maximum of about 10 per cent of the total radiation received, depending on the location, the time of year, and many other factors.

The relationship of mutation rate to dose in man has not been adequately established. This is because very large numbers of persons must be observed at various levels of radiation before the dose relationship can be ascertained. The doses commonly used in Drosophila are very

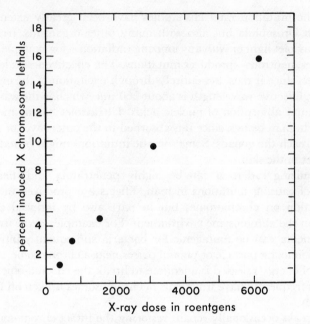

Figure 10-7. The yield of X-chromosome lethals induced by irradiation of Drosophila males with X rays. (Data from Oliver, 1930.)

much higher than those to which man is exposed. Human beings are killed by radiation that does little harm to Drosophila. The straight-line relationship between single-hit or point mutations and dose, amply demonstrated at high levels of radiation in Drosophila (Fig. 10-7), has not been thoroughly studied at very low radiation intensity. Russell's results in mice suggest that the response may not be linear at very low intensity. Instead, the yield of mutations per unit of radiation is less for certain types of cells.

There is much yet to be learned about the effects of radiation. At the present time, statements concerning the effects of radiation on man are based on meager evidence for which the confidence limits are very wide.

Chemical Mutagens

The ability of chemicals to induce mutations was first demonstrated in 1940 by C. Auerbach, using mustard gas and related compounds in experiments with Drosophila. Since then, many compounds ordinarily considered to be nontoxic have been shown to be mutagenic in specific situations. Any agent that affects the chemical environment of chromosomes is likely to influence, at least indirectly, the stability of DNA and its ability to replicate without error. However, a key factor in chemical mutagenesis is the necessity for the agent to enter the cell, usually the nucleus itself, in order for mutation to occur. The membranes of cells are quite selective in permitting substances to pass. Thus, high concentration of a substance outside a cell is no guarantee that the substance is present in the nucleus. For this reason, results of studies of chemical mutagens cannot be transferred readily from one species to other species, especially if the species are not closely related.

The mutagenic effect of some chemicals involves direct effects on DNA. This occurs either through chemical alteration of the DNA, as in the reaction of HNO_2 with amino groups of the purine and pyrimidine bases, or through substitution of a base analogue for one of the natural bases. For example, 5-bromouracil is similar to thymine and can be incorporated by many organisms into DNA in place of thymine. Such altered DNA appears to direct some normal functions, but errors in replication occur more readily than with unaltered DNA. Inorganic compounds can induce mutations under some circumstances. Manganese chloride is mutagenic for many organisms, as are compounds that bind calcium and thus interfere with the integrity of the chromosome structure. Indeed, almost any substance is likely to influence chromosome stability adversely if it enters the nucleus in metabolically abnormal amounts.

Genetic Effects

Genetic stability is influenced by specific genes in the genome as well as by external agents. This has been demonstrated for several organisms, notably bacteria and Drosophila. The influence can be to make the entire gene complement either more mutable or more stable. Neel (1942) demonstrated the presence in certain strains of Drosophila of a specific gene that increases the mutation rate. That genes themselves should influence mutational stability is to be expected, since they determine to a large extent the metabolic environment of the chromosomes. The ability to handle introduced chemical substances or metabolically produced mutagens, such as peroxides, is dependent on the array of enzymes whose synthesis is directed by the genes.

Temperature

The rates of all chemical reactions are influenced by temperature. It is not surprising then that temperature can be mutagenic. While the effects of temperature are unpredictable for specific organisms and situations, in general the mutation rate increases with increasing temperature. In Drosophila, an increase of 10° C increases the mutation rate two- or threefold. Temperature probably affects both thermal stability of the DNA and the rate of reaction of other substances with DNA.

A study of Swedish nudists indicated that the scrotal temperature of human males in ordinary clothing is about 3° C higher than that of nude males. The higher temperatures could well increase the mutation rate nearly twofold, leading the investigators to suggest that the wearing

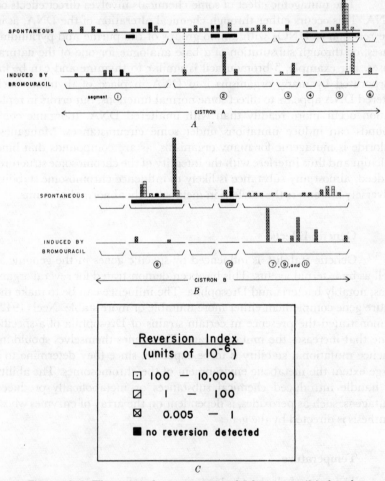

Figure 10–8. The maps of spontaneous and 5-bromouracil induced mutants at the *rII* locus of bacteriophage T4. The order of mutants within segments was not established. (From Benzer and Freeze, *Proc. Natl. Acad. Sci.* (U.S.) 44:112–119, 1958, by permission.)

of pants has possibly been much more dysgenic than fallout from testing of nuclear devices threatens to be. They suggested the wearing of kilts as one solution.

Genetic Fine Structure

The mutation rates of different loci in a particular organism usually fall in the same range. This does not extend down to the nucleotide level, however. Benzer and others have shown that specific points (nucleotides?) along the DNA of bacteriophage are much more prone to mutation than are other points (Fig. 10–8). These "hot spots" are distributed among different genes in the genome, so that the mutation rate per locus, which is the sum of all the mutable sites in the gene, is about the same for different loci. Since there are only four types of DNA bases in most organisms, the existence of hot spots must reflect the interaction of bases with each other and possibly with specifically localized non-DNA components. Different mutagenic agents induce mutations at different rates along the gene. A point that mutates frequently in response to one agent may mutate rarely with another. A second agent may induce a different hot spot.

Cell Cycle

The yield of mutations from radiation in mice is influenced by the stage of meiosis at the time of radiation exposure. Russell has shown that irradiation of mature sperm in mice produces approximately twice as many mutations as does irradiation of spermatogonia. The differing metabolic environments of the various cell stages influence the likelihood of mutations.

REFERENCES AND SUGGESTED READING

BENDER, M. A. 1957. X-ray induced chromosome aberrations in normal diploid human tissue cultures. *Science* 126: 974–975.

BENZER, S., and FREESE, E. 1958. Induction of specific mutations with 5-bromouracil. *Proc. Natl. Acad. Sci.* (U.S.) 44: 112–119.

CRICK, F. H. C., BARNETT, L., BRENNER, S., and WATTS-TOBIN, R. J. 1961. General nature of the genetic code for proteins. *Nature* 192: 1227–1232.

CROW, J. F. 1961. Mutation in man. *Progr. Med. Genet.* 1: 1–26.

CROWE, F. W., SCHULL, W. J., and NEEL, J. V. 1956. *A Clinical, Pathological, and Genetic Study of Multiple Neurofibromatosis.* Springfield, Ill.: Charles C Thomas, 181 pp.

EHRENBERG, L., V. EHRENSTEIN, G., and HEDGRAN, A. 1957. Gonad temperature and spontaneous mutation-rate in man. *Nature* 180: 1433–1434.

FREESE, E. 1962. Molecular mechanism of mutations. In *Molecular Genetics,* Part I (J. H. Taylor, ed.). New York: Academic Press, pp. 207–269.

JAMES, A. P., and NEWCOMBE, H. B. 1964. The quantitative assessment of hereditary damage induced by radiation. *Progr. Med. Genet.* 3: 217–259.

LYNAS, M. A. 1958. Marfan's syndrome in Northern Ireland: An account of 13 families. *Ann. Human Genet.* 22: 289.

MCKUSICK, V. A. 1964. *Human Genetics.* Englewood Cliffs, N. J.: Prentice-Hall, p. 40.

MULLER, H. J. 1927. Artificial transmutation of the gene. *Science* 66: 84–87.

NEEL, J. V. 1942. A study of a case of high mutation rate in *Drosophila melanogaster. Genetics* 27: 519–536.

———. 1962. Mutations in the human population. In *Methodology in Human Genetics* (W. J. Burdette, ed.). San Francisco: Holden-Day, pp. 203–224.

———. 1963. *Changing Perspectives on the Genetic Effects of Radiation.* Springfield, Ill.: Charles C Thomas.

———, and SCHULL, W. J. 1956. *The Effect of Exposure to the Atomic Bombs on Pregnancy Termination in Hiroshima and Nagasaki.* Washington, D. C.: National Academy of Sciences—National Research Council, Publ. 461.

OLIVER, C. P. 1930. The effect of varying the duration of X-ray treatment upon the frequency of mutation. *Science* 71: 44–46.

PENROSE, L. S. 1961. Mutation. In *Recent Advances in Human Genetics* (L. S. Penrose and H. Lang Brown, eds.). London: J. and A. Churchill, pp. 1–18.

REED, T. E., and NEEL, J. V. 1955. A genetic study of multiple polyposis of the colon. *Am. J. Human Genet.* 7: 236–263.

———, and ———. 1959. Huntington's chorea in Michigan. 2. Selection and mutation. *Am. J. Human Genet.* 11: 107–136.

RUSSELL, W. L. 1951. X-ray-induced mutation in mice. *Cold Spring Harbor Symp. Quant. Biol.* 16: 327–336.

———. 1962. An augmenting effect of dose fractionation on radiation-induced mutation rate in mice. *Proc. Natl. Acad. Sci.* (U.S.) 48: 1724–1727.

———, RUSSELL, L. B., and CUPP, M. B. 1959. Dependence of mutation frequency on radiation dose rate in female mice. *Proc. Natl. Acad. Sci.* (U. S.) 45: 18–23.

SCHOLTE, P. J. L., and SOBELS, F. H. 1964. Sex ratio shifts among progeny from patients having received therapeutic X-radiation. *Am. J. Human Genet.* 16: 26–37.

SCHULL, W. J., and NEEL, J. V. 1958. Radiation and the sex ratio in man. *Science* 128: 343–348.

SHAW, M. W., FALLS, H. F., and NEEL, J. V. 1960. Congenital aniridia. *Am. J. Human Genet.* 12: 389–415.

STRAUSS, B. S. 1964. Chemical mutagens and the genetic code. *Progr. Med. Genet.* 3: 1–48.

VOGEL, F. 1957. Neue Untersuchungen zur Genetik des Retinoblastoms (Glioma retinae). *Z. menschl. Vererb. -u. Konstit.* 34: 205–236.

———. 1961. Die spontane Mutabilität menschlicher Gene. *Arch. Julius Klaus-Stift.* 36: 149–166.

PROBLEMS

1. Define:

somatic mutation	Muller-5 test
germinal mutation	prototroph
point mutation	auxotroph
"reading frame"	phenocopy
lethal mutants	roentgen
visible mutants	"hot spot"

Chapter Eleven

PROBABILITY

When a chemist makes measurements such as temperature, the observations are limited in accuracy only by the instruments used. If better instruments were available, more accurate observations could be made. Temperature is a measure of the mean kinetic energy of a population of molecules. Very few of the molecules actually possess energy equal to the mean, however, for the majority move faster or slower than the mean value. If one were to select ten molecules at random, they would very likely not include a molecule with the mean energy of the parent population. Furthermore, the mean of the ten molecules would almost certainly vary slightly from the population mean.

Chemists commonly deal with 10^{20} molecules at a time rather than 10. The chance deviations that occur with ten molecules do not happen when observations are made on such immense numbers, and sampling error can therefore be safely ignored. Biologists, however, commonly make observations on small numbers where chance deviation can occur. It is necessary to recognize the possibility of chance deviation and to estimate the reliability of observations. Geneticists in particular have been faced with this problem. Mendel recognized the chance nature of gene transmission and the possibility of deviation from ideal ratios, although the statistical procedures for evaluating the significance of deviations were not available to him.

This chapter will be concerned with some of the basic laws of probability and how they are used to solve some genetic problems. Many of the statistical techniques commonly in use require more background than can be assumed or provided in this treatment. The material given here should provide an appreciation of the nature of statistical inference as well as a means of solving many of the simpler problems encountered in genetics.

SOME BASIC CONCEPTS OF PROBABILITY

A statement of probability is the likelihood of a "favorable" event among all possible events. Favorable, as used in this context, merely means the event or events of interest, whether or not they might be rated desirable by other criteria. Probability can vary from 0 to 1, 0 indicating no possibility of the favorable event, and 1 indicating no alternate possibility; that is, the event is the only one possible. If $p = \frac{1}{2}$, then half of the time a favorable event will occur.

Probability can be expressed symbolically as

$$p(e_f) = \frac{\Sigma e_f}{\Sigma e_i}$$

where $p(e_f)$ is the probability of a favorable event (e_f), Σe_f is the sum of all events that are favorable, and Σe_i is the sum of all events that are possible. The values e_f and e_i may be in any units that express the relative frequency of each event. Since the units appear both in numerator and denominator, they cancel out.

Consider a die with six sides, each equally likely to appear when the die is thrown. If we ask what the probability is that a 3 will be thrown, the answer is $p(3) = \frac{1}{6}$. The probability of any specific side is $\frac{1}{6}$ and there are six sides. The total number of choices is expressed by $6 \times \frac{1}{6} = 1$. Therefore

$$p(3) = \frac{1/6}{6 \times 1/6} = \frac{1}{6}$$

To calculate the probability of obtaining an even number, one must sum the favorable outcomes, in this case 2, 4, or 6. Then

$$p(\text{even}) = \frac{3 \times 1/6}{6 \times 1/6} = \frac{1}{2}$$

The various possibilities need not be equally likely. Suppose we place 100 marbles into a jar. Ten are yellow, 30 are red, 15 are white, 20 are black, and 25 are green. The probability of drawing a red marble is

$$p(\text{red}) = \frac{30}{10 + 30 + 15 + 20 + 25} = 0.30$$

If the black marbles are removed from the jar, the probability of drawing a red marble becomes

$$p(\text{red}) = \frac{30}{10 + 30 + 15 + 25} = 0.375$$

Thus, reducing the number of unfavorable events increases the likelihood of a favorable event.

Suppose that in the original series of 100 marbles, we wish to know the probability of drawing either a white or black marble. In this case, two possible outcomes are favorable, and

$$p(\text{black or white}) = \frac{15 + 20}{10 + 30 + 15 + 20 + 25} = 0.35$$

The same answer is obtained by calculating the separate probabilities for black and white, followed by addition; for example, $p(\text{black}) = 0.15$, $p(\text{white}) = 0.20$, $\therefore p(\text{black or white}) = 0.35$.

The last example illustrates the important principle that if there are two or more favorable and mutually exclusive events, the total probability can be obtained by summing the probabilities of the separate events.

Another important principle is the independence of chance events from previous trials. When a coin is flipped, the probability of a head or tail is ½ for each. If a given trial yields a head, the next flip still has equal chances for a head or tail. Even if a sequence of five heads is thrown, the sixth still has a half chance of being a head. This has been expressed as "Probability has no memory."

This fact permits the computation of probabilities for complex sequences and combinations of events. The probability of a sequence of events is simply the combined product of each event taken separately. The probability of throwing three heads is

$$p(3H) = p(H) \cdot p(H) \cdot p(H)$$
$$= 1/2 \cdot 1/2 \cdot 1/2 = 1/8$$

This procedure is the same whether one coin is tossed three times or three coins are tossed together. In either case each component event contributes its probability.

The Binomial Expansion

A type of problem frequently arises in genetics that can be readily handled by a binomial expansion of the type $(x + y)^n$. In the preceding example, the probability of three heads was shown to be ⅛. This is also the probability for three tails or for any specific sequence, such as a head followed by two tails. Frequently the interest is in the combination—in this case, one head and two tails—rather than in the sequence by which it was obtained. The same totals could have been obtained by two other sequences: tail, head, tail; and tail, tail, head. Each sequence has the probability ⅛, and since each is a favorable outcome, the total probability of two tails and a head can be obtained by adding them to get ⅜.

Such enumeration is simple in the example but may become complex for larger numbers. Fortunately, the binomial expansion permits calculation of the terms appropriate for any combination of events. The two probabilities associated with two alternate events, for example, heads versus tails, are designated p and q. The binomial is then expressed as

$$(p + q)^n$$

where n is the number of events in the combination. In the above example, n was 3, corresponding to three coins or three tosses. The expansion of $(p + q)^3$ is

$$p^3 + 3p^2q + 3pq^2 + q^3$$

For $p = q = ½$, the expansion becomes

$$1/8 + 3/8 + 3/8 + 1/8 = 1$$

If p is the probability of a head, then the four terms are the probabilities of three heads, two heads and a tail, one head and two tails, and three tails.

The binomial expansion for any value of n can always be obtained by multiplying the quantity $(p + q)$ by itself n times. This is not necessary, however. Each term in the expansion consists of two parts—the algebraic terms p and q with their exponents, and the coefficient. The exponents correspond to the events of probability p and q respectively. For example, a combination of 10 heads and 20 tails would give $p^{10}q^{20}$. This expression, however, is the probability of a specific sequence of 10 heads and 20 tails. There are many possible sequences, the exact number being given by the coefficient.

There are two convenient ways to arrive at coefficients for individual terms in the expansion. For small values of n, and particularly if the entire expansion is desired, the Pascal triangle is helpful. Consider the expansion for small values of n.

$n = 0$	1
1	$1p + 1q$
2	$1p^2 + 2pq + 1q^2$
3	$1p^3 + 3p^2q + 3pq^2 + 1q^3$
4	$1p^4 + 4p^3q + 6p^2q^2 + 4pq^3 + 1q^4$

Regularities in the exponents of p and q are obvious and familiar. The coefficients also fit into a regular pattern somewhat less obviously. Each is the sum of the two nearest coefficients in the line above. With this information, one can construct a Pascal triangle that yields any desired coefficient.

$$
\begin{array}{ccccccccccccc}
n = 0 & & & & & & 1 & & & & & \\
1 & & & & & 1 & & 1 & & & & \\
2 & & & & 1 & & 2 & & 1 & & & \\
3 & & & 1 & & 3 & & 3 & & 1 & & \\
4 & & 1 & & 4 & & 6 & & 4 & & 1 & \\
5 & 1 & & 5 & & 10 & & 10 & & 5 & & 1 \\
6 & 1 & 6 & & 15 & & 20 & & 15 & & 6 & 1 \\
\end{array}
$$

etc.

The Pascal triangle is very useful for small values of n. But n may be very large, and there are $(n + 1)$ terms in the expansion. Furthermore, interest may be limited to only a few terms. The general formula for any term in the expansion is

$$\frac{n!}{x!(n - x)!} p^x q^{n-x}$$

also written
$$\binom{n}{x} p^x q^{n-x}$$

where x is the exponent appropriate for p. In a complete expansion, x varies from n to zero. Suppose we wish to calculate the probability of tossing four heads and two tails. In this case, $x = 4$ and $n = 6$. The appropriate term in the expansion of $(p + q)^6$ is

$$p(4H,2T) = \frac{6!}{4!2!} p^4 q^2$$

$$= \frac{1 \cdot 2 \cdot 3 \cdot 4 \cdot 5 \cdot 6}{1 \cdot 2 \cdot 3 \cdot 4 \cdot 1 \cdot 2} p^4 q^2$$

$$= 15 p^4 q^2$$

which is the same answer given in the Pascal triangle for $n = 6$. Substituting for p and q gives

$$p(4H,2T) = 15(1/2)^4(1/2)^2$$

$$= 15/64$$

Similarly, the probability of throwing any combination of 50 heads and 50 tails is

$$p(50H,50T) = \frac{100!}{50!50!} \, p^{50}q^{50}$$

$$= 0.08$$

This is a small number, which can be calculated readily even though the calculations involve very large numbers.

Sample Distributions

In the example given earlier of three coins tossed, the probabilities of three heads, two heads and one tail, one head and two tails, and three tails were ⅛, ⅜, ⅜, and ⅛ respectively. This may be shown graphically as in Figure 11–1. The probability associated with any number of tails for $n = 3$ can be obtained by reading the ordinate for that number. Note that the most probable value for a large number of tosses, half heads and half tails, is not possible for $n = 3$, but the distribution is symmetrical around the hypothetical 1.5 tails. For $n = 10$, the curve shown in Figure 11–2 is obtained. In this case, the curve is much smoother and is clearly centered around five heads and five tails. The probability of obtaining exactly five heads and five tails is only ²⁵²⁄₁₀₂₄. In other words, one is more likely to get some combination other than five heads and five tails, even though that is the single most probable value. But in contrast to $n = 3$, the likelihood of getting all heads has dropped to ¹⁄₁₀₂₄.

For larger values of n, the likelihood of all heads or tails is infinitesimal. Equal numbers of heads or tails is the most likely combination, but the probability of obtaining this combination now is very small. The distribution of probabilities gives the familiar bell-shaped normal or Gaussian distribution.

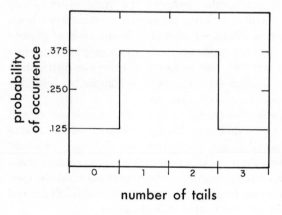

number of tails

Figure 11–1. Probability distribution for a toss of three coins, each with equal likelihood of landing heads or tails.

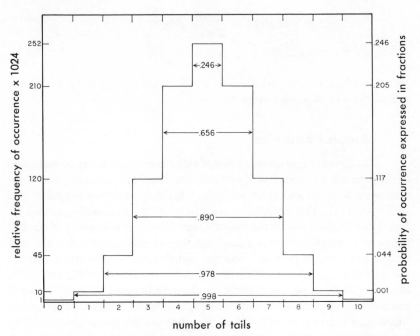

Figure 11–2. Probability distribution for a toss of ten coins. There are $(\frac{1}{2})^{10}$ = 1024 possible sequences, giving eleven combinations in the relative frequencies shown. The left ordinate is the number of sequences corresponding to a given combination of heads and tails. The right ordinate is the same divided by 1024 to convert to fractions. The figures inside the distribution are sums of areas as indicated. These values represent the total probability of any combination within the area.

TESTS OF SIGNIFICANCE

In genetics, as in many other sciences, the question frequently arises as to whether a set of observations conforms to a certain hypothesis. This often takes the form of asking whether the classification of persons as affected or unaffected yields a ratio compatible with simple Mendelian inheritance. This problem is the same as asking whether the distribution of heads and tails in a number of coin tosses is compatible with the hypothesis of equal chances for each to turn up.

In order to answer the question, one must formulate a null hypothesis; that is, there is no difference between the theoretical value of p and the value in the population studied. In terms of a coin, we would say the ratio of heads and tails is not different from that expected if heads and tails are equally likely. If we can prove the hypothesis unlikely, then we may wish to conclude that heads and tails are not equally likely and that the coin lands on one side more often than the other.

The procedure for testing the hypothesis can be illustrated by a sequence of ten tosses. If five heads and five tails were tossed, this would be the most probable value for $p = 0.5$ and would be obtained 0.246 of the time (Fig. 11–2). Clearly, this is compatible with $p = 0.5$. If six heads and four tails were tossed, a value this much deviant from 5:5 would be obtained 0.754 of the time ($1 - 0.246$). Seven heads and three tails, or the equally deviant three heads and seven tails, would occur less than 0.344 of the time, but this is often enough not to invalidate $p = 0.5$. An 8:2 ratio would occur less than 0.110 of the time, a 9:1 less than 0.022, and a 10:0 less than 0.002 of the time. Since a deviation in either direction might occur, it is necessary to sum the probabilities on either side of the expected value.

At what point should the null hypothesis be rejected? The answer will depend on the likelihood of alternate explanations and the consequences of a wrong decision. For most investigations, a result that will happen only 5 percent of the time by chance under a hypothesis is considered adequate to reject the hypothesis. If the results could happen only 1 percent of the time by chance, the hypothesis can be rejected with greater confidence. On occasions, erroneous rejection of a hypothesis may have serious consequences. A more conservative level, such as 0.1 percent, might then be used.

In the example given, a 10:0 distribution will occur only 0.002 of the time when heads and tails are in fact equally likely. If this distribution were tossed, one could conclude that the coin results were biased and expect to be right 99.8 percent of the time. A 9:1 distribution would also lead one to discard the null hypothesis, but in this case, an error would be made 2.2 percent of the time. An 8:2 distribution would lead to error 11 percent of the time if the hypothesis were rejected. For most purposes this error is too large, and the hypothesis would be allowed to stand pending more data.

The Normal Distribution

Most studies are based on more than ten observations. Calculation of the probability distribution by means of the binomial expansion is unwieldy for these cases. Instead, a normal distribution can be constructed using calculus. This distribution assumes infinitesimal divisions along the abscissa and hence is continuous, as shown in Figure 11–3. The abscissa is graduated in units of standard deviation, which, for a simple proportionality such as heads *versus* tails, is given by

$$s = \sqrt{\frac{pq}{n}}$$

NORTHWEST MISSOURI STATE COLLEGE LIBRARY

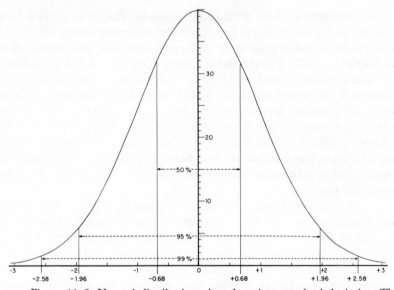

Figure 11–3. Normal distribution plotted against standard deviation. The total area under the curve approaches 1 as the curve is extended on both sides, although the height of the curve approaches zero. The area under a particular portion of the curve equals the probability that a deviation from the mean will fall within that portion. For example, the area bounded by −0.68 S.D. and +0.68 S.D. = 0.50. Therefore, 50 percent of the time, the mean value of a sample will fall within ±0.68 S.D. of the true population mean. The boundaries for 95 percent and 99 percent of the area also are indicated.

where p and q are the theoretical frequencies to be tested and n is the number of observations. The observed deviation of a set of observations is given by

$$z = \frac{p_o - p}{s}$$

where p_o is an observed proportion of events, such as heads, and p the hypothetical.

Evaluation of z can be illustrated by the following. A coin is tossed 100 times. Heads turn up 40 times and tails 60. Can we conclude that the chances of heads *versus* tails are not equal? Let us set up the hypothesis that the chances are equal, that is, $p = 0.5$. The observed $p_o = 0.4$. The observed deviation, expressed as units of standard deviation, is then

$$z = \frac{0.4 - 0.5}{\sqrt{\dfrac{(0.5)(0.5)}{100}}}$$

$$= -2.00$$

Referring to Figure 11–3, we see that a deviation of 2.00 along the abscissa includes just over 95 percent of the area of the curve. Therefore, a 40:60 deviation will occur less than 5 percent of the time by chance when $p = 0.5$. We may therefore reject the hypothesis that $p = 0.5$, with only a 5 percent risk of making an error. Had the deviation been large enough to yield $z > 2.58$, the risk would have been only 1 percent.

Chi-square Analysis

The χ^2 (chi-square) analysis is related in theory to the normal deviate analysis outlined above. However, it has some special applications that justify separate consideration.

A measure of deviation from theory of a set of observations can be measured by χ^2, given by the formula

$$\chi^2 = \Sigma \frac{(E - O)^2}{E}$$

where E = expected value, O = observed value, and Σ indicates summation for all categories. In the problem of the previous section, the expected values (on the hypothesis of $p = 0.5$) would be fifty heads and fifty tails. The observed values were 40 and 60. Therefore,

$$\chi^2 = \frac{(50 - 40)^2}{50} + \frac{(50 - 60)^2}{50}$$

$$= 4.00$$

This value of 4.00 is the square of 2.00 obtained by the earlier method, since, for the special case of two alternatives (heads or tails), $\chi^2 = z^2$.

In order to decide whether the value of χ^2 is too large to represent chance occurrence, it is necessary to consult a table of χ^2, such as is given in Table 11–1. To use the table, one must know the degrees of freedom. The degrees of freedom (df) are the number of categories that can be varied independently without changing the total number of observations. In the above problem, there is one degree of freedom, since only one category can be varied, either heads or tails. If the proportion of heads is arbitrarily specified to be 0.45, then the proportion of tails must be 0.55. If one were studying the distribution of dice scores, there would be five degrees of freedom since a die has six sides.

For one degree of freedom, a χ^2 of 3.84 is larger than 95 percent of the values obtained by chance. The χ^2 of 4.00 exceeds this value, indicating that a 40:60 distribution would occur less than 5 percent of the time by chance, the same conclusion reached by the earlier method.

Chi square can readily be applied to data consisting of more than one category. In the cross $AaBb \times aabb$, four types of offspring are expected: $AaBb$, $aaBb$, $Aabb$, and $aabb$. In the absence of linkage or other factors, they should be in equal proportions. Actual observation gave 45 $AaBb$, 40 $aaBb$, 60 $Aabb$, and 55 $aabb$. Are these values compatible with independent assortment? The expected value for each category is 50; hence,

$$\chi^2 = \frac{(50 - 45)^2}{50} + \frac{(50 - 40)^2}{50} + \frac{(50 - 60)^2}{50} + \frac{(50 - 55)^2}{50}$$

$$= 5.00, \text{df} = 3$$

For three degrees of freedom, χ^2 must exceed 7.8 to invalidate the hypothesis.

TABLE 11-1

Distribution of χ^2. The Values of P Are the Probability That χ^2 Will Exceed by Chance the Value Given in the Table.

DEGREES OF FREEDOM	P						
	0.99	0.95	0.50	0.10	0.05	0.02	0.01
1	0.00016	0.0039	0.45	2.71	3.84	5.41	6.64
2	0.0201	0.103	1.39	4.61	5.99	7.82	9.21
3	0.115	0.35	2.37	6.25	7.82	9.84	11.35
4	0.297	0.71	3.36	7.78	9.49	11.67	13.28
5	0.554	1.15	4.35	9.24	11.07	13.39	15.09
10	2.56	3.94	9.34	15.99	18.31	21.16	23.21

Abridged from Table III, R. A. Fisher, *Statistical Methods for Research Workers*. Edinburgh: Oliver and Boyd, Ltd., by permission of the author and publishers.

CONTINGENCY.   Another important use of χ^2 is in testing for contingency or association. The example just cited is a test of association between the A locus and the B locus. Since a specific cross was tested and simple Mendelian inheritance was involved, it was possible to arrive at the "expected" values on theoretical grounds and independently of the data to be tested. In other cases, it is desirable to test for association between two traits in the absence of external hypotheses from which to derive expected values.

An example would be the association between hair color and eye color. Do blonds tend to have blue eyes more often than brown eyes? Or perhaps they tend to have brown eyes. Observation of 100 persons gave 35 blue-eyed blonds, 10 brown-eyed blonds, 15 blue-eyed brunettes, and 40 brown-eyed brunettes. A contingency table is set up as follows:

observed	blue eyes	brown eyes	totals
blond	35	10	45
brunette	15	40	55
totals	50	50	100

In order to calculate χ^2, it is necessary to compute a table of expected values. From the marginal totals, it is seen that $^{50}/_{100}$ of the persons have blue eyes and $^{45}/_{100}$ are blonds. We wish to test the null hypothesis of no association. Absence of association would lead us to expect that $^{50}/_{100}$ of the 45 blonds would have blue eyes. Similarly, $^{50}/_{100}$ of the 55 brunettes should have blue eyes, etc. A table of expected values can be constructed by these procedures, for example,

expected	blue eyes	brown eyes	totals
blond	22.5	22.5	45
brunette	27.5	27.5	55
totals	50	50	100

Note that the marginal totals must agree with those in the table of observed data. It is necessary to calculate only one of the entries by multiplication. The remaining three can be obtained by subtraction from the marginal totals. For this reason, there is only 1 df in a 2 × 2 contingency table.

Calculation of the χ^2 is as before:

$$\chi^2 = \frac{(22.5 - 35)^2}{22.5} + \frac{(22.5 - 10)^2}{22.5} + \frac{(27.5 - 15)^2}{27.5} + \frac{(27.5 - 40)^2}{27.5}$$

$$= 25.25$$

This value clearly exceeds that required for 1 percent level of significance for 1 df. We must conclude that the null hypothesis is incorrect and that there is indeed association between hair color and eye color, there being an excess of blue-eyed blonds and brown-eyed brunettes, and a deficiency of blue-eyed brunettes and brown-eyed blonds.

Contingency tables can be constructed larger than the 2 × 2 illustrated. The degrees of freedom in an $m × n$ table is $(m - 1) \cdot (n - 1)$.

YATES CORRECTION FOR χ^2. The χ^2 table is derived from a continuous curve, although the distribution of χ^2 itself is discontinuous.

This approximation is of little significance unless the numbers of observations are small. If the numbers are small, χ^2 is likely to be erroneously large, and a hypothesis may be incorrectly rejected.

Yates has suggested a means of correction. It consists in adding or subtracting ½ in each of the four cells so that the marginal totals remain the same but the vaues $(E - O)$ are reduced. On the left is an example of raw data and on the right the corrected values.

8	4	12		7.5	4.5	12
6	7	13		6.5	6.5	13
14	11	25		14	11	25

The χ^2 based on uncorrected data is 1.066 and on the corrected table is 0.396. There is no fast rule to decide when to use Yates correction. If the expected values in each cell are under 10, then the correction probably will make a difference.

REFERENCES AND SUGGESTED READING

DIXON, W. J., and MASSEY, F. J., JR. 1957. *Introduction to Statistical Analysis*, 2d ed. New York: McGraw-Hill, 488 pp.

FISHER, R. A. 1958. *Statistical Methods for Research Workers*, 13th ed. Edinburgh: Oliver and Boyd, 356 pp.

KEMPTHORNE, O. 1954. *Statistics and Mathematics in Biology*. Ames: Iowa State College Press, 632 pp.

———. 1957. *An Introduction to Genetic Statistics*. New York: Wiley, 545 pp.

SNEDECOR, G. W. 1956. *Statistical Methods*, 5th ed. Ames: Iowa State College Press, 534 pp.

WALKER, H. M., and LEV, J. 1953. *Statistical Inference*. New York: Holt, Rinehart and Winston, 510 pp.

PROBLEMS

1.   If a coin is thrown ten times, what are the probabilities of the following combinations?
     a. all heads

    b. the sequence HHTTHHTTHT
    c. the sequence THTHTHTHTH
    d. five heads and five tails
    e. one or more heads
    f. two or more heads
    g. no fewer than two heads and two tails

2. Among sibships of five, give the probabilities for
    a. all boys
    b. three boys and two girls
    c. all combinations with both boys and girls

3. Phenylketonuria is a recessive trait. Two normal people have an affected child.
    a. What is the probability that the next child will be affected?
    b. What is the probability that the next two children will be affected?
    c. What is the probability that the next three children will be affected?
    d. What is the probability that one of the next three children will be affected?

4. Albinism is a recessive trait. The first child of two normal parents is albino.
    a. What is the probability that the mother of the albino is a carrier?
    b. What is the probability that the maternal grandfather is a carrier?
    c. What is the probability that the next child will be a carrier?
    d. What is the probability that an offspring of a normal brother of the albino is a carrier?
    e. What is the probability that any one sibling of the albino will be affected?
    f. What is the probability that there will be no affected persons among the next three siblings of the albino?
    g. What is the probability that the next three siblings will consist of one affected and two unaffected?
    h. What is the probability that the next three siblings will consist of two carriers and one homozygous normal?

5. There are 60 boys and 40 girls in a class.
    a. What is the random expectation that seat number 36 will be occupied by a girl?
    b. What is the expectation that the first four seats will have two girls and two boys?

   c. Is the sex ratio in the class significantly different from the expected 50:50 in the general population?

6. In one group of 78 people, 41 percent had blue eyes. Among 98 people from an adjacent town, 49 percent had blue eyes. May we conclude that these two populations are different with respect to the frequency of blue eyes?

Chapter Twelve

TESTS OF GENETIC HYPOTHESES

When a trait or disease is thought to be inherited, confirmation may be obtained by showing that transmission follows a definite predictable pattern. The first step in deciding the mode of inheritance is the formulation of a genetic hypothesis—usually that the trait is transmitted as a simple Mendelian dominant or recessive. Such a hypothesis entails predictions, which may be shown to be incorrect, proving the hypothesis to be incorrect. If the hypothesis cannot be proved incorrect, it may be accepted until additional tests are made.

The logic of scientific proof should be kept clearly in mind. It is never possible to prove that a hypothesis is correct. Rather, one can only prove that the alternatives are incorrect or unlikely. If such "proof" is to carry weight, all reasonable hypotheses must be tested for compatibility with the observations. As knowledge increases, previously "unreasonable" hypotheses sometimes become reasonable, necessitating re-examination of older proofs. Failure to disprove a hypothesis may happen because the hypothesis is correct or because experimental observations are inadequate.

In many experimental organisms, genetic hypotheses are relatively easy to test. The usual procedure is to cross two pure strains to give an F_1 hybrid, which in turn is allowed to self-fertilize to give the F_2 or which may be backcrossed to the apparently recessive parental strain. If the variation under study is influenced by a single pair of alleles, then the F_2 generation yields $AA:Aa:aa$ in a 1:2:1 ratio ideally. The backcross yields Aa and aa in equal numbers. Deviation from either ratio is sufficient evidence that the trait does not follow simple Mendelian rules. It would then be necessary to consider the influence of other genetic loci and the environment.

In theory, the same types of genetic tests can be used for investigation of human traits. Occasionally, it is possible to pool families to give simple 1:1 or 3:1 ratios. More often, it is necessary to introduce corrections. In the following sections, some of the frequently used tests for human traits are considered. Genes on sex chromosomes show a special pattern of transmission. The methods described in this chapter apply only to autosomal inheritance.

TESTS FOR DOMINANT INHERITANCE

⌣ Dominant inheritance can usually be recognized by inspection of pedigrees, since every affected child should have an affected parent and a pair of unaffected parents should not have an affected child. Exceptions to these rules may occur when persons with the dominant genotype fail to express the related phenotype. This may happen because other genetic or environmental factors influence the gene expression. Some genes are not expressed until a person is an adult or perhaps even in advanced age, an obvious example being baldness. In such cases, a person may die before he expresses his true phenotype, leading to apparent inconsistencies with simple genetic interpretation. Such factors as mutation and illegitimacy also may give rise to deviation from these rules.

Dominant inheritance is the simplest type of inheritance to test. If the dominant gene is rare, the likelihood of homozygous dominant individuals is very small. Every person with the trait may thus be considered heterozygous. Since such persons will nearly always marry homozygous recessive partners, the marriages are comparable to a backcross of F_1 to homozygous recessive parental type. The ratio of children with the dominant gene to children who lack it is 1:1. Since these sibships can be identified through a parent who exhibits the trait, all the sibships can be pooled to give a good estimate of the genetic ratio. If the ratio of affected to normal offspring is 1:1 among marriages of affected to normal, the trait may be considered to result from a dominant gene.

For most rare dominant traits, there is little error in assessing the genetic ratio, provided adequate attention is given to the manner in which the data are collected. In actual practice, each individual or family bearing the trait of interest must be ascertained (identified as possessing the trait). Serious bias may be introduced by the method of ascertainment. In the case of simple dominant inheritance, bias can be avoided if only the descendants of propositi are considered. (The *propositus,* also called *proband* or *index case,* is the person bearing the trait under investigation through whom a family is located.) Inclusion of the sibships of the propositi leads to error because of the greater likelihood of locating sibships that by chance have more than the usual number of affected persons. A correction can be introduced, as in the following section on recessive inheritance, enabling use of index sibships. However, the usual practice is to avoid use of index sibships.

As an example of testing for simple dominant inheritance, consider the sibships given in Figure 12–1. Sibships of two and three persons are given with distributions of dominant and homozygous recessive

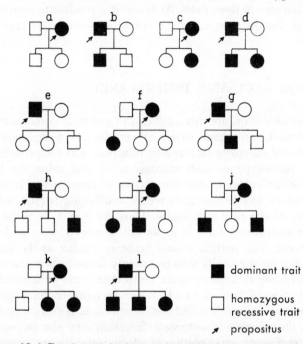

Figure 12–1. Dominant inheritance in sibships of two and three persons.

phenotypes in the combinations predicted by the binomial theorem. In each case, the parent was the propositus, so that sibships with no dominant phenotypes are observed, and sibships with different numbers of dominant phenotypes are found in the same relative frequency in which they occur in the population. There are 32 offspring total, 16 with the dominant phenotype and 16 homozygous recessive. The conforms to the expected 1:1 distribution in a backcross. But in some sibships, all members carry the dominant gene, and in other sibships none carry it.

While this test for dominant inheritance appears to be simple to apply, it is sometimes rather difficult with the available data. This is because pedigrees of very rare dominant genes tend to be noted because of an unusual concentration in the pedigree of persons having the dominant phenotype. An unsophisticated observer is apt to be more impressed by family l of Figure 12–1 with four members of dominant phenotype than by family e with only one, although the latter is just as important in genetic analysis as the former. Thus, most published pedigrees suggesting dominant inheritance are useless for testing segregation ratios. The basic assumption that all families will come to the attention of the investigator in the same proportion that they occur in the general population is not met in these cases. At times, it is possible to correct for this assumption, but in most cases the correction cannot be applied with confidence.

TESTS FOR RECESSIVE INHERITANCE

Recessive traits are more difficult to test than dominants because matings of two heterozygous persons are usually ascertained only through the existence of homozygous recessive offspring. But the probability of a dominant phenotype in such matings is ¾, and using the binomial theorem we can calculate that the portion of matings which by chance fails to produce any homozygous recessive offspring is $(¾)^n$, where n is the number of offspring in a family. Thus, for $n = 1$, ¾ of the matings will not be ascertained; for $n = 2$, $\frac{9}{16}$ will be missed; for $n = 3$, $\frac{27}{64}$ will be missed, etc. The portion missed becomes smaller as the family size increases. But for the family sizes commonly found in Western countries, this portion never diminishes to the point that it can be ignored.

Selection of families in which one or more combinations of offspring is not ascertained is called *truncate* selection. If every type of family is located, the selection is *nontruncate*. Selection may also be complete or single, depending on what portion of affected sibships are located. Complete selection implies that in a given population every sibship produced by appropriate matings is located in the case of nontruncate selection. In the case of truncate selection—the more common situation—every sibship with at least one affected individual should be located. In the case of single selection, only a sample of total possible sibships is located.

The statistical significance in distinguishing between complete and single selection lies in the different frequencies of various types of sibships under the two situations. In the case of complete selection, sibships are found in the same proportion in which they occur in the population. In single selection, sibships with two affected persons are twice as likely to be ascertained as those with one; those with three affected are three times as likely; etc. The differences between complete and single truncate selection are illustrated in Figure 12–2 for sibships of size three.

Since the binomial theorem permits us to predict with certainty the proportion of families missed, it is possible to test for Mendelian ratios, even in recessive inheritance. The methods to be discussed are appropriate for matings of two heterozygotes; matings in which one parent also shows the proposed recessive phenotype should not be considered.

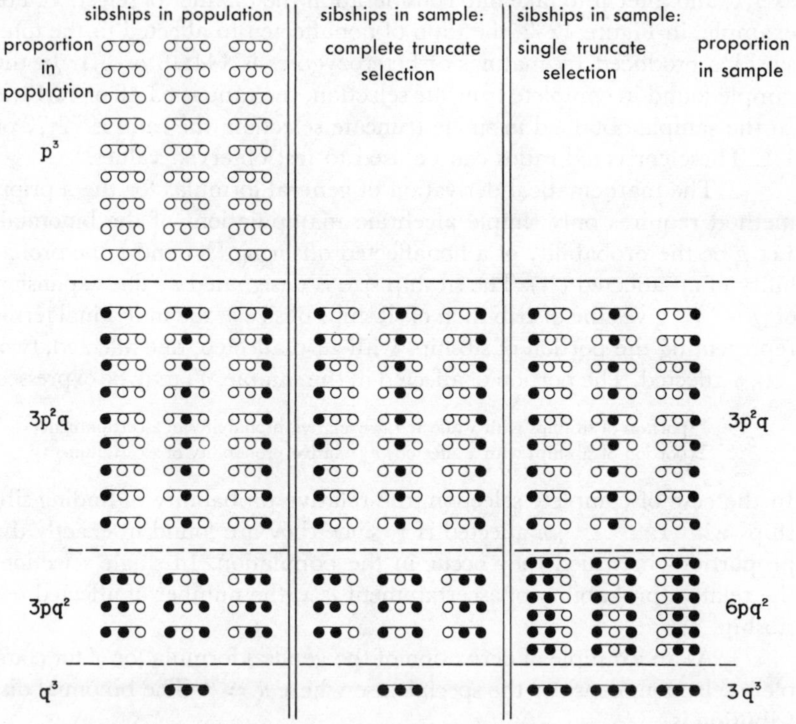

Figure 12–2. Sibships of size three in the proportions in which they occur: (1) in the general population, (2) in complete truncate selection, and (3) in single truncate selection. Only sibships that are offspring of two heterozygous parents are considered. Thus, p = probability of nonaffected offspring = $\frac{3}{4}$; q = probability of affected offspring = $\frac{1}{4}$. Solid circles indicate affected and open circles nonaffected offspring.

For most recessive conditions, particularly those resulting in abnormalities, the genes are rare enough so that only matings of two heterozygotes lead to homozygous recessive persons.

Genetic ratios can also be tested for recessive traits which are sufficiently common so that matings of homozygous recessive with heterozygous persons are likely to occur. Treatment of this situation requires first a consideration of population genetics.

The a Priori Method (Method of Apert)

One procedure for testing for ratios in recessive sibships involves calculating the ratio of affected to unaffected in the actual sample. In order to make such a calculation, it is necessary to assume a ratio, such as 3:1, and alter it to take into consideration the manner of selection. For example, in Figure 12–2, the ratio of nonaffected to affected in the total sibships produced by matings of heterozygotes is 144:48 or 3:1. In the sample found in complete truncate selection, the ratio is 63:48 or 1.313:1. In the sample obtained in single truncate selection, the ratio is 72:72 or 1:1. These corrected ratios can be used to test observed values.

The mathematical derivation of general formulas for the a priori method requires only simple algebraic manipulations of the binomial. Let p be the probability of a nonaffected offspring ($\frac{3}{4}$) and q the probability of an affected ($\frac{1}{4}$). The sibship size is designated n. The expansion of $(p + q)^n$ gives the distribution of sibships of size n, the individual terms representing the portion of sibships with zero affected, one affected, two, . . . , n affected. The portion of affected in the sample, q', may be expressed

$$q' = \frac{\Sigma(\text{portion of sibships with } x \text{ affected})(x)(\text{relative probability of ascertainment})}{\Sigma(\text{portion of sibships with } x \text{ affected})(n)(\text{relative probability of ascertainment})}$$

In the case of complete selection, the relative probability of finding sibships with 1, 2, . . . , n affected is 1, since they are found in exactly the proportions in which they occur in the population. In single selection, the relative probability of ascertainment is x, the number of affected per sibship.

As an example of derivation of the general formula for q' for complete selection, consider the special case where $n = 3$. The binomial distribution is

$$p^3 + 3p^2q + 3pq^2 + q^3$$

The portion of affected in the total group of sibships is

$$q = \frac{(0)(p^3) + (1)(3p^2q) + (2)(3pq^2) + (3)(q^3)}{(3)(p^3) + (3)(3p^2q) + (3)(3pq^2) + (3)(q^3)}$$

Since the first term in the denominator represents the sibships with no affected persons, this term would not appear in the calculation of q', and

$$q' = \frac{3p^2q + 6pq^2 + 3q^3}{9p^2q + 9pq^2 + 3q^3}$$

Dividing by 3 and remembering that $3p^2q + 3pq^2 + q^3 = 1 - p^3$,

$$q' = \frac{q(p^2 + 2pq + q^2)}{1 - p^3}$$

$$= \frac{q(p + q)^2}{1 - p^3}$$

$$= \frac{q}{1 - p^3}$$

It can be shown that for any value of n,

$$q' = \frac{q}{1 - p^n}$$

For $n = 3$, $q' = (\frac{1}{4})/[1 - (\frac{3}{4})^3] = {}^{64}\!/_{148}$, which is the same as the 48:63 ratio obtained earlier.

For single ascertainment, and again considering the case $n = 3$,

$$q' = \frac{(1)(3p^2q) + (2)(6pq^2) + (3)(3q^3)}{3[3p^2q + (2)(3pq^2) + (3)(q^3)]}$$

Dividing numerator and denominator by $3q$,

$$q' = \frac{p^2 + 4pq + 3q^2}{3}$$

$$= \frac{p^2 + 2pq + q^2 + 2pq + 2q^2}{3}$$

$$= \frac{(p + q)^2 + 2q(p + q)}{3}$$

$$= \frac{1 + 2q}{3}$$

For any value of n,

$$q' = \frac{1 + (n - 1)q}{n}$$

For $n = 3$, $q' = [1 + 2(\frac{1}{4})]/3 = \frac{1}{2}$. The ratio obtained from Figure 12-2 was 1:1, showing agreement.

Since the values of q' are dependent solely on q and n, they need be calculated only once. Table 12-1 gives the values of q' for the two methods of ascertainment. The following example illustrates the use of the a priori method for complete ascertainment.

Stevenson and Cheeseman located all persons with hereditary

TABLE 12–1

Corrected Expectation of q (q') for Complete and Single Truncate Ascertainment for Sibships of Various Sizes n. The Product nq' Also Is Given for Convenience.

	COMPLETE ASCERTAINMENT		SINGLE ASCERTAINMENT	
n	q'	nq'	q'	nq'
1	1.0000	1.0000	1.0000	1.0000
2	.5714	1.1428	.6250	1.2500
3	.4324	1.2972	.5000	1.5000
4	.3657	1.4628	.4375	1.7500
5	.3278	1.6390	.4000	2.0000
6	.3041	1.8246	.3750	2.2500
7	.2885	2.0195	.3571	2.5000
8	.2778	2.2224	.3438	2.7500
9	.2703	2.4327	.3333	3.0000
10	.2649	2.6490	.3250	3.2500
11	.2610	2.8710	.3182	3.5000
12	.2582	3.0984	.3125	3.7500
13	.2561	3.3293	.3077	4.0000

TABLE 12–2

Distribution of Deaf and Normal Offspring In Families In Which Both Parents Are Normal. Data from Stevenson and Cheeseman (1956)

SIBSHIP SIZE n	NUMBER OF SIBSHIPS x	TOTAL OFFSPRING nx	OBSERVED AFFECTED	OBSERVED UNAFFECTED	EXPECTED AFFECTED $nq'x$
1	21	21	21	0	21.00
2	35	70	40	30	40.00
3	39	117	50	67	50.59
4	34	136	41	95	49.74
5	35	175	48	127	57.37
6	49	294	68	226	89.41
7	34	238	57	181	68.66
8	33	264	69	195	73.34
9	15	135	32	103	36.49
10	6	60	10	50	15.89
11	3	33	6	27	8.61
12	4	48	10	38	12.39
13	1	13	1	12	3.33
	309	1604	453	1151	526.82

Observed affected (less $n = 1$ sibships) =   432
Observed unaffected   = 1151
Expected affected (less $n = 1$ sibships) =   505.82
Expected unaffected: $1583 - 505.82$ = 1077.18
    $\chi^2 = 15.83$, 1 df, $P < 0.01$

deaf mutism in Northern Ireland. Many of these had one or both parents also deaf. However, there were 309 sibships with at least one deaf member, both parents having normal hearing. The data on these sibships are given in Table 12–2. There are 1151 normal and 453 deaf persons. Is this compatible with a corrected 3:1 ratio? The expected number of affected persons is calculated as indicated. Sibships consisting of one affected person only are ignored, since these can only have a ratio of 1 affected:0 unaffected and therefore are uninformative.

The large χ^2 is incompatible with simple recessive inheritance as the explanation for all cases of deaf mutism. Inspection of Table 12–2 indicates a deficiency of affected persons for sibships of all sizes greater than three. More extensive analysis of these and related data indicates that, although a large portion of congenital deafness is due to homozygosity for recessive genes, there are many cases whose etiology is different. These cases might be due to more complex inheritance or to environmental factors. The data of Table 12–2 have an excess of families with only one affected person. Presumably some of these are not due to simple recessive inheritance.

Simple Sib Method

Where the a priori method corrects the expected 3:1 ratio to match a particular set of observations, the *simple sib method* corrects the observed values so that they can be tested against the theoretical 3:1 ratio. The rationale behind the sib method is found in the relationships of the terms in the expansion $(p + q)^n$ to those in $(p + q)^{n-1}$. Let us consider the specific case of $n = 5$, giving on expansion

$$p^5 + 5p^4q + 10p^3q^2 + 10p^2q^3 + 5pq^4 + q^5$$

Multiplying each term by the number of affected gives

$$(0)p^5 + (1)5p^4q + (2)10p^3q^2 + (3)10p^2q^3 + (4)5pq^4 + (5)q^5$$

Dividing each term by the common factor $5q$ does not change the *relative* magnitude of the terms and gives

$$p^4 + 4p^3q + 6p^2q^2 + 4pq^3 + q^4$$

But this is the expansion of $(p + q)^4$.

The utility of this relationship arises from the fact that truncate selection provides a series of terms complete except for the first. These terms are present in a definite proportion. By adjusting the size of the terms by multiplying by a factor equal to the number of affected individuals in each sibship, a new series is obtained that has all the terms corresponding to sibships of one less person. If we then consider each term as representing the combination of individuals for the $n - 1$ series, a 3:1 ratio of dominant and recessive phenotypes should result. In this procedure, sibships of five persons with one affected, represented in the original expansion by $5p^4q$, would be *counted* as sibships of four persons with no affected.

An example drawn from Figure 12–2 will illustrate the procedure. In the population, the ratio of one affected, two affected, and three affected among sibships of three is 27:9:1. This is also the ratio in complete selection. Multiplying each number by the affected persons gives (1)27:(2)9:(3)1 or 27:18:3 (9:6:1). The sibships of Figure 12–2 would then be counted as 27 with *two unaffected sibs,* 18 with *one unaffected* and *one affected,* and 3 with *two affected.* This gives a total of 72 unaffected and 24 affected persons—a 3:1 ratio.

A sample drawn by single selection is already altered by the influence of the number of affected persons on the likelihood of ascertaining a sibship. As demonstrated earlier, the effect is to increase each term of the expansion by a factor equal to the number of affected persons in the sibship. This is the same operation just indicated as the simple sib correction; hence in single ascertainment the sibships already occur in the corrected proportions. It is merely necessary to subtract one affected person from each sibship before counting. Thus, in Figure 12–2 the sample resulting from single truncate ascertainment has 27 sibships with one affected, 18 with two affected, and 3 with three affected. These are to be counted as 27 with two unaffected, 18 with one affected and one unaffected, and 3 with two affected, giving 72 unaffected and 24 affected, as in the earlier example.

In the case of single ascertainment, there is only one propositus per sibship, and each sibship is counted only once. In complete ascertainment, each sibship needs to be counted as many times as there are affected persons. Since each affected person is an independent propositus, one should count the siblings of each propositus in turn. Thus, a sibship of three with two affected is counted as a total of two affected and two unaffected, because there are two propositi, each of which has one affected and one unaffected sibling.

Once values are obtained for the corrected number of unaffected and affected persons, they can be tested for conformity to a 3:1 ratio by the usual χ^2 test.

DIFFICULTIES IN TESTING GENETIC HYPOTHESES

It is relatively simple to develop corrections for truncate ascertainment and for complete *versus* single ascertainment. Collecting data for which these corrections are strictly applicable is quite another matter. Complete ascertainment means that no homozygous recessive person should escape detection. With the improved medical diagnosis and recording of the present time, complete ascertainment can sometimes be approached if the homozygous recessive state results in a readily characterized condition. In general, ascertainment is possible because a person has sought medical aid; hence, only those conditions which require medical aid are candidates for this type of investigation.

Single ascertainment assumes that sibships are detected in proportion to the number of homozygous recessives per sibship. A variety of factors make this assumption incorrect. Not all segments of society are equally likely to seek medical attention. In some cases, a person is more likely to visit a doctor if a relative with the same apparent condition has benefited from medical attention. Families may more readily recognize the need for medical attention if they have already gained experience with a particular disease. This would lead to an excess of multiply affected sibships compared to singly affected sibships.

A variety of corrections have been developed to compensate for deviations from the ideal situations treated above. These corrections are somewhat complicated and are beyond the scope of this text. Further discussion can be found in the references listed at the end of the chapter. In practice, many investigators attempt as nearly as possible to collect data that conform to the assumptions outlined above, with the hope that uncorrected deviations will not jeopardize their conclusions. This is generally possible in a *prospective* study. Sometimes the data are collected for other purposes and are made available to the geneticist to use in the best way he can. In this case, the data are not likely to match one of the simple models discussed in this chapter, and more complex models must be used.

REFERENCES AND SUGGESTED READING

BAILEY, N. T. J. 1951. A classification of methods of ascertainment and analysis in estimating the frequencies of recessives in man. *Ann. Eugen.* 16: 223–225.

FISHER, R. A. 1934. The effect of methods of ascertainment upon the estimation of frequencies. *Ann. Eugen.* 6: 13–25.

HALDANE, J. B. S. 1932. A method for investigating recessive characters in man. *J. Genet.* 25: 251–255.

HOGBEN, L. 1931. The genetic analysis of familial traits. I. Single gene substitutions. *J. Genet.* 25: 97–112.

MORTON, N. E. 1959. Genetic tests under incomplete ascertainment. *Am. J. Human Genet.* 11: 1–16.

STEINBERG, A. G. 1959. Methodology in human genetics. *J. Med. Educ.* 34: 315–334. Reprinted in *Am. J. Human Genet.* 11(2): Part 2.

STEVENSON, A. C., and CHEESEMAN, E. A. 1956. Hereditary deaf mutism, with particular reference to Northern Ireland. *Ann. Human Genet.* 20: 177–231.

WEINBERG, W. 1912. Weitere Beiträge zur Theorie der Vererbung. 4. Über Methode und Fehlerquellen der Untersuchung auf Mendelsche Zahlen beim Menschen. *Arch. Rass. u. Ges. Biol.* 9: 165–174.

PROBLEMS

1. Define:

propositus	truncate selection
ascertainment	complete selection
single selection	proband

2. Huntington's chorea is a rare autosomal dominant trait in man. Among 200 offspring of affected individuals, 85 are found also to be affected. Is this a significant departure from theoretical expectation?

3. In many pedigrees, brown eyes appear to be inherited as a dominant trait. Matings of brown-eyed × blue-eyed parents, where the brown-eyed parent had a blue-eyed parent, were ascertained. These matings subsequently produced 45 brown-eyed and 55 blue-eyed offspring. Does this ratio support simple dominant inheritance?

4. In a certain population, there are a total of 110 sibships of the variety of muscular dystrophy thought to be inherited as an autosomal recessive. Of these, 25 are single-child sibships, 40 have two children, 35 have three, and 10 have four. A total of 147 affected individuals were observed in this group. Is this ratio compatible with simple recessive inheritance?

5. Suppose that you wish to test the theory that deafness is inherited as a simple recessive trait. A random sample of 100 sibships were found to consist of the following: 17 with a single affected individual; 15 with two affected; 43 with one affected and one unaffected; 5 with

three affected; 5 with two affected and one unaffected; and 15 with one affected and 2 unaffected. Are these results compatible with a simple recessive theory?

6.   Cystic fibrosis is thought to be caused by homozygosity for an autosomal recessive gene. A small sample of 100 sibships yielded 30 two-child sibships, 40 three-child sibships, and 30 four-child sibships. These contained 165 affected individuals. Is this number compatible with simple autosomal recessive inheritance?

Chapter Thirteen

ANALYSIS OF PEDIGREES

Genetic ratios within sibships permit testing for Mendelian inheritance using a single generation. It is particularly useful for testing for recessive inheritance, where affected persons often occur only in one sibship of a family. Obtaining data free of bias is sometimes difficult, and deviations from regular Mendelian ratios sometimes occur that are intrinsically very interesting but impossible to recognize purely on the basis of sibships.

Analysis of pedigrees complements sibship analysis and is suited to answer some questions about which single sibships are uninformative. It consists largely in drawing family trees and attempting to establish the genotype of each person on the basis of his relationship to others. Most of the principles used are inherent in the original paper of Mendel except for genes on the X chromosome. In this chapter, we will review some of the major patterns of inheritance.

Separation of traits into dominant and recessive is somewhat arbitrary, as discussed in the chapters on gene action and production of phenotype. If the presence of an allele in the genome is perceived when one copy is present, it is said to be dominant. If two copies are required, it is recessive. The heterozygous effect of a gene may differ considerably from its homozygous effect, and the means of observation may or may not discriminate between the two. Also the ability to recognize the hetero-zygote may depend on the sensitivity of techniques used.

Whether a gene is dominant or recessive thus depends on the observer. For any given level of observation, it is useful to specify the pattern of inheritance, since it permits prediction of additional persons who may bear the gene in question or who may be free of it. The terms dominant and recessive are time honored, having been introduced by Mendel, and they will not confuse those who understand the nature of gene action.

AUTOSOMAL INHERITANCE

The action of genes located on autosomes or X chromosomes is presumably similar. The patterns of inheritance are different and will be treated separately.

Simple Dominant Inheritance

A dominant trait can be recognized when its allele is in heterozygous combination with a different allele. Most "wild-type" alleles appear to be largely dominant. This implies that departures from wild type are likely to be recessive. More refined methods of observation show many recessive genes to have a dominant effect. The term dominant is sometimes interpreted to mean that the homozygous dominant and heterozygous phenotypes are similar—an idea that clearly is not true in many cases.

The primary usefulness of pedigree analysis is for cases in which most of the matings are $Aa \times aa$, where A is the dominant allele. This type of mating is prevalent when the frequency of A is small compared to a. Most of the genes of clinical significance are characterized by low frequency. It is usually possible to construct a pedigree showing transmission of A through two or more generations. A pedigree of dominant inheritance is shown in Figure 13–1.

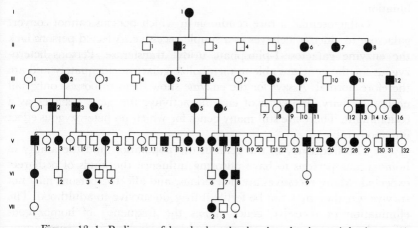

Figure 13–1. Pedigree of brachydactyly showing dominant inheritance. A portion of this pedigree was reported by Farabee in 1905 as the first example of Mendelian inheritance in man. The pedigree was revised in 1962. (From V. A. Mc-Kusick, *Human Genetics.* Englewood Cliffs, N.J.: Prentice-Hall, 1964, by permission.)

Several requirements for autosomal dominant inheritance must be met in order to merit that designation. (1) Every affected person must have at least one affected parent. (2) Both males and females should be affected and should be capable of transmitting the trait, provided the trait does not cause sterility. (3) There is no skipping of generations or alternation of sexes. Father to son and mother to daughter transmission should be as frequent as father to daughter and mother to son. (4) An affected person should transmit the trait to half his offspring if the mating is $Aa \times aa$. A discussion of the difficulties of assessing ratios is given in the previous chapter.

In counseling, one is frequently asked to predict the genetic status of relatives of affected persons. For a dominant trait that is uniformly penetrant at an early age, there is no difficulty. Persons who do not have the trait will not develop it and will not transmit it to their children. It is necessary to modify such statements when dealing with traits of late onset or low penetrance.

Simple Recessive Inheritance

As more sensitive techniques have been developed, it has become increasingly apparent that few genes are completely recessive. Many genes that must be in homozygous combination to show the "characteristic" expression can be detected nevertheless in heterozygous combination.

Galactosemia, a rare condition in which persons cannot convert galactose to glucose, behaves as a simple recessive. Affected persons lack the enzyme galactose-1-phosphate uridyl transferase. Persons heterozygous for the gene are able to metabolize galactose adequately and are therefore normal. Assays for the enzyme show them to possess only half normal activity. In terms of enzyme activity, the gene behaves as a codominant. There are still many genes for which no heterozygous effect is demonstrable.

The frequency of the gene in the population and the ability of homozygous persons to have offspring influence the kinds of pedigrees expected. Many recessives are deleterious, and affected persons may not survive. Or they may not be fertile if they do survive to adulthood. The elimination of recessive genes causes the frequency of homozygous affected persons to remain at very low levels. Under such circumstances, all homozygotes are produced by matings of the type $Aa \times Aa$. A typical pedigree therefore consists of a single sibship with affected persons, all other sibships being normal. An example of a pedigree showing inheritance of a relatively benign recessive trait is shown in Figure 13–2.

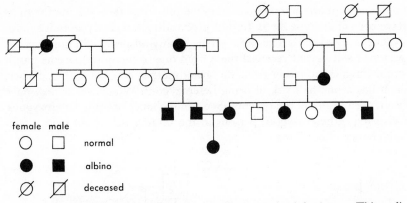

Figure 13-2. Pedigree of albinism showing recessive inheritance. This pedigree was obtained from the Hopi Indians, where the gene for albinism is unusually frequent. Therefore, pedigrees may show several generations to be affected. Superficially, such pedigrees may resemble dominant inheritance with reduced penetrance. (From C. M. Woolf and R. B. Grant, 1962, *Am. J. Human Genet.* 14: 391–400, by permission.)

The genetic nature of recessive traits is sometimes difficult to prove. Some rare environmental factor might also lead to isolated sibships with more than one affected member. Evidence of the genetic basis is of two sorts. For more common traits, the most important is a 3:1 ratio of normal to affected (the necessity to correct for method of ascertainment must be kept in mind). For very rare traits, there is an increase in consanguinity among parents of affected persons; that is, the parents are more likely to be related than other parents in the same population. The quantitative aspects of consanguinity are discussed in a later chapter. A few traits have been observed in only one person. These have been attributed to recessive genes on the basis of highly specific enzyme defects. Such an interpretation is reasonable on the basis of what is known of gene action, but it should be remembered that direct evidence favoring genetic etiology is lacking.

Less deleterious genes may attain sufficient frequency so that $Aa \times aa$ matings sometimes occur. The presence of affected persons in two generations has been misinterpreted by some as evidence for a dominant form of the condition. However, a few pedigrees of this type will occur by chance, even if the gene is rare, and they may occur more often if the gene is common. There may indeed be both a dominant and a recessive form of a trait. Care should be exercised that the evidence for both forms is adequate.

It is frequently of interest to know the likelihood of heterozygosity for a recessive gene among the relatives of an affected person. Some simple rules will enable the calculation to be made. If two normal parents have one or more homozygous recessive offspring, then the mating must have been of the type $Aa \times Aa$. The probability that each parent is heterozygous is $p(Aa) = 1$. The same is true of any offspring of a homozygous person. Each parent received the a from one of the grandparents, but it could have come either from the grandmother or grandfather. Hence, each has a one-half risk of being heterozygous. Whichever it may have been, normal sibs of the parents have a half chance of being heterozygous. Offspring of heterozygous persons in the mating $AA \times Aa$ have a one-half chance of receiving a.

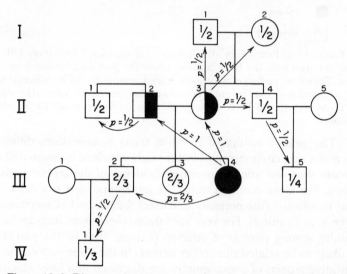

Figure 13-3. Diagram showing probability of heterozygosity for persons related to a homozygous recessive. Figures on arrows are probabilities of heterozygosity, assuming that the person the arrow is pointing from is heterozygous (except in the case of the homozygous recessive). Figures inside the symbols are the total probabilities of heterozygosity.

Normal sibs of aa persons are of two types if the parents are both Aa. Some are AA and others Aa. The usual F_2 ratios should apply, giving $1AA:2Aa:1aa$. Since only normal sibs are under consideration, the ratio is $1AA:2Aa$; that is, $p(AA) = \frac{1}{3}, p(Aa) = \frac{2}{3}$.

The probability that a relative of an affected person is heterozygous for the gene is obtained by combining the probabilities of persons through whom they are related. Since a specific combination of events is required, the probabilities are multiplied together. An example is in Figure 13-3. The probability that III-5 is Aa is

$$p(Aa) = (1)(1/2)(1/2) = 1/4$$

Similarly, the probability for IV-1 is

$$p(Aa) = (2/3)(1/2) = 1/3$$

Occasionally, prospective marriage partners, each with an affected relative, wish to know the likelihood of their having affected children. The pedigree is drawn and the probability that each parent is heterozygous is calculated. The probability that both are heterozygous is the product of the probabilities for each. If both parents are heterozygous, each child would have a one-fourth chance of being affected and a three-fourths chance not to be. The probability that the first child would be affected is

$$p(aa) = p(Aa \text{ mother}) \times p(Aa \text{ father}) \times 1/4$$

The probability that all of three children would be affected is

$$p(3 \, aa) = p(Aa \text{ mother}) \times p(Aa \text{ father}) \times (1/4)^3$$

The probability that none would be affected is $1 - p(1 \text{ or more affected})$. For n children it is

$$p(\text{no } aa) = 1 - [p(Aa \text{ mother}) \times p(Aa \text{ father}) \times (1 - (3/4)^n]$$

These calculations ignore the possibility of introduction of an a allele through other relatives. The likelihood that this might occur is very small unless a is common.

INHERITANCE ON THE SEX CHROMOSOMES

X-Linked Recessive Inheritance

A special pattern characterizes genes on the X chromosome. Since females have two X chromosomes and males only one, genes that are recessive in females are expressed in males.

The transmission of X chromosomes provides the basis for the pattern of X-linked, frequently called sex-linked, recessive inheritance. Affected males transmit the gene to all daughters and to no sons. Father to son transmission of a trait rules out X-linked genes, although the possibility should always be recognized that the son may by chance receive a similar gene from his mother. Unless the gene frequency is very high, most women carrying a gene a will be heterozygous Aa and will not express a. They will transmit a to half of their sons, who will express the trait. They will also transmit a to half their daughters, where it will be in combination with the paternal allele, usually A.

In addition to the higher frequency of expression of X-linked recessives in males, affected persons often occur in alternate generations. This is because of the pattern of affected father–unaffected carrier daughter–affected grandson. This pattern is the origin of the common misconception that skipping of generations is evidence for genetic etiology of a trait. It is evidence only for X-linked traits and only if the skipping follows a definite pattern. Since carrier mothers give rise to carrier daughters half the time, affected males may be related in ways other than grandfather and grandson. An affected male may have an affected maternal uncle if the gene was transmitted from his maternal grandmother.

One of the classical examples of X-linked inheritance is the hemophilia in many of the royal families of Europe. A pedigree is given in Figure 10–1. Affected males have a severe defect of the blood-clotting mechanism and are apt to bleed to death from minor cuts. Carrier females are normal. The first appearance of the hemophilia gene in the royal families was in a son of Queen Victoria. This is evidence that it probably arose as a mutation in Queen Victoria or in a segment of the germinal tissue of her parents.

The unique pattern of X-linked inheritance readily enables the assignment of genes to the X chromosome. By contrast, no definite assignment of any gene to an autosome has been achieved. A list of genes on the X chromosome is given in Table 13–1. With few exceptions, these alleles are recessive to the normal allele, heterozygous females showing little if any effect.

While the pattern of X-linked inheritance is straightforward, a few conditions are difficult to classify because of the possibility of sex limitation. Traits may be expressed only in males because the gene is on the X chromosome and is so rare that homozygous females are unlikely to be encountered. On the other hand, some genes may be expressed only in the presence of typically male phenotypes. A gene influencing beard pattern is not likely to be expressed in females, even though they may carry the proper combination of genes.

Testicular feminization illustrates the difficulty that may be encountered, even if rarely. A pedigree of this condition is given in Figure 6–1. The gene causing the abnormality is rare, and homozygous persons have not been observed, nor could they occur, since persons with an XY karyotype who also have the gene are females externally. The condition is described in more detail on page 66. It is compatible with either auto-

TABLE 13–1

Some of the Traits Thought to be Controlled by Genes on the X Chromosome*

1. partial color blindness, deutan series
2. partial color blindness, protan series
3. total color blindness; most cases are autosomal, however
4. glucose-6-phosphate dehydrogenase structure
5. Xg blood group system
6. Duchenne type muscular dystrophy
7. muscular dystrophy of Becker
8. hemophilia A (AHG deficiency)
9. hemophilia B (Christmas disease; PTC deficiency)
10. agammaglobulinemia
11. gargoylism (Hurler syndrome); there is also an autosomal form
12. late spondylo-epiphyseal dysplasia
13. Aldrich syndrome
14. hypophosphatemia (vitamin D-resistant rickets)
15. hypoparathyroidism
16. diabetes insipidus, nephrogenic type
17. diabetes insipidus, neurohypophyseal type
18. Lowe syndrome
19. hereditary hypochromic anemia
20. angiokeratoma diffusum corporis
21. dyskeratosis congenita
22. hereditary bullous dystrophy, macular type
23. keratosis follicularis spinulosa decalvans cum ophiasi
24. ichthyosis vulgaris
25. anhidrotic ectodermal dysplasia
26. amelogenesis imperfecta, hypomaturation type
27. amelogenesis imperfecta, hypoplastic type
28. absence of central incisors
29. congenital deafness; there are autosomal forms also
30. progressive deafness
31. mental deficiency; a small portion of cases show X linkage
32. Börjeson syndrome
33. spinal ataxia
34. cerebellar ataxia with extrapyramidal involvement
35. spastic paraplegia
36. progressive bulbar paralysis
37. peroneal muscular atrophy (Charcot-Marie-Tooth)
38. diffuse cerebral sclerosis (Pelizaeus-Merzbacher)
39. diffuse cerebral sclerosis (Scholz)
40. hydrocephalus. Most cases are not X linked.
41. Parkinsonism; only one kindred shows X linkage
42. ocular albinism
43. external ophthalmoplegia and myopia
44. microphthalmia
45. microphthalmia or anophthalmos with other anomalies
46. hereditary nystagmus
47. megalocornea
48. hypoplasia of iris with glaucoma
49. congenital total cataract
50. congenital cataract with microcornea
51. congenital stationary night blindness
52. choroideremia
53. retinitis pigmentosa
54. macular dystrophy
55. retinoschisis
56. pseudoglioma
57. van der Bosch syndrome
58. Menkes syndrome

* For many of these traits, there are also causes other than inheritance by means of an X-linked gene. This list is taken from a review by McKusick, 1962. For a fuller description of the diseases, see the original. There are a number of other conditions for which X linkage has been suggested but for which evidence is meager.

somal or X-linked inheritance. The most important evidence against X-linked genes—father to son transmission—cannot be observed, because affected persons cannot be fathers.

X-Linked Dominant Inheritance

Although the catalogue of X-linked recessive genes is quite large, the first X-linked dominant genes, apart from the common "wild-type" alleles, were recognized very recently and only a few are known. The reason is probably because selection has favored survival on the X chromosome of alleles whose function can be fully satisfied by a single copy. In contrast, there are always two genes for each autosomal locus, and, if one is defective, the other frequently does not compensate 100 percent, even though it compensates adequately. With the discovery of X-chromosome differentiation, this argument will perhaps require modification, although inactivation may not affect the entire X chromosome.

The rules for X-linked dominant inheritance are similar to those for recessive, except that heterozygous females express the condition. Since females have twice as many X chromosomes as males, they have a higher frequency of affected persons. For rare traits and in the absence of interactions with other factors, two thirds of affected persons should be female. An affected female, if she is heterozygous, will transmit the gene to half her offspring, regardless of sex. An affected male will not transmit to his sons, but all his daughters will be affected.

Probably the best example of an X-linked dominant trait is G6PD (glucose-6-phosphate dehydrogenase) deficiency. This enzyme occurs in many tissues of the body, including red blood cells, where it is most readily assayed. Males with the deficiency allele show greatly reduced quantities of active enzyme. Homozygous deficient females are similar to males. Heterozygous females vary in phenotype from normal to fully defective, with most showing intermediate levels. The gene is dominant in that it can be detected in most although not all heterozygotes. The deficiency gene is sufficiently frequent in some populations to produce pedigrees with apparent father to son transmission. Additional study has shown that these families consist of heterozygous mothers with essentially normal phenotype married to affected fathers. The affected sons receive their gene from the apparently normal mother.

Several electrophoretic variants of G6PD are also known. These are structural alterations in the enzyme, detected by mobility differences in an electric field. They are controlled by genes on the X chromosome, presumably alleles of the G6PD deficiency gene. A pedigree of one of the uncommon variants is given in Figure 13–4.

Y-Linked (Holandric) Inheritance

Y-linked inheritance should be the easiest to recognize. Every son of an affected father should be affected, and no daughter should be affected or transmit the trait as a carrier. A number of examples of Y-linked inheritance have been suggested, but evidence in most cases is poor and in some is incompatible.

The most famous example of Y linkage was the Lambert family of porcupine men. The condition consisted in changes in the skin sufficiently striking so that affected persons exhibited themselves in circuses.

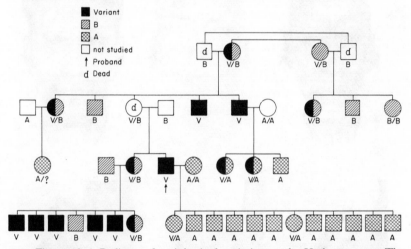

Figure 13–4. Pedigree of an inherited variation on the X chromosome. The various forms of the enzyme glucose-6-phosphate dehydrogenase are inherited as codominant traits, with great phenotypic variation in females because of X-chromosome inactivation (Chapter 9). Genotypes are indicated below the symbols. (From W. K. Long, H. N. Kirkman, and H. E. Sutton, 1965, *J. Lab. Clin. Med.* 65: 81–87, by permission.)

The Lamberts lived in England during the eighteenth century. The first pedigree prepared showed seven generations of affected males conforming to the exacting demands of Y linkage. In 1957, Stern and L. S. Penrose re-examined such records as were available and concluded that the traditional pedigree had been colored by the demands of show business and that the true pedigree was incompatible with Y linkage.

At the present time, no gene has been satisfactorily established on the Y chromosome. The trait for which the best evidence has been collected is hairy pinnae (hairy ears). An example of this trait is shown in Figure 13–5. The difficulty encountered with this trait is possible sex limitation. The sexual dimorphism in body and facial hair may limit the expression to males, even though females may carry the gene. Also, there is an age effect, the trait not appearing in some men until late middle age. Many of the pedigrees obtained can be interpreted in more than one way. The critical study in Israel by Slatis and Apelbaum favors Y linkage. Additional data will be necessary before the question can be completely resolved.

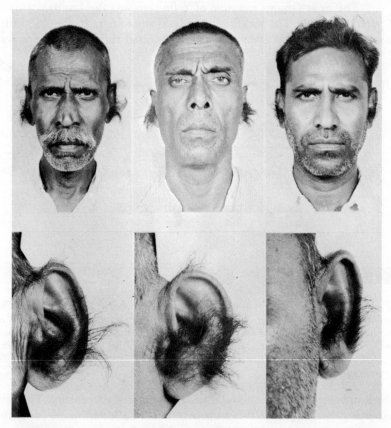

Figure 13–5. Photograph showing the trait "hairy ears," common in parts of India and in some other Caucasian groups. It has been suggested that this trait is controlled by a locus on the Y chromosome. (From C. Stern, W. R. Centerwall, and S. S. Sarkar, 1964, *Am. J. Human Genet.* 16:455–471, by permission.)

The Y chromosome is remarkably free of genes at the present time. This should not cause surprise, since any function required by both men and women would have to be controlled from another chromosome. As pointed out in an earlier chapter, the Y chromosome does determine maleness in human beings. Therefore, it has one very important function for half of the population.

Partial Sex Linkage

In some organisms with XY sex determination, portions of the X and Y chromosomes are homologous. Genes occurring within this region are said to be partially sex linked. They can recombine by crossing over.

The results of early attempts to detect partial sex linkage in human beings seemed to favor its existence. Diagrams of human X and Y chromosomes showing a homologous region are still encountered. Later studies, however, have failed to confirm partial sex linkage in man, and it is now considered not to exist.

REFERENCES AND SUGGESTED READING

FARABEE, W. C. 1905. Inheritance of digital malformations in man. *Papers Peabody Museum Amer. Arch. Ethnol., Harvard Univ.* 3: 65–78.

LONG, W. K., KIRKMAN, H. N., and SUTTON, H. E. 1965. Electrophoretically slow variants of glucose-6-phosphate dehydrogenase from red cells of Negroes. *J. Lab. and Clin. Med.* 65: 81.

MC KUSICK, V. A. 1962. On the X chromosome of man. *Quart. Rev. Biol.* 37: 69–175.

———. 1964. *Human Genetics.* Englewood Cliffs, N. J.: Prentice-Hall, 148 pp.

SLATIS, H. M., and APELBAUM, A. 1963. Hairy pinna of the ear in Israeli populations. *Am. J. Human Genet.* 15: 74–85.

STERN, C. 1957. The problem of complete Y-linkage in man. *Am. J. Human Genet.* 9: 147–166.

———, CENTERWALL, W. R., and SARKAR, S. S. 1964. New data on the problem of Y-linkage of hairy pinnae. *Am. J. Human Genet.* 16: 455–471.

WOOLF, C. M., and GRANT, R. B. 1962. Albinism among the Hopi Indians in Arizona. *Am. J. Human Genet.* 14: 391–400.

PROBLEMS

1. Indicate the genotypes for all persons in Figure 13–2. If more than one genotype is possible, indicate the probability of each.

2.

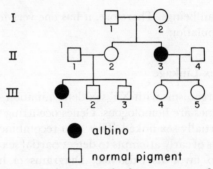

● albino

□ normal pigment

a. Which persons are known to be heterozygous for albinism?
b. What is the probability that III-2 is a carrier?
c. If III-3 and III-4 marry, what is the probability that their first child will be albino?
d. If III-3 and III-4 have many children, what is the probability of at least one affected?
e. What is the probability that a grandchild of III-1 will be a carrier?

3.

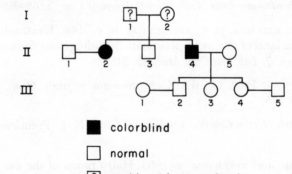

■ colorblind

□ normal

? could not be examined

a. What are the genotypes and phenotypes of I-1 and I-2?
b. What are the genotypes of II-3 and II-5?
c. What are the chances that male offspring of II-1 and II-2 will be colorblind? Female offspring?
d. What are the chances that male offspring of III-1 and III-2 will be colorblind? Female offspring? Assume III-1 to be homozygous.
e. What are the chances that male offspring of III-4 and III-5 will be colorblind? Female offspring?

4. Distinguish between sex-linked inheritance, sex-limited inheritance, and partial sex linkage. A given inherited trait is found in 20 percent of males but in only 4 percent of females. Why is this evidence for sex linkage rather than sex limitation?

Chapter Fourteen

COMPLEX GENETIC TRAITS
AND POLYGENIC INHERITANCE

The discussion thus far has dealt with traits, variation of which is due to single gene differences. Many human traits, especially diseases or traits that are observed at the biochemical level, can be described as single gene variations, or simple Mendelian traits, as they are frequently called. On the other hand, many very important traits, such as intelligence or special aptitudes, cannot be described in such simple terms. Nevertheless, it is legitimate to ask whether the obvious variations in normal intelligence can be ascribed in part or entirely to genetic variation.

CONTINUOUS VARIATION

A trait that is measured quantitatively and that may assume any value on a scale (or limited portion of a scale) is said to be continuous. An example is height. Between the shortest person and the tallest person, there are no values that cannot correspond to someone's height. If the distribution of heights in a population is plotted, the values fall into a curve similar to the normal distribution of Figure 11–3. It is apparent that the techniques used to detect the effects of heredity on discontinuous traits or attributes cannot be applied without modification to continuous traits.

Traits that show continuous variation are difficult to study but present no difficulties so far as genetic theory is concerned. The genes involved in continuous traits are not unusual. The only special feature is that variation among several sets of genes influences one trait. Such traits are said to show *polygenic* or *multigenic* inheritance. If there exist only the alternatives *A* and *a* to influence some trait—for example, skin color—persons would be relatively simple to classify with respect to the *A* locus. But if, at the same time, variation at the *B* locus is important, the task is more difficult, since there are nine genotypes to consider: *AABB*, *AABb*, *AAbb*, *AaBB*, *AaBb*, *Aabb*, *aaBB*, *aaBb*, and *aabb*. Dominance might reduce the number of useful distinctions. Even if *A* is completely dominant to *a* and *B* to *b*, there remain four distinctive combinations. Addition of a third and fourth locus rapidly leads to a system so complicated that analysis with confidence would be difficult.

In the case of skin color, it would be necessary to recognize very subtle differences in order to attempt an analysis based even on four loci. Environmental influences and errors of measurement must be considered also. A person's skin may be lighter or darker, depending on his exposure to sun. And every measure has its limit of accuracy that imposes a limit on the recognizable number of gene combinations.

In spite of these difficulties, it is frequently useful to have an estimate, however crude, of the contribution of heredity to a given variation. A variety of techniques appropriate to different experimental organisms have been developed to ascertain genetic components of variation. Plant and animal breeders in particular have been interested in knowing to what extent a certain variation is hereditary in order to decide whether the environment or selective breeding would be more likely to influence the trait.

It is important to understand the nature of estimates of heritability. As in all areas of genetics, *variation* is the object of investigation. A statement that height is 80 percent inherited means that 80 percent of the variation in height can be attributed to variation of genes. But such a statement is meaningless without reference to a specific population and environment.

Consider two populations that are under investigation for heritability of height, and assume that environmental variables are equal for the two populations. On an arbitrary scale of variability, population I might be represented as in Figure 14–1. Suppose, however, that population II is homozygous at several of the loci that influence height and for which population I has two or more alleles. The genetic variability of population II will be less than population I, and the total variability also

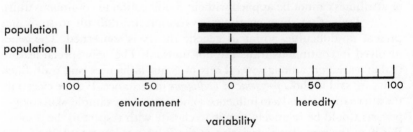

Figure 14–1. Diagram showing relative contributions of heredity and environment for two populations with equal environmental variability but different total variability.

will be less. Heritability estimates in the two populations would be 80 percent for I and 67 percent for II. The corresponding contributions of environment would be 20 percent and 33 percent, even though the absolute magnitude of the environmental component is the same. Similarly, if the environmental variation increases, the portion of the total variation attributable to genetic variation will decrease.

The complexity of genetic and environmental interactions is illustrated by certain skills. Skill at a game such as tennis is generally considered to depend largely on good instruction and practice. Estimation of the genetic component of skill of the total population would very likely yield an answer near zero. Many persons will have played very little and would perform poorly; those who do play would perform largely according to the amount of exposure to the game. Environment would appear to be all-important because the total variation in skill is so large and most of it is due to environment.

On the other hand, an outstanding player must have excellent neuromuscular coordination, and persons vary in the limits to which their coordination can be trained. Among a cross section of the population exposed to intensive instruction and practice in tennis, some would excel and others would do poorly. At least part of the reason for difference in performance would lie in inherent—presumably genetic—differences in neuromuscular makeup. By reducing the environmental variation through training, the genetic components may have an opportunity to be expressed.

Still other results might be obtained if observations were limited to champion tennis players. Is the achievement of such persons limited primarily by inherited anatomical and physiological variations, or is practice all-important? Our democratic ideology emphasizes environment and individual opportunity. These are the variables that can be manipulated readily. We should be aware, however, of the limitations and opportunities attributable to genetic variation.

It is thus very difficult to arrive at estimates of genetic or environmental contributions that have general significance. Any such estimate is valid at best for a particular population in a particular environment. A statement that the variation in yield of corn from a specific strain in a certain environment is 50 percent heritable is useful, since it suggests that selective breeding should increase the average yield to match that of the best plants. Conversely, if the variation in yield is 50 percent environmental, then control of the environment should also increase the yield. In the case of human populations, estimates of heritability are useful as indicators of the traits that are most likely to respond to environmental manipulation. But it must not be forgotten that persons at one end of the scale may show a responsiveness to environmental changes different from those in the middle or at the other end of the scale.

TWINS IN GENETIC RESEARCH

In experimental plants and animals, the genetic component of variation can be estimated by comparing genetically related with genetically unrelated organisms in a variety of environments. In man, the experimental designs developed by plant and animal breeders cannot be applied. Instead, one must make observations on such experiments of nature as occur by chance.

One such experiment in man is the occurrence of multiple births —twins, triplets, etc. Because of their greater prevalence, twin births provide most of the opportunities for observations. The utility of twin births arises from the existence of two kinds of twins, the so-called identical (monozygotic) and fraternal (dizygotic) twins. Monozygotic (MZ) twins arise from a single zygote that divides into two separate embryos very early in gestation. Since only one zygote is involved, the twins are genetically identical. Dizygotic (DZ) twins arise from two zygotes that are produced by fertilization of two separate ova. Thus, they have the same genetic relationship as ordinary sibs. They may be either like-sexed (two boys or two girls) or unlike-sexed (a boy and a girl). Monozygotic twins must be like-sexed.

Persons who are genetically identical provide a means of estimating the effects of environment, since any differences between cotwins must have a nongenetic origin. It should be noted that environment, as defined by this test, comprises all nongenetic effects, including the internal environment of the body and unequal distribution of cytoplasmic constituents in cell division. Dizygotic twins may differ from each other both for environmental as well as for genetic reasons.

Diagnosis of Twin Zygosity

The usefulness of twins in genetic research depends on correctly assessing the zygosity. The criteria of zygosity determination vary somewhat with the investigator but ultimately depend on whether or not a *genetic* difference can be demonstrated between the members of a twin pair. If a difference is present, the twins are classified as dizygotic. If no reliable difference can be detected, they are classified as monozygotic. The thoroughness with which one investigates zygosity varies with the situation. For a comparison of measurements on 100 MZ twins with those on 100 DZ twins, the presence of a few DZ twins among the MZ sets is not likely to influence conclusions. However, for transplantation of a kidney, possible at present only between genetically identical persons, it is necessary to establish zygosity with great certainty.

The first step in establishing zygosity is to classify subjects for simple genetic traits. The simplest is sex; as indicated earlier, twins of different sex arise from different zygotes. Other traits include the blood groups, plasma protein types, and salivary secretion of antigens, all of which follow simple Mendelian patterns of inheritance. A difference in any one system is adequate evidence for classifying a pair of twins as DZ, although, purely by chance, DZ twins may agree for all of the traits tested. More complex traits may also be considered: finger and palm prints, hair color, eye color, and morphology of skeletal and other tissues, such as teeth, ears, and nostrils. Reliable judgments of complex traits can be made by experienced observers.

Zygosity of twins has often been judged erroneously by the nature of the fetal membranes. Both MZ and DZ twins may have two separate placentas with separate amnions and chorions. Conversely, both types of twins may have a single fused placenta. DZ twins always have two chorions, but they may be so fused that they cannot be distinguished without special examination. A high portion of MZ twins have separate amnions with a single chorion. The birth membranes may sometimes help establish monozygosity, but more than casual examination is required.

The most rigorous test of zygosity is skin grafting. Because of the surgical procedure involved, transplanting of skin is done only if it is important to establishing zygosity with certainty. The body normally responds to the introduction of foreign material (antigens) by the formation of antibodies. These are proteins (gamma globulins) that form complexes with foreign material. The reaction is highly specific, and minute differences in structure can be recognized by formation of antibody complexes with particular antigens.

The various antigens that elicit antibody formation and that determine whether a tissue is "foreign" to the host are under genetic control. Closely related persons share more antigens in common than do unrelated persons. A skin graft between closely related persons is likely to remain viable much longer than if the persons are unrelated. But, unless persons are genetically identical, antibodies to the graft will eventually be formed and the graft will be rejected. This is not true for monozygotic twins, since they are genetically identical. Permanent acceptance of a skin graft ordinarily is evidence of genetic identity.

Investigation of Genetic Problems with Twins

The simplest use of twins is in testing for concordance of monozygotic twins for a trait suspected to be hereditary. If a trait is entirely genetic, all monozygotic twin pairs should be concordant. All exceptions are evidence against hereditary factors as sole causes. Although studies of twins may give useful information in this type of investigation, the yield of information is low for the effort necessary to collect a new body of twin data. For fairly simple genetic traits, answers can be obtained more easily through family studies. Furthermore, twin studies give very little information on the mechanism of heredity, whereas family studies may yield information that clarifies the precise mode of inheritance.

The principal contribution of twins to genetic research is in the area of complex traits that show continuous variation. Traits such as physical size, intelligence or other mental abilities, or levels of blood components—for example, cholesterol—may be investigated for genetic components by the twin method. Twins do not reveal *how* genes operate, but they may tell us *whether* genetic variation is present and approximately how much of the variation is genetic.

The question to be answered is whether monozygotic twins vary less than dizygotic twins. An affirmative answer supports the hypothesis of a genetic component of variation. Ideally, the most effective use of twins would be a comparison of monozygotic twins reared apart with pairs of unrelated persons of the same age, socioeconomic level, etc. The variability of the unrelated group should equal the variability of the general population from which they were drawn and should reflect both genetic and environmental differences among the group. Expressed symbolically,

$$V_U = V_G + V_E$$

where V_U is the variability among unrelated persons, V_G is the portion attributable to gene differences, and V_E is the portion attributable to environmental differences.

Some pairs by chance will have similar environments; others will have very different environments. But the average difference in environment within pairs should be similar, irrespective of whether the pair is a twin or not. Since $V_G = 0$ for MZ twins,

$$V_M = V_E$$

where V_M is the variability within monozygotic twin pairs, and

$$V_G = V_U - V_M$$

This formula is straightforward, but requires a class of persons—MZ twins reared apart—that is too small and difficult to locate to be of practical use. The alternative is to use MZ twins reared together. In this case, the twins are exposed to similar environments, and it is necessary to compare them to pairs of related persons living together so that V_E will be constant. Since age and sex are important in determining environment, DZ twins of like sex are used. The assumption is that the similarity of environment for MZ twins is equal to that for DZ twins. For many traits this probably is correct; for others, such as personality traits, it is not. The experience of being an identical twin is apt to be different from the experience of being a nonidentical twin. The relations among twins may be symbolized as before:

$$V_{DZ} = V_G + V_E$$

$$V_{MZ} = V_E$$

$$V_G = V_{DZ} - V_{MZ}$$

But the meanings have changed slightly. V_E for twins reared together is certainly smaller than the same quantity for persons reared apart. Furthermore, V_G for DZ twins is much smaller than the genetic variability of unrelated persons, since DZ twins share many genes in common by virtue of having the same parents. For these reasons, the results obtained from comparisons of MZ and DZ twins are not true measures of the size of the genetic and environmental components. But if V_G can be shown to be greater than zero, then genetic factors are considered to contribute to the variability of the trait in question.

A variety of statistical techniques have been used for the analysis of twin data. If the distribution of twin-pair differences is Gaussian, then V may be measured as the variance and the ratio V_{DZ}/V_{MZ} used to test for the contribution of genetic variation. The calculation of variance ratios is discussed in most textbooks of statistics. When appropriate, this is the most satisfactory method of testing for genetic effects. The answer obtained—when genetic effects can be detected—is usually only a crude estimate of the magnitude of the effects. If a very large number of twin pairs were examined, sufficiently good estimates of V_{DZ} and V_{MZ} might be obtained so that V_G could be computed. With the number usually available, it is not meaningful to attempt to calculate a value for V_G.

Less elegant statistical techniques may be used with sacrifice of some of the information in the data. An example of the distribution of differences between twin pairs for height is shown in Figure 14–2. As expected, the most frequently encountered values are very low, since DZ twins share many genes in common as well as a common environment.

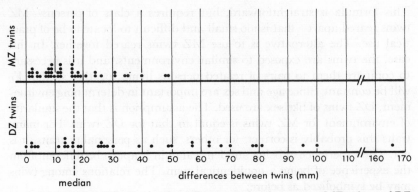

Figure 14–2. Distribution for differences in height between MZ twins and DZ twins.

However, the large values that may occur in DZ twins are very rare in MZ twins. From inspection of such a distribution, it may be surmised that the variability of DZ twins is larger than MZ twins, and hence genetic factors must be operating. A more objective evaluation is required for conclusions to be drawn scientifically.

One technique that may be used is to divide the distribution of values arbitrarily so that a χ^2 test of heterogeneity may be applied. This is done by selecting some value, such as the median, to classify the twins as having "large" or "small" differences. Fifty percent of the twins will have small differences by this definition, and 50 percent will have large differences. If there is no association of magnitude of the difference with zygosity, then 50 percent of the MZ twins should fall into each category as should 50 percent of the DZ twins. On the other hand, if MZ twin pairs contribute relatively more of the small values and DZ pairs more of the large, then a χ^2 test will show heterogeneity in the combined distribution.

In the example of Figure 14–2, division at the median gives 28 MZ twins with low values and 15 with high. There are 12 DZ twins with low and 24 with high. A 2 × 2 test for heterogeneity gives a χ^2 of 7.92 with one degree of freedom, a value significant at the 1 percent level. Since the two types of twins therefore do not represent one population, the conclusion is that they are different with respect to height, and it is postulated that the two populations are different because DZ twins have genetic variation as well as environmental, but MZ twins have only environmental variation.

Because it ignores extremes of distribution, this test is less powerful than the more complicated analysis of variance. The very large differences that may occur between DZ twins are counted the same as differences just large enough to fall in the upper 50 percent. For a trait with a large genetic component, differences between MZ twins may never match the differences commonly found in DZ twins. Because the dividing value usually will be chosen so that high and low categories will include both MZ and DZ twins, no weight is given to the DZ values that are large. One may choose a dividing line that maximizes the differences between MZ and DZ distributions, but this leads to circularity that invalidates the significance test.

In practice, the type of information to be gained from twins is very limited in scope. The principal contribution is to our recognition of the complex variables that may partially reflect genetic variation. Unsatisfactory as the results may be, in some cases there is virtually no alternative route to this answer.

REFERENCES AND SUGGESTED READING

CLARK, P. J. 1956. The heritability of certain anthropometric characters as ascertained from measurements of twins. *Am. J. Human Genet.* 8: 49–54.

DAHLBERG, G. 1926. *Twin Births and Twins from a Hereditary Point of View.* Stockholm: Bokförlags-A. B. Tidens Tryckeri.

KEMPTHORNE, O. (ed.) 1960. *Biometrical Genetics.* New York: Pergamon.

MATHER, K. 1949. *Biometrical Genetics: The Study of Continuous Variation.* London: Methuen, 162 pp.

NEWMAN, H. H., FREEMAN, F. N., and HOLZINGER, K. J. 1937. *Twins, a Study of Heredity and Environment.* Chicago: University of Chicago Press, 369 pp.

ROBERTS, J. A. F. 1964. Multifactorial inheritance and human disease. *Progr. Med. Genet.* 3: 178–216.

VERSCHUER, O. VON. 1927. Die Vererbungsbiologische Zwillingsforschung, Ihre biologischen Gundlagen. *Ergeb. Inn. Med. Kinderheilk.* 31: 35–120.

PROBLEMS

1. Define:

    continuous variable   monozygous
    polygenic inheritance   dizygous
    heritability

Chapter Fifteen

LINKAGE

Mendel's second law states that different loci assort into gametes independently of one another. The genetic markers that he used did assort independently, as do most pairs of markers chosen at random in any organism. Mendel's work was prior to the recognition of chromosomes as the physical structures on which genes are located. Had he been aware of this arrangement, he would have realized that there are more genes than chromosomes and therefore some genes must be together on the same chromosome. Since chromosomes retain their integrity during meiosis and cell division, the genes on a particular chromosome cannot assort independently.

It was observed by early workers in genetics that genes present together on a single chromosome may become separated in offspring. The possible physical basis for this was recognized in the formation of chiasmata. During meiosis, homologous chromosomes synapse. As they begin to separate, it can be seen that the attachment at certain points is very strong, forming "bridges" (chiasmata), which might serve as points of exchange of chromatid segments. This process of exchange is known as crossing over.

Chiasmata are seen to form at positions all along the chromosome. Presumably, crossing over can occur anywhere, although the likelihood need not be uniform. The greater the physical separation of two genes on a chromosome, the more likely that crossing over will occur between them. Thus, it should be possible to measure the relative position of genes along a chromosome by the relative frequencies of crossing over between pairs of loci, provided, of course, that genes are arranged in a linear sequence along the chromosomes.

In 1913, Sturtevant reported confirmation of this hypothesis through studies of X-linked genes in Drosophila. He found that the distance between two loci could be measured in terms of the percent of recombinant (crossover) gametes. When three loci are studied, the distance between the outer pair, measured directly, is the sum of the distances between the middle and outer loci. Stated symbolically, in the sequence ABC, $AC = AB + BC$.

Experimentally, one must have a system in which recombinant and nonrecombinant gametes can be distinguished. Sturtevant used F_1 females from the cross ♀ $MMpp$ × ♂ mP, where M (normal wings) is dominant to m (rudimentary wings) and P (normal red eyes) to p (vermilion eyes). (See Fig. 15–1.) The F_1 females were double heterozygotes, $MmPp$. Furthermore, M and p had to be on one chromosome, and m and P on the other because of the parental genotypes. When these Mp/mP females were mated with the F_1 males (Mp/Y), the recombinants and nonrecombinants could be distinguished in F_2 males. Mp and mP chromosomes were present in the F_1 females, but MP and mp chromosomes could arise only by crossing over between the two loci. Of 405 F_2 males tested, 109 were recombinant, giving a crossover frequency of 26.9 percent (26.9 crossover units).

For autosomal loci, an analogous method of testing is used, the F_1 double heterozygote being backcrossed to a double homozygous recessive. For example, the parental cross AB/AB × ab/ab gives F_1 type AB/ab. If this is crossed to ab/ab, nonrecombinant offspring are of types AB/ab and ab/ab. Recombinants are Ab/ab and aB/ab. The arrangement of the alleles in the F_1 generation is unimportant, so long as it is known. The F_1 could have been Ab/aB, the nonrecombinants then being Ab/ab and aB/ab.

Alleles that are on the same chromosome are said to be *cis* with respect to each other. If they are on opposite chromosomes, they are in the *trans* position. The terms *coupling* and *repulsion*, equivalent to *cis* and *trans* respectively, were introduced earlier by Bateson and are still encountered.

Unlinked genes recombine with a frequency of 50 percent. If the A and B loci are on different chromosomes, the double heterozygote $AaBb$ will form four types of gametes, AB, Ab, aB, and ab, in a 1:1:1:1 ratio, regardless of the parental origin of the alleles. Fifty percent is thus the maximum recombination frequency that can be directly observed. At map distances approaching 50 percent, the frequency of double crossovers becomes important but cannot be estimated with only two loci. A double crossover between two marker genes preserves the original combination of alleles and is counted as a nonrecombinant, although it should be counted as two. For this reason, measurements made directly on widely separated loci are underestimates and will be smaller than

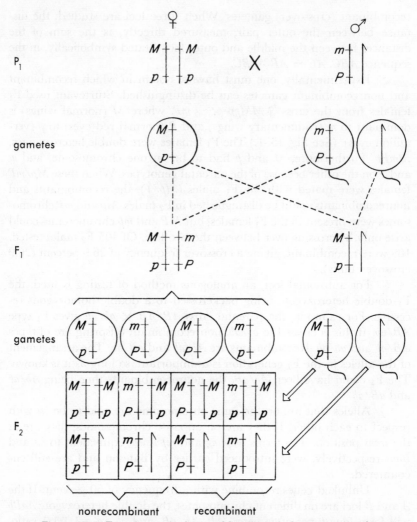

Figure 15–1. Experimental scheme of Sturtevant's demonstration that genes on the same chromosome do not reassort freely. *M* (normal wings) is dominant to *m* (rudimentary wings), and *P* (normal red eyes) is dominant to *p* (vermilion eyes). Both loci are on the X chromosome.

the sum of component map distances using intermediate loci. The best figures for long distances therefore are obtained by summing component short distances.

Many chromosomes are so long that multiple crossing over is likely to occur in every synapsis. Summing the map distances between close genetic markers gives values greater than 100 map units. Genes

located at opposite ends of these chromosomes assort at random in meiosis. They belong to the same linkage group, but they fail to show linkage in a direct test. Failure to find linkage between a pair of loci therefore
does not constitute evidence that they are on different chromosomes. In
practice, it is usually not feasible to demonstrate linkage between loci
greater than 40 map units apart, and in some experimental studies, the
limit is still lower.

The use of three genetic markers permits detection of double
crossovers. For intermediate distances, the two crossovers occur more or
less at random with respect to each other. If the three markers are very
close, the likelihood of a double crossover is less than would be expected
by chance. This phenomenon is called *interference* and is visualized as
resulting from the physical difficulty in the chromosomes bending back
to form two unions in so short a distance.

Certain lower organisms (bacteria, viruses) also show recombination of genetic markers, although the mechanism may differ from
crossing over. It is possible to study extremely short map distances in
these organisms. At such short distances (0.01 to 0.1 units), the likelihood
of a double recombinant is increased rather than decreased. This has
been designated *negative interference*. The mechanism is not understood.

CORRELATION BETWEEN RECOMBINATION MAP AND PHYSICAL MAP

In most organisms, little detail in chromosome morphology can
be observed. Exceptions are found in certain *Diptera,* including Drosophila. The salivary glands of Drosophila larvae have giant polytene
chromosomes that are readily visible at interphase. In 1933, Painter
developed a technique that permitted examination of fine details of
morphology of these chromosomes. They were found to have highly characteristic sequences of deeply staining bands (chromatic regions) in an
achromatic matrix (Fig. 15–2). The chromosomes of old larvae undergo
somatic pairing, homologous points lining up in a very precise manner.
Any alteration in the sequence of bands, such as deletions or inversions,
can be readily recognized by the pairing figures.

Because of the individuality of bands, short deletions of chromosomal material can be readily recognized. The deleted genes sometimes
can be identified by standard genetic procedures, and the genes can be
mapped in the manner outlined earlier in the chapter. It is then possible
to compare the recombination map, based on crossover frequencies, with
the cytological map.

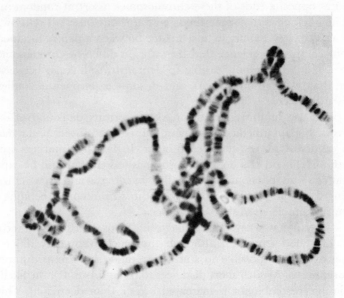

Figure 15–2. Polytene chromosomes of Drosophila salivary glands, showing bands. (Courtesy B. H. Judd.)

Painter's initial studies gave the results shown in Figure 15–3. The genes map in the same sequence in which they occur on the chromosome. However, units of recombination are not equal along the chromosome. In some areas, crossing over is frequent; in others it is infrequent. The demonstration that the recombination map has physical meaning was an important milestone in genetics.

DETECTION OF LINKAGE IN MAN

Theoretically, the techniques for measuring linkage in lower organisms can also be used in man. In practice, the difficulties in applying such techniques are enormous. The mating of a double heterozygote of known chromosomal arrangement (*cis* or *trans*) with a double homozygous recessive is rarely encountered. In order to know the chromosomal arrangement of the double heterozygote, it is necessary that the parents be available and that they be of certain genotypes. It is generally more efficient to use more complicated methods of analysis that can be applied to more readily available data.

A number of special methods for analysis of linkage in human

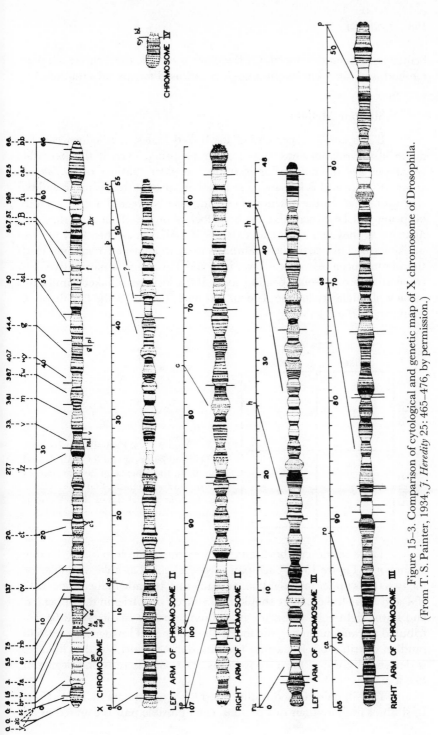

Figure 15–3. Comparison of cytological and genetic map of X chromosome of Drosophila. (From T. S. Painter, 1934, *J. Heredity* 25: 465–476, by permission.)

187

beings have been developed. Of the older methods, the Penrose sib pair method is of some interest because it is still used for special situations.

Sib Pair Method

If parents are segregating for linked genes, predictions can be made about relationships among their offspring, even if the parental genotypes are unknown. For example, consider matings of $AB/ab \times ab/ab$. If the A and B loci are close together, most of the offspring will be AB/ab or ab/ab. In the absence of crossing over between A and B, pairs of offspring will be either alike for both loci or unlike. That is, if they are alike for A, they will also be alike for B; if unlike for A, then they will be unlike for B. This particular example is from an informative mating. Had the mating been $Ab/ab \times ab/ab$, it would have been uninformative, because all offspring would be alike for b. If the loci are unlinked, similarity or lack of similarity for the A locus has no influence on the likelihood of similarity at the B locus.

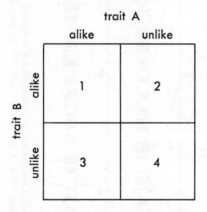

Figure 15–4. Each sib pair is scored as being alike or unlike for trait A and trait B. In the absence of linkage, entries will be at random in the four cells, reflecting only the frequencies of chance resemblance. Linkage leads to an excess in 1 and 4.

These results can be analyzed by setting them into a 2×2 table as shown in Figure 15–4. Each pair of sibs is scored as alike or unlike for the two traits under investigation, and an entry is made in the proper cell. If A and B are linked, there should be an excess of entries in the upper left and lower right cells. Offspring from uninformative matings will be distributed at random among the four cells. Absence of linkage also leads to random distribution. Departure from randomness, attributed to linkage, is detected by use of the χ^2 test for association. There is one degree of freedom.

The sib pair method is illustrated with actual data in Table 15–1. In sibships of more than two persons, each possible pair is counted as an

TABLE 15-1

Test for Linkage between *MN* Locus and *Hp* Locus by Sib Pair Method of Penrose. These Data Do Not Depart Significantly from a Random Distribution and Therefore Do Not Support Linkage.

SIBSHIP	HP TYPE	MN TYPE	SIBSHIP	HP TYPE	MN TYPE
A	2–1	Ms	F	2–1	Ns
	1–1	Ms		1–1	Ns
	O	MNs			
			G	1–1	MNs
B	2–1	Ms		1–1	MNs
	1–1	MNS		1–1	MNs
C	2–1	MNs	H	2–2	MNSs
	2–1	MNs		2–2	MSs
	2–1	MNs		O	MNSs
	1–1	Ns			
	1–1	Ns	I	2–1	Ms
				1–1	MSs
D	2–1	MNs			
	2–2	Ns	J	2–1	Ms
	2–1	Ns		2–1	MNs
E	2–1	MSs	K	1–1	MNs
	2–2	MSs		1–1	Ms
	2–1	MSs		1–1	Ns
				1–1	MNs
			L	1–1	MNs
				1–1	MNs

The *Hp* locus determines serum haptoglobin types and the *MN* locus determines red cell antigens of the MNSs series. S and s are attributes of the MN types that frequently are not tested.

MN		Hp Like	Hp Unlike	
	Like	10	6	$\chi^2 = 1.80$
	Unlike	8	12	df $= 1$; $P > 0.05$

independent entry. If there are three sibs, there will be three entries. Four sibs give six entries, etc. Large sibships are thus more informative for a given amount of data.

An advantage of the sib pair method is its application to traits whose inheritance is unknown. It has been used to test for linkage between genes contributing to variation of physical traits, such as height. Such traits appear to be largely inherited but controlled by many loci. If a major locus for height were closely linked to a major locus for head breadth, it should be detectable by the sib pair method. The dilution from other loci and from uninformative families is a serious problem, and no convincing linkage has been detected by this approach.

The Lod (Log Odds) Score Method

A much more efficient means of detecting linkage has been developed in the past decade. Morton has been particularly instrumental in developing the method. A full exposition is beyond the scope of an introductory text but, briefly, the approach is to set up a series of hypotheses regarding linkage relationships of specific pairs of loci. Each hypothesis includes a statement of the map units separating the loci. The probability of obtaining a particular set of observations is then calculated for a number of linkage values, for example, 10, 20, 30, 40, and 50 units. The probability can be plotted against map distance, and the point of maximum probability is the best estimate of the linkage.

The procedure is complicated but exceedingly useful. It is applicable to large families, which are very informative. Only a few large families may be sufficient to establish linkage.

ESTABLISHED LINKAGE GROUPS IN MAN

Although many studies have been undertaken with the objective of detecting linkage in man, only a few have given positive results that could be verified. One reason for the failure to detect linkage is the lack of genetic marker genes. A variety of blood types, plasma protein types, and so on, occur with frequencies that make them useful as markers. But the number is small compared to the number of chromosomes in a haploid complement. Furthermore, genes separated by more than 20 map units require extensive data in order to demonstrate linkage.

Some of the rare genes undoubtedly are linked to each other, but the likelihood of finding a person heterozygous for two rare genes is small. Also, such a person must mate with another of the appropriate genotype and produce offspring. It is not surprising that in the few established cases of linkage, at least one of the loci is a common marker; that is, it has two or more alleles of high frequency.

Sex Linkage

The most promising group of genes to examine for linkage are the X-linked genes. Table 13–1 is a summary of genes known to exist on the

X chromosome. They all therefore belong to the same linkage group. Arranging them into a linear sequence is difficult because most are too rare. A few, however, are sufficiently common to enable linkage tests.

Linkage on the X chromosome is somewhat simpler to investigate than autosomal linkage. This is illustrated by the work of Sturtevant cited earlier. A doubly heterozygous female is the only source of X chromosomes for her sons; her mate therefore, is of no concern. The configuration of the genes on her X chromosomes can be ascertained from the phenotype of her father. Whatever his combination of genes on the X chromosome, it must be transmitted intact to his daughters. In order to measure map distance, one need only establish the chromosomal combinations in a woman, then count the number of nonrecombinant and recombinant sons.

There are two very useful marker genes on the X chromosome. These are red-green colorblindness and the red blood cell antigen Xg^a. Approximately 8 percent of males are colorblind and 17 percent of females are heterozygous for colorblindness. Normal daughters of colorblind men are heterozygous for the gene for color vision. The Xg^a red cell type has been recognized only since 1962. Red cells of persons who have the antigen agglutinate with immune antibodies formed against $Xg(a+)$ cells. Xg^a immune antiserum is very rare, since only one person is known ever to have produced antibodies against $Xg(a+)$ cells, although thousands of $Xg(a-)$ persons have received positive cells repeatedly through transfusion. Approximately 60 percent of males are $Xg(a+)$, a favorable frequency for linkage studies.

A third marker is available in some populations. The gene that results in an abnormal type of the enzyme glucose-6-phosphate dehydrogenase (G6PD) is on the X chromosome. The enzyme defect is called primaquine sensitivity, because it was first detected when persons with the defect responded abnormally to the antimalarial primaquine. Most populations do not have the G6PD deficiency gene. It has a high frequency in some other populations, however, such as Sardinians, Oriental Jews, and African Negroes. In addition to the allele that results in deficiency, Negroes have an allele that leads to enzyme of normal activity but with altered electrophoretic mobility.

Three rare X-linked conditions have been investigated for linkage with these markers. These are Duchenne-type muscular dystrophy, hemophilia A (so-called classical hemophilia), and hemophilia B (Christmas disease). Of these three rare diseases, only hemophilia A is located close enough to the markers to be placed. Although the results are still somewhat tentative, the map obtained thus far is given in Figure 15–5.

An interesting pedigree has been reported by Graham et al. The position of the hemophilia B locus (He_B) is known to be outside the seg-

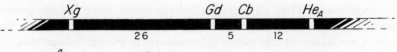

Xg: Xgᵃ   *Gd:* Glucose-6-phosphate dehydrogenase
Heₐ: Hemophilia A   *Cb:* Colorblindness, both deutan and protan

Figure 15–5. Map of portion of human X chromosome. The map distances shown are approximate only, but the order of loci seems certain. There is evidence that the *Cb* locus is actually two loci, mutations at one giving rise to deutan color defect and mutations at the other to protan defect. Recombination between the two loci has not been observed, however. The loci for hemophilia B and for Duchenne-type muscular dystrophy appear not to be closely linked to the above group.

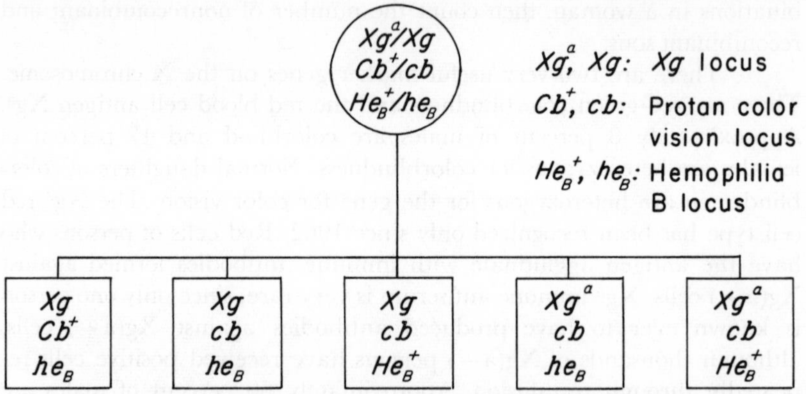

$$
\begin{array}{c}
Xg^a/Xg \\
Cb^+/cb \\
He_B^+/he_B
\end{array}
$$

Xgᵃ, Xg: Xg locus
Cbᵗ, cb: Protan color vision locus
He_Bᵗ, he_B: Hemophilia B locus

| *Xg* *Cbᵗ* *he_B* | *Xg* *cb* *he_B* | *Xg* *cb* *He_Bᵗ* | *Xgᵃ* *cb* *he_B* | *Xgᵃ* *cb* *He_Bᵗ* |

Figure 15–6. Pedigree showing recombination of loci on X chromosome, with at least one son being a double recombinant. (From Graham *et al.*, 1962.)

ment between *cb* and *Xg*, although the direction is not known. In the pedigree of Figure 15–6, the mother is heterozygous for Xgᵃ (*Xgᵃ/Xg*), hemophilia B (*He_B+/he_B*), and colorblindness (*Cb+/cb*). Since her parents could not be examined, the coupling of the genes on her X chromosomes cannot be established. There are two possible sequences of genes and four possible coupling options. Whichever is correct, at least one of the sons resulted from a double crossover.

Autosomal Linkage

Only three satisfactory cases of autosomal linkage have been established in man. Many others have been suggested, and several will perhaps prove valid when further data are collected.

ABO BLOOD GROUPS AND NAIL-PATELLA SYNDROME.   The first such linkage to be established clearly was for the *ABO* blood group locus and the locus for nail-patella syndrome. The blood group locus is responsible for the common blood types that have been known for many years. There are three common alleles, I^A, I^B, and I^O, the first two being further divided into several closely related alleles. The nail-patella syndrome is a rare dominant condition in which there are a variety of skeletal defects. These include defective fingernails and defective or absent patella. A number of pedigrees of nail-patella syndrome have been investigated for linkage with various genetic markers. The results show that the nail-patella gene is about 10 map units from the ABO locus.

RH BLOOD GROUPS AND ELLIPTOCYTOSIS. The Rh blood groups are antigens on the red blood cells. Inheritance is rather complex, there being a large series of alleles at the Rh locus. Elliptocytosis is a benign condition of red cells, in which the cells have an ellipsoid shape rather than the ordinary round disc shape. It is a rare, dominantly inherited condition.

By studying several very large pedigrees of elliptocytosis, Morton found that the previously reported linkage between genes for Rh type and elliptocytosis was valid only for some families. In some, the genes are close together, approximately 3 units apart. In others, linkage could not be detected. The most likely interpretation is that elliptocytosis can result from either of two defects, the responsible genes being unlinked.

LUTHERAN AND SECRETOR TYPES. The Lutheran (Lu) blood types also involve differences in antigenic structure of red blood cells. Secretor types refer to whether a person secretes soluble ABO antigen in saliva and other body fluids. Se/Se or Se/se persons secrete antigens; se/se persons do not. These loci are approximately 15 units apart. This linkage was first reported to exist between Lu and the Lewis blood group. This was prior to understanding of the rather complex interactions of the Lewis and secretor phenotypes. This linkage was actually the first detected, although several years elapsed before it was completely elucidated.

Chromosomes and Autosomal Linkage Groups

The three linkage groups detected have not been assigned to specific chromosomes. There is no way to recognize which linkage groups belong to which chromosomes purely by genetic analysis. It is necessary to associate unusual inheritance of markers with a chromosome anomaly in order to establish a relationship. One association that has been suggested is the ABO locus and chromosome 21. The data are still inconclusive, but it will be instructive to consider the methodology.

If the gene distinction is restricted to O or non-O types, then in a diploid population the frequencies of genotypes should be described by the binomial expansion:

$$(p + r)^2 = p^2 + 2pr + r^2$$

where p is the frequency of $I^A + I^B$ and r is the frequency of I^O. For trisomics, if the two alleles received from one parent come from different parental chromosomes, the genotype distribution would be

$$(p + r)^3 = p^3 + 3p^2r + 3pr^2 + r^3$$

Such is the case for first meiotic nondisjunction without crossing over between the gene locus and the centromere. It also is the case for second meiotic nondisjunction with crossing over. In second meiotic nondisjunction without crossing over, no distortion of the O:non-O ratio occurs. In first meiotic nondisjunction with crossing over, the expectation is intermediate between the two formulas. These relationships can be readily verified by simple diagrams. If $r = 0.6$, the frequency of type O ($I^O I^O$) persons would be 0.36 by the first formula, and the frequency of $I^O I^O I^O$ would be 0.216 by the second.

Where the expectation of homozygous I^O persons is altered by nondisjunction, it is always in the direction of fewer such persons. Demonstration of a decrease in homozygous recessive persons among trisomic conditions can be interpreted as due to location of the gene on the chromosome involved. In a study of 1000 patients with trisomy 21 syndrome, Shaw and Gershowitz found the frequency of type O persons to be 40.5 percent compared to the expected frequency of 45.6 percent for that population. Among the possible explanations is that the ABO locus is on chromosome 21.

In addition to the statistical approach for trisomic persons, linkage can also be demonstrated by investigation of chromosomal aberrations. For example, a translocation chromosome can be treated in some respects as a dominant trait. If a particular gene were found never to dissociate in a given family from the translocation chromosome, linkage could be adduced.

REFERENCES AND SUGGESTED READING

ADAM, A., *et al.* 1963. Data for X-mapping calculations, Israeli families tested for Xg, g-6-pd and for colour vision. *Ann. Human Genet.* 26: 187–194.

DAVIES, S. H. *et al.* 1963. The linkage relations of hemophilia A and hemophilia B (Christmas disease) to the Xg blood group system. *Am. J. Human Genet.* 15: 481–492.

GRAHAM, J. B., TARLETON, H. L., RACE, R. R., and SANGER, R. 1962. A human double cross-over. *Nature* 195: 834.

JACKSON, C. E., SYMON, W. E., and MANN, J. D. 1964. X chromosome mapping of genes for red-green colorblindness and Xg^a. *Am. J. Human Genet.* 16: 403–409.

MANN, J. D., *et al.* 1962. A sex-linked blood group. *Lancet* 1: 8–10.

MATHER, K. 1957. *The Measurement of Linkage in Heredity,* 2d ed., revised. London: Methuen, 149 pp.

MOHR, J. 1954. *A Study of Linkage in Man.* Copenhagen: Munksgaard, pp. 1–119.

———. 1963. The Lutheran-secretor linkage: Estimation from combined available data. *Acta Genet. Statist. Med.* 13: 334–342.

MORTON, N. E. 1955. Sequential tests for the detection of linkage. *Am. J. Human Genet.* 7: 277–318.

———. 1956. The detection and estimation of linkage between the genes for elliptocytosis and the Rh blood type. *Am. J. Human Genet.* 8: 80–96.

———. 1957. Further scoring types in sequential linkage tests, with a critical review of autosomal and partial sex linkage in man. *Am. J. Human Genet.* 9: 55–75.

———. 1962. Segregation and linkage. In *Methodology in Human Genetics* (W. J. Burdette, ed.). San Francisco: Holden-Day, pp. 17–52.

PAINTER, T. S. 1934. Salivary chromosomes and the attack on the gene. *J. Heredity* 25: 465–476.

PORTER, I. H., SCHULZE, J., and MCKUSICK, V. A. 1962. Genetical linkage between the loci for glucose-6-phosphate dehydrogenase deficiency and colour-blindness in American Negroes. *Ann. Human Genet.* 26: 107–122.

RENWICK, J. H. 1961. Elucidation of gene order. In *Recent Advances in Human Genetics* (L. S. Penrose and H. Lang Brown, eds.). London: J. and A. Churchill, pp. 120–138.

———, and LAWLER, S. D. 1955. Genetical linkage between the *ABO* and nail-patella loci. *Ann. Human Genet.* 19: 312–331.

SANGER, R., and ADAM, A. 1964. Xg and g-6-pd in Israeli families: An addendum. *Ann. Human Genet.* 27: 271–272.

————, and RACE, R. R. 1958. The Lutheran-Secretor linkages in man: Support for Mohr's findings. *Heredity* 12: 513–520.

SHAW, M. W., and GERSHOWITZ, H. 1963. Blood group frequencies in mongols. *Am. J. Human Genet.* 15: 495–496.

SMITH, C. A. B. 1959. Some comments on the statistical methods used in linkage investigation. *Am. J. Human Genet.* 11: 289–304.

STURTEVANT, A. H. 1913. The linear arrangement of six sex-linked factors in Drosophila, as shown by their mode of association. *J. Exptl. Zool.* 14: 43–59.

PROBLEMS

1. Define:

recombination	*trans*
crossing over	coupling
chiasma	repulsion
linkage group	interference
cis	

2. A strain of mice homozygous for two dominant genes *AABB* is crossed to a strain recessive at both loci, *aabb*. The F_1 is backcrossed to the recessive parent, producing 115 *AaBb*, 88 *Aabb*, 86 *aaBb*, and 111 *aabb* offspring. Are these loci linked?

3. In mice, albinism may result from homozygosity for recessive genes at either of two loci, *A* and *B*. When the F_1 from a cross of *AABB* × *aabb* was backcrossed to the double recessive *aabb*, 288 offspring were albinos and 112 were pigmented. Are the two loci linked?

4. A man with nail-patella syndrome and type B blood married a normal woman with type A blood. The man's father also had the syndrome and type O blood. The woman's father was normal with type O blood. With respect to these two loci, what types of offspring would be expected and in what proportions?

5. In the following pedigree, which of the offspring in generation III are nonrecombinant, which are recombinant, and which are uncertain?

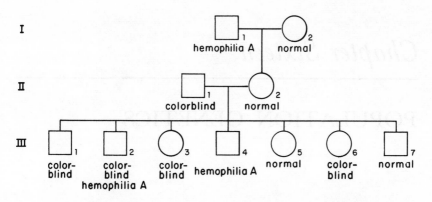

6. If a man with G6PD deficiency and color blindness marries a woman who is homozygous normal, what will be the expected genetic status of his grandchildren? Give all possible combinations and the probability for each. Assume that only normal genes are introduced through marriages.

7. Write out all the possible gene combinations for Figure 15–6, indicating which are nonrecombinant, which involve single crossovers, and which involve double crossovers.

Chapter Sixteen

POPULATION GENETICS

Although genes are expressed only in individuals, many problems of genetics concern groups of people and can be solved only by considering the entire group. This aspect of genetics is known as population genetics. As later chapters will illustrate, there are major health issues that rely heavily on concepts of population genetics for formulation and interpretation.

Population genetics is a quantitative science. Mathematical models are used extensively, and the assumptions and properties of the models must be understood in order to appreciate their limitations in biological applications. Many polemics would be avoided if the distinction between the mathematical model and the vastly more complex biological event were remembered.

THE HARDY-WEINBERG LAW

The basis of population genetics is the Hardy-Weinberg law. Although this law is only a special case of the binomial theorem for $n = 2$, its applicability to genetics was not fully appreciated until 1908 when Hardy, a British mathematician, and Weinberg, a German physician, independently pointed out its utility. The short paper by Hardy is particularly interesting as an example of a concise statement of a very important principle.

The basis of the Hardy-Weinberg law is the randomness with which genes are combined in persons. The frequency of a gene (or allele) in a population may be expressed without regard to the combinations in which it actually occurs. If there are two alleles, A and a, the frequency of A may vary from zero to one, with the frequency of a being the difference between one and A. It is customary to let p and q stand for the frequencies of two alleles, in this case A and a, respectively. If there are only two alleles in the population, $p + q = 1$, and $p = 1 - q$.

In earlier chapters, the binomial was given as $(p + q)^n$, where n is the number of events taken at a time. A person may be considered a random sample of genes taken two at a time; therefore, $n = 2$. Expanding the binomial gives the familiar

$$(p + q)^n = p^2 + 2pq + q^2$$

where p^2 is the frequency of persons both of whose alleles are A, $2pq$ is the frequency of heterozygous Aa persons, and q^2 is the frequency of aa persons. If 40 percent of the alleles at a particular locus are A and 60 percent are a, then $p = 0.4$ and $q = 0.6$. Substituting into the formula gives 16 percent AA, 48 percent Aa, and 36 percent aa persons.

An example will demonstrate the random combinations of alleles in a population. Human red cells may be classified by the presence of various antigens on the cell surfaces. Most antigens show simple Mendelian inheritance, and a number of different antigenic systems are known. For one of these, the MN system, based on the reaction with the two common antisera, there are three types of persons—M, MN, and N, corresponding to the genotypes $L^M L^M$, $L^M L^N$, and $L^N L^N$.

In a group of 147 randomly selected persons, there were 45 of type M, 69 of type MN, and 33 of type N. These 147 persons possess 294 L genes, either L^M or L^N. Since each M person possesses two L^M alleles and each MN person possesses one, the total number of L^M alleles is 159. The frequency of L^M is 159/294 or 0.54. The frequency of L^N must be $1 - 0.54 = 0.46$. These values were arrived at by direct counts of alleles independently of the combinations of alleles. Therefore, they can be used to test whether the actual distribution of genotypes matches that predicted. Substituting $p = 0.54$ and $q = 0.46$, one would expect $0.54^2 L^M L^M$, $2(0.54)(0.46) L^M L^N$, and $0.46^2 L^N L^N$ persons. Expanding the coefficients gives 0.2916, 0.4968, and 0.2116 respectively. Multiplying these values by the number of persons (147) gives 43 $L^M L^M$, 73 $L^M L^N$, and 31 $L^N L^N$ persons expected. These values are close to 45, 69, and 33 observed, as can be verified statistically. The combinations of alleles therefore are random.

The frequencies of the three genotypes can be calculated readily from the frequency of either allele. The change in genotype frequencies with gene frequency is shown in Figure 16–1. The frequency of heterozygotes never exceeds 0.5, a value it attains when $p = q = 0.5$. On the other hand, the heterozygotes are never the least frequent class. They increase rapidly as p or q moves away from zero, and for values of p or q between 0.33 and 0.67, the heterozygotes are the prevalent class.

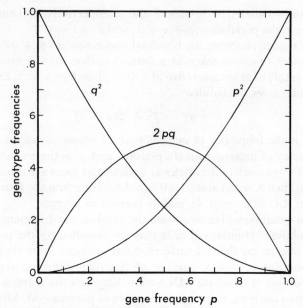

Figure 16–1. Relative frequencies of homozygous and heterozygous persons plotted against gene frequency p, where $p + q = 1$.

The Assumptions of the Hardy-Weinberg Law

The Hardy-Weinberg law can be expected to apply only if the assumptions upon which it is based are met in the populations to which it is applied. The most important requirement is random mating or *panmixis*. When mates are chosen, the various genotypes must have a chance

TABLE 16–1

Frequencies of Parental and Offspring Genotypes for a Two Allele System

MATING TYPE	FREQUENCY	PROBABILITY OF OFFSPRING			MATING FREQUENCY × PROBABILITY OF OFFSPRING		
		AA	Aa	aa	AA	Aa	aa
$AA \times AA$	p^4	1	0	0	p^4	0	0
$AA \times Aa$	$4p^3q$	½	½	0	$2p^3q$	$2p^3q$	0
$AA \times aa$	$2p^2q^2$	0	1	0	0	$2p^2q^2$	0
$Aa \times Aa$	$4p^2q^2$	¼	½	¼	p^2q^2	$2p^2q^2$	p^2q^2
$Aa \times aa$	$4pq^3$	0	½	½	0	$2pq^3$	$2pq^3$
$aa \times aa$	q^4	0	0	1	0	0	q^4

total AA offspring $= p^4 + 2p^3q + p^2q^2 = p^2(p^2 + 2pq + q^2) = p^2$
total Aa offspring $= 2p^3q + 4p^2q^2 + 2pq^3 = 2pq(p^2 + 2pq + q^2) = 2pq$
total aa offspring $= p^2q^2 + 2pq^3 + q^4 = q^2(p^2 + 2pq + q^2) = q^2$

of being chosen exactly proportional to their frequencies. The frequencies of the mating types can be expressed by expansion of $(p^2 + 2pq + q^2)^2$ to give the results in Table 16–1. As is seen from the offspring totals, the frequencies of genotypes among the offspring generation are also random and are the same as among their randomly mated parents.

A second assumption is equal viability of the different genotypes. If the genotype aa does not survive as well as AA or Aa, then the frequency of aa will be less than q^2. In an extreme case, it may approach zero, and many such examples are known. Differential viability of genotypes is known as selection and will be discussed in Chapter 17.

MEASUREMENT OF GENE FREQUENCIES

Autosomal Genes

Since genes cannot be observed directly, their presence must be inferred from phenotypes. In some systems, this is easy; in others, it is difficult. In the MN blood types, each genotype corresponds to a distinguishable phenotype. The numbers of L^M and L^N alleles can be counted accurately by observing the frequencies of M, MN, and N persons. The frequency of L^M is the number of L^M alleles divided by the $L^M + L^N$ alleles. Such an estimate is frequently called a direct gene count, even though it is based on phenotypes only.

In the MN system, the alleles are codominant. Had one been recessive, the heterozygote would not have been distinguishable from the homozygous dominant and an allele count would not have been possible. The Rh blood groups, considering only the distinction Rh+ and Rh−, behave as a two-allele system with the Rh+ allele dominant to the Rh−. The Rh+ allele can be subdivided into several alleles, but these can be grouped under the allelic designation R. The allele that, when homozygous, gives Rh− phenotype is designated r. On the basis of these two alleles, there are three genotypes, RR, Rr, and rr. RR and Rr produce red cells that react with anti-Rh_0 serum; rr cells do not react and are therefore Rh −. The frequencies of the alleles cannot be counted directly, since the proportion of Rh positives who are RR versus those who are Rr cannot be ascertained. However, if the population is assumed to be in Hardy-Weinberg equilibrium, then the frequency of rr should be q^2, where q is the frequency of the r allele. If 16 percent of the population is Rh −, the frequency of r should be $\sqrt{q^2} = \sqrt{0.16} = 0.4$. The frequency of R is $1 - 0.4 = 0.6$. The frequency of RR ($p^2 = 0.36$) and of Rr ($2pq = 0.48$) in the total population can then be calculated.

If more than two alleles are present at a locus, the preferred method for estimating frequencies will depend on the exact dominance relationships among the alleles. In theory, the frequency of a recessive allele can always be estimated as the square root of the phenotype frequency. In practice, this estimate may be inaccurate if the frequency of the recessive phenotype is low. If several phenotypic distinctions are possible in a multiallele system, the most accurate estimates would come from simultaneous consideration of all the phenotypes. This can be done by the *maximum likelihood method*. Information on this method should be sought in more advanced texts. Briefly, it consists in finding the gene frequency values that, when substituted into the equation describing the distribution of phenotypes, give the best fit to the data.

Sex-Linked Genes

The fact that males have only one X chromosome makes estimates of genes on the X chromosome particularly easy. The phenotypes of X-linked genes ordinarily are expressed in males, so that the presence of colorblindness or normal vision, hemophilia or normal clotting time, glucose-6-phosphate dehydrogenase deficiency or normal enzyme are reliable expressions of the male genotype. The frequency of these genes is thus the frequency of phenotypes among males. In a population in which 8 percent of the males are colorblind, the gene frequency of colorblindness is 0.08.

Sex-linked genes in females follow the same rules in general as autosomal genes. It should be possible therefore to estimate gene frequencies from females or at least to include data from females in a general formula for distribution of phenotypes. Difficulties arise because of the large variability of expression of X-linked genes in females, now thought to be explained by the Lyon hypothesis (Chapter 9). Females heterozygous for X-linked genes may show primarily the effects of only one allele. Females heterozygous for glucose-6-phosphate dehydrogenase deficiency may have normal, intermediate, or deficient amounts of enzyme. The error in classification is very large as a consequence. For other sex-linked genes, such as colorblindness, the error in classifying females is much smaller. However, the rarity of females homozygous for many recessive traits requires examination of very large numbers of females in order to obtain reliable estimates of phenotype frequencies. If the frequency of colorblindness in males (q) is 0.08, the expected frequency in females (q^2) would be 0.0064. Examination of a thousand males would yield approximately 80 affected persons; in a thousand females, only six would be expected, with a proportionally larger chance of sampling error. Furthermore, a few heterozygous females have sufficient color vision defect to make classification difficult.

Accuracy of Gene Frequency Estimates

All measures of gene frequency are made from observations of a finite sample that is considered to be representative of a larger population. If a very large sample is observed, the gene frequency estimate may be quite accurate. If only twenty persons are observed, the estimate may be unreliable.

The usual means of expressing confidence in an estimate is by calculation of the *standard error of the mean*. This quality, symbolized as SE, expresses the chances that the real frequency in the population, as opposed to the frequency found in a sample of the population, lies within a certain range of the observed value. The statement that $p = 0.50$ and $SE = 0.10$, often written $p = 0.50 \pm 0.10$, means that the observed value of p is 0.50 and that in 68 percent of samples the real value of p will lie between 0.40 and 0.60. Two standard errors, ± 2 SE, includes 95 percent of the real values, and ± 3 SE includes 99.7 percent. (The derivation of these quantities may be found in elementary statistics textbooks.) A standard error of 0.02 indicates a more reliable observation, at least in terms of sampling, than a standard error of 0.10.

Calculation of the standard error for direct allele counts is simple. The general formula for proportions is

$$SE = \sqrt{\frac{pq}{n}}$$

where n is the number of alleles, or twice the number of persons. (Compare with the formula on p. 139.) If, among 50 persons, there are 10 of blood type M, 23 of type MN, and 17 of type N, the frequency p of L^M would be 0.43 and the frequency q of L^N would be 0.57. The standard error would be 0.0495. Thus, 68 percent of the time, the frequency of L^M in the parent population from which the sample of 50 persons was drawn will lie between 0.38 and 0.48. Ninety-five percent of the time the correct value will lie between 0.33 and 0.53.

When the gene frequency must be calculated from the frequency of homozygous recessive phenotypes, the formula for the standard error is

$$SE = \sqrt{\frac{1 - q^2}{2n}}$$

For large values of q, the standard error is relatively small for a given sample size. For small values, it is quite large.

DEVIATIONS FROM HARDY-WEINBERG EQUILIBRIUM

In a random mating population, each genotype should be present in a frequency that is a function only of the frequencies of various alleles in that population. If it can be shown that the genotypes are not distributed randomly, it is then necessary to examine the population or the genetic theory, or both, to see in what way these fail to satisfy the Hardy-Weinberg law.

Test for Equilibrium

The usual procedure for testing for equilibrium is to calculate the expected genotypes on the basis of gene frequencies and to test for deviation from the observed frequencies. In most applications, the gene frequencies have to be ascertained from the sample population. For direct allele counts, the gene frequency estimates are not based on assumptions of equilibrium. Consequently, these can be used to test for equilibrium. In the example used earlier of 50 persons consisting of 10 M, 23 MN, and 17 N, the frequency of L^M was 0.43 and of L^N was 0.57. If these alleles were distributed at random among the 50 persons, the distribution of genotypes would be $50(p^2 + 2pq + q^2) = 50[0.43^2 + 2(0.43)(0.57) + 0.57^2] = 9.25$ M $+ 24.51$ MN $+ 16.25$ N. These figures closely match the 10, 23, and 17 observed, and therefore this sample would indicate the population to be at equilibrium.

The observed and expected values do not always agree so closely. In that event, it is necessary to use a statistical test to assess the chances that the deviation is significant. A χ^2 can be calculated in a manner similar to the problems of Chapter 11. For the examples given the procedure would be

$$\chi^2 = \Sigma \frac{(O - E)^2}{E}$$

$$= \frac{(10 - 9.25)^2}{9.25} + \frac{(23 - 24.51)^2}{24.51} + \frac{(17 - 16.25)^2}{16.25}$$

$$= 0.188$$

Although there are three terms in this χ^2, there is only one degree of freedom, since the expected values were derived from the observed data. For problems of this particular type, the number of degrees of freedom is equal to the number of phenotypes minus the number of alleles. For this value of χ^2 and 1 df, $.70 > P > .50$. Thus, the observed deviation could happen by chance more than half the time. Had the observed deviation been so large that it would happen by chance rarely, it would be appropriate to conclude that the population from which the sample was drawn probably was not in equilibrium.

In many genetic systems, gene frequencies are computed from the square root of the recessive phenotype(s). This procedure *assumes* the population to be in equilibrium; hence, it is not possible subsequently to test for equilibrium.

Reasons for Departure from Equilibrium

The demonstration that a population is not in equilibrium is evidence that the assumptions necessary for equilibrium have not been met. Two primary assumptions were noted earlier—random mating and equal likelihood of survival of different genotypes. Most departures from equilibrium are due to nonrandom mating. In genetic terms, nonrandom mating means that mates are selected because of their genotype. It is convenient to distinguish several causes of nonrandom mating, although the genetic effects are equivalent.

STRATIFICATION.   When a population consists of two or more subpopulations with different gene frequencies, it is said to be stratified. The most common example in the United States is the Negro and Caucasian populations. These two groups differ in the frequencies of a number of genes, and failure to recognize the presence both of Negroes and Caucasians in a population may lead to erroneous gene frequency estimates. There are many other subpopulations that may also be important. The distribution of genes varies within and among the countries of Europe, and populations that are closely related may yet differ in the frequencies of some alleles. A typical American city, with populations originally from Ireland, Germany, Poland, Italy, West Africa, and so on, has many groups that must be recognized for genetic studies. America may be the melting pot, but the mixture hasn't completed melting yet.

For many purposes, it may be possible to group together related populations with similar gene frequencies. The decision will depend on the use to be made of the information. Deviation from expected equilibrium values is frequently small when two populations are mixed, even though the gene frequencies may differ. The effect of pooling is to produce too many homozygotes and fewer heterozygotes. The test for equilibrium makes detection of pooling of two similar populations unlikely unless the data are based on large numbers of observations.

ASSORTATIVE MATING.   Persons who choose mates because of particular traits are said to mate assortatively. If mating partners resemble each other for a trait, the assortative mating is positive; if partners are chosen because they are different, assortative mating is negative. Every mating is assortative with respect to some traits and random with respect to others. People tend to marry into their own ethnic group, thereby maintaining the population strata. This may not be a question of ethnic preference so much as the opportunity for social contacts. Persons often are encouraged to marry within the religious denomination to which they belong. In many communities, certain denominations are drawn primarily from one ethnic group, and marriages within the denomination therefore are likely to be between persons of similar ethnic and genetic background. Numerous other social institutions might be cited that tend to perpetuate ethnic differences.

These examples of assortative mating are basically the same as stratification, since the preferred mate is selected from the same subpopulation. In addition, there is assortative mating within a population if mates select each other for similar characteristics. Tall people tend to marry tall; short people marry short; intelligent people marry intelligent; and so on. This type of assortative mating is of genetic interest only to the extent that the traits selected are under genetic control. Only traits apparent to the marriage partners can be selected. Generally, blood types are not known, and even if known, they are not likely to play an important role in mate selection. Most of the traits important in assortative mating are complex genetically.

UNEQUAL VIABILITY OF GENOTYPES.   Even though the mating structure of a population may be random, persons of different genotypes do not necessarily have the same chances of survival. An extreme case would be complete lack of viability of one genotype. This occurs with zygotes homozygous for certain genes. A genetically equivalent situation would be failure of persons born with a certain genotype to survive to an age when they would be included in the survey of genotypes. Ideally, surveys should be carried out on newborn infants. A more common procedure is to work entirely with adults.

There are many examples of unequal viability of genotypes. For most recessive traits where viability of the homozygous recessive is greatly reduced, the frequency of the recessive gene has so diminished that surveys of random groups of people are unrewarding. The frequency can be more efficiently, if less accurately, estimated from ascertainment of affected persons only, provided the size of the population from which they are drawn is known.

An example of a common deleterious trait is sickle cell anemia. In many populations, there is a moderately high frequency of the gene for abnormal hemoglobin, $Hb_\beta{}^S$, which in the homozygous state causes sickle cell anemia. Persons heterozygous for the $Hb_\beta{}^S$ gene can be recognized by electrophoresis of their hemoglobin (see Chapter 8). Persons who are homozygous rarely survive to adulthood, but in certain parts of the world heterozygotes seem to have a slight advantage over persons homozygous for the normal allele, $Hb_\beta{}^A$, because of increased resistance to malaria. A survey of the frequency of these two alleles among infants would show the three genotypes to be in approximately the proportions predicted by the Hardy-Weinberg law. If the survey were conducted among adults, there would be only a few persons found homozygous for $Hb_\beta{}^S$.

UNEQUAL ASCERTAINMENT OF GENOTYPES.   Genotypes may be equally viable but nevertheless may not be present in a particular sample of the population in the same proportions in which they occur at birth. This would be the case if the persons actually examined were not representative of the parent population because of association between genotype and likelihood of being selected for study.

In practice, a random sample of a population is virtually impossible to assemble. Institutionalized persons are almost never included as part of the population from which they are drawn. Genotypes that are likely to lead to institutionalization will be underrepresented in the non-institutional population. The same is true of hospitalized patients or persons whose health does not permit them to assume an active role. In some instances, surveys are limited to a narrow segment of the population —for example, workers in a particular factory, admissions to a maternity hospital, or students in a school. These particular examples might lead to overascertainment of genes associated with physical robustness, fertility, or intelligence, respectively. To the extent that a gene under investigation is associated with the above traits, the genotypes may be disproportionately represented in the sample.

It will be easier to avoid confusion concerning ascertainment if the concepts of *incidence* and *prevalence* are clearly separated. Incidence is defined as the frequency of a characteristic at birth among a defined number of persons in a population. Prevalence is the frequency of a characteristic in the living population. Two diseases might have equal incidence in that they affect an equal portion of the population. But if one disease lasts twice as long, there would be twice as many persons affected at a given time (if the risk were constant with time). Incidence of genetic traits refers to the frequency at birth of a given genotype among all genotypes. Prevalence refers to the frequency of the genotype at a given time after natural selection for and against various gene combinations has occurred.

INCORRECT GENETIC THEORY. In a two-allele system, the maximum frequency of heterozygotes is 0.50 (Fig. 16–1). Occasionally, the heterozygote frequency is higher. This may be caused by sampling error, but χ^2 analysis should show the distribution of genotypes not to be significantly different from that predicted by the Hardy-Weinberg law. Rarely, the frequency of heterozygotes may be much higher. This is more likely to be observed if genetic theory has been formulated on one racial group and sampling is then done on another. For example, human gamma globulins can be classified into several types, depending on their ability to react in a complex mixture of red cells, "incomplete" Rh antibodies, and serum from some patients with rheumatoid arthritis. The gamma types were found to be under genetic control, the main types first detected being Gm(a+b−), Gm(a+b+), and Gm(a−b+), corresponding to genotypes Gm^a/Gm^a, Gm^a/Gm^b, and Gm^b/Gm^b. In a sample of American Negroes, Steinberg, Stauffer, and Boyer (1960) found the frequency of Gm(a+b+) to be 0.95, a figure greatly in excess of that predicted by the Hardy-Weinberg law. They proposed and subsequently established that in Negroes there exists an allele Gm^{ab} that leads to the reactions of both Gm^a and Gm^b and that is present in very high frequency.

The frequency of the Gm^{ab} allele is very high in Negroes but very low in other groups tested. It was the high frequency of apparent heterozygotes that led to recognition of the new allele. Such possibilities must be kept in mind when testing new populations for genetic traits.

GENE FREQUENCIES IN MIXED POPULATIONS

There are numerous examples in the history of man in which two or more populations, each with its characteristic gene frequencies, have united to form a single new panmictic population. The frequency of inherited traits in the new population is a function of the frequencies in the parent populations. In order to arrive at the new frequencies, one must keep in mind that the frequency of various allele combinations is expressed in terms of the frequency of the individual alleles. Calculation of the allele frequencies in the new population is therefore the first step in predicting the frequency of allelic combinations.

The general formula for averaging frequencies is

$$pt = ap_a + bp_b + cp_c + \ldots + np_n$$

where p_t is the frequency of a specific allele in the new population; a, b, $\ldots$, n are the relative contributions of the parent populations; and p_a, p_b, $\ldots$, p_n are the corresponding allele frequencies in the parent populations. The various p_a, p_b, $\ldots$, p_n may have any value from zero to one, but $a + b + \ldots + n = 1$.

Consider the example of Rh$-$ persons who are homozygous for the r allele. Among North American Caucasians, the frequency of Rh$-$ persons is approximately 15 percent. Among the Bantu of Africa, it is about 5 percent. On the basis of other genetic systems, American Negroes are known to have received about 70 percent of their genes from African ancestors and about 30 percent from Caucasian. To arrive at the predicted frequency of Rh$-$ persons among American Negroes, it is necessary first to calculate the frequency of the r allele in the present population. Thus, the frequency in Bantus q_B is $\sqrt{0.05} = 0.22$, and the frequency in Caucasians q_C is $\sqrt{0.15} = 0.39$. The gene frequency in American Negroes is then

$$q_N = (0.70)(0.22) + (0.30)(0.39) = 0.27$$

The frequency of Rh$-$ persons among American Negroes is $(0.27)^2$ or 0.073. This corresponds to an observant frequency of approximately 8 percent.

Often it is desirable to calculate the relative contributions of two parent populations to a new population, knowing the phenotype frequencies in all three populations. In this case, p_t, p_a, and p_b are known. Substitution into the general equation, remembering that $a + b = 1$, permits calculation of the values of a and b.

REFERENCES AND SUGGESTED READING

HARDY, G. H. 1908. Mendelian proportions in a mixed population. *Science* 28: 49–50.

LI, C. C. 1955. *Population Genetics*. Chicago: University of Chicago Press.

———. 1961. *Human Genetics*. New York: McGraw-Hill, 218 pp.

STEINBERG, A. G., STAUFFER, R., and BOYER, S. H. 1960. Evidence for a Gm^{ab} allele in the Gm system of American Negroes. *Nature* 188: 169–170.

PROBLEMS

1. Define:

    panmixis   assortative mating
    mean   incidence
    standard error of mean   prevalence
    stratification

2. Consider blue eyes to be a simple recessive trait. In a certain pan-
    mictic population, 16 percent of the persons have blue eyes.
    a. What portion of the brown-eyed persons are heterozygous for
       blue eyes?
    b. What would be the frequency of blue-eyed children among off-
       spring of parents, both of whom are brown eyed?

3. Phenylketonuria has been reported to occur once in approximately
    10,000 births. Pedigree studies indicate the disease to be due to
    homozygosity for a recessive gene.
    a. What is the frequency of the gene?
    b. What percentage of the population is heterozygous for the gene?
    c. What will be the frequency of marriages involving two hetero-
       zygotes?

4. In a certain population, color blindness occurs 25 times more fre-
    quently in males than in females. What is the frequency of the gene
    for color blindness? What is the frequency of heterozygous females?

5. Cystic fibrosis of the pancreas is due to an autosomal recessive gene.
    The frequency of the gene is approximately 0.02 in Caucasian pop-
    ulations.
    a. What is the frequency of affected individuals?
    b. What is the frequency of carriers?
    c. What is the frequency of marriages of carriers with homozygous
       normals?
    d. What is the frequency of marriages of carriers with carriers?

6. The observed frequencies of blood groups at the MN locus in a par-
    ticular population are: Type M, 110; type MN, 180; type N, 110.
    What are the gene frequencies of L^M and L^N? Is the population at
    equilibrium? If this population undergoes random mating with one
    twice as large in which the frequency of $L^M = 0.7$, what will be the
    expected frequencies of phenotypes in the new population?

Chapter Seventeen

SELECTION

Selection is said to operate when there is inequality in fitness of genotypes. Fitness is to be understood in a broad sense, being measured ultimately in terms of the number of offspring produced. A person may be fit functionally in that he is healthy, but, if he fails to leave offspring, he is scored genetically as "dead." By the same token, long survival beyond the reproductive age does not make a person more fit than one who leaves as many offspring but dies at a young age.

Fitness is a property of a whole organism in a particular environment. Therefore the factors that contribute to fitness are many and complex. It is possible, nevertheless, to measure the relative fitness of two groups of phenotypes that differ on the average by a single particular gene.

It is common to speak of *positive* or *negative* selective advantage. The terms are somewhat arbitrary, since there is no absolute scale with unit advantage. But an allele can be said to have positive selective advantage if it leads to greater fitness than the alternate alleles under consideration. It has negative selective advantage if it leads to lesser fitness.

Sets of alleles at a particular locus are sometimes said to be selectively neutral if the various genotypic combinations appear to have equal fitness. It is possible that true selective neutrality never exists. Every difference, no matter how slight, could lead to equally slight but significant differences in fitness. However, alleles whose only difference is a substitution of one amino acid for another very similar amino acid in some protein may have very similar fitness values. The estimates of relative fitness must be based on observation rather than biochemical reasoning, since very small changes, as in hemoglobins S, C, and A, may cause significant differences in fitness.

Selection occurs at all stages of the life cycle. Most familiar is the selection against certain genotypes subsequent to birth. Persons homozygous for hemoblobin S rarely survive to reproduce. Until the availability of insulin, persons with juvenile diabetes were at a great disadvantage compared to nondiabetics. Resistance to infectious diseases, although poorly understood from the genetic point of view, was an important feature of selection prior to the advent of antibiotics.

It has been suggested that modern medical practices have largely eliminated natural selection. It is true that persons with diseases have a much better chance of survival than formerly. But survival of persons is only the most obvious area in which selection operates. If the entire life cycle is considered—formation of gametes, survival of gametes, formation of zygote, development of fetus, survival of newborn through reproductive period—there are many points at which selection can operate without leading to visible elimination of certain genotypes or to medical intervention.

An example of selection in gametogenesis is found in Drosophila. The *segregation-distorter (SD)* locus has two known alleles. Normal segregation of chromosomes occurs with the wild-type allele. Males heterozygous for the mutant allele, under certain conditions of environment, show a marked departure from the 1:1 ratio expected from genes on the SD chromosome. Apparently, the mutant allele is able to cause the normal chromosome to break during spermatogenesis, so that few of the sperm contain the normal allele. This interaction of homologous genes during meiosis is called *meiotic drive*. The extent to which it may occur in man is unknown. Loss of gametes is experimentally difficut to establish as are small deviations from Mendelian ratios.

Even though mature gametes are formed, not all are equally likely to give rise to a zygote. This is most clearly seen in *gametic* or *prezygotic* selection involving sperm. The cervical secretions of many women contain antibodies against certain of the ABO blood groups. Sperm contain these blood group substances, and there is unsubstantiated evidence that sperm from an AB male consist of half A sperm and half B, presumably reflecting the haploid genetic content. It seems possible that in the mating of an AB man and an A woman, the A sperm should be favored over B sperm, leading to more A children than are expected from a 1:1 ratio. The quantitative importance of this kind of selection is yet to be established, but the possibilities are obvious.

There is little information on the genetic constitution of aborted fetuses. Spontaneous abortions, many too early to be recognized as such, are frequent. Many abortions involve malformed fetuses; in other cases, a defect is not obvious, although many metabolic defects would likely be undetected. Judging from studies on laboratory animals, a large portion of abortions are genetic in origin. Such abortions represent natural selection in operation.

Finally, in spite of the great progress with many human diseases, there are still many that have not yielded to therapy. Some of these are inherited and subject to selection.

SELECTION AGAINST DELETERIOUS TRAITS

The simplest situations to consider quantitatively are those in which a mutant gene, either dominant or recessive, leads to reduced fitness compared to the nonmutant "wild-type" phenotype. There are thus only two fitness classes to consider.

Selection against Dominant Genes

If a dominant gene is lethal, resulting either in death or in sterility, selection is rapid and effective. A fully penetrant gene with zero fitness would be virtually eliminated in one generation, since it would not be transmitted to offspring. Mutation would produce new copies of the mutant gene, but, since the mutation rate is characteristically very low, few persons would carry the dominant gene because of a new mutation.

Examples of deleterious genes meeting these requirements are not known. There are many rare conditions in which affected persons are unable to reproduce. In order to prove that a trait is genetic, it must be transmitted. Dominants that cannot be transmitted therefore cannot be distinguished from environmentally induced traits.

Although not a single gene mutation, trisomy 21 syndrome illustrates some of the difficulties in interpretation of defects that result in sterility. (The few cases of fertility now known among trisomy 21 patients were mostly found after the chromosomal basis of the disease was established.) The disease occurs too often for each case to represent a new mutation of a conventional gene. However, the only association with environmental factors was with maternal age. The absence of opportunity for transmission to offspring of affected persons prevented recognition of the genetic basis of the disease. It was as easily explained by unidentified environmental factors.

It seems likely that all genes undergo mutation. Many such mutations, in heterozygous combination, almost certainly lead to nonviability. This could result in a stillbirth or a spontaneous abortion, the latter possibly occurring so early in gestation as to be unrecognized. Or the mutation may be compatible with viability in the somatic sense but not in the genetic; that is, the person is sterile. The frequency of a condition of this type due to mutation at a specific locus would be very rare, approximately twice the mutation rate. Based on an average mutation rate of 1×10^{-5} per locus per gamete, zygotes heterozygous for specific new mutations would occur with an incidence of about 1/50,000. Thus, some of the very rare abnormalities may result from new mutations that cannot be demonstrated by conventional genetic means.

Many dominant genes, although deleterious, are still compatible with fertility. The efficiency of selection is less than in the previous case and is proportional to the loss of fitness of heterozygous persons. The loss of fitness of a genotype can be expressed by the *coefficient of selection, s*. The fitness of a genotype is symbolized by $w = 1 - s$. If the frequency, p_o, of a dominant gene A is very low in the parent or zeroth generation, so that AA persons are rare, the effects of selection for one generation can be expressed by

$$p_1 = \frac{2p_oq_ow}{2(2p_oq_ow + q_o^2)} = \frac{p_ow}{2p_ow + q_o}$$

As p becomes very small compared to q, the denominator approaches 1. The equation is then

$$p_1 \simeq p_ow$$

For additional generations

$$p_n = p_ow^n \tag{1}$$

where n is the number of generations of selection.

For any value of w less than 1, the frequency p will approach zero as n becomes very large. Theoretically, it will not become zero, but as the number of persons with the gene becomes small, chance may cause fluctuations from the predicted frequency. Eventually, since the deleterious genes are also being formed through mutation, the rate of loss through selection will equal the rate of gain through mutation.

Selection against Recessive Genes

Deleterious recessive genes are removed from the population just as are dominants. However, the process is much less efficient because only a portion of the genes are in the homozygous combination and therefore subject to removal. If the appropriate terms of the binomial expansion are multiplied by the number of recessive alleles, the fraction of recessive genes in homozygotes is given by the expression

$$2q^2/(2pq + 2q^2) \tag{2}$$

which reduces to q. For rare genes, only a small portion would be subject to removal by selection; even for common genes, selection is inefficient.

For complete selection against the recessive phenotype corresponding to genotype aa, the rate of change of gene frequency, q, can be readily calculated. Consider a population consisting of the usual three gene combinations involving two alleles. The distribution would be

$$p_0^2 + 2p_0q_0 + q_0^2$$

If the aa persons represented by the term q_0^2 do not reproduce, then the frequency of a in the next generation will be the same as in the $AA + Aa$ persons of the original generation, thus

$$q_1 = \frac{2p_0q_0}{2(p_0^2 + 2p_0q_0)} \tag{3}$$

It is necessary to multiply the denominator by 2 since each person has two alleles, whatever his genotype. Dividing by $2p_0$ and remembering that $p_0 = 1 - q_0$ yields

$$q_1 = \frac{q_0}{1 + q_0} \tag{4}$$

The frequency of recessive genotypes would be $q_1^2 = q_0^2/(1 + q_0)^2$. The frequency of a after two generations of selection can be obtained by substituting for q_1 in the formula $q_2 = q_1/(1 + q_1)$. This yields

$$q_2 = \frac{q_0}{1 + 2q_0} \tag{5}$$

Similarly, it can be shown that for any number of generations n,

$$q_n = \frac{q_0}{1 + nq_0} \tag{6}$$

The change of q versus n is shown in Figure 17–1. Although q approaches zero, it does so very slowly. This is because an increasing portion of the recessive genes are in heterozygous combination and not selected against as q becomes small. For any particular value of q, the portion of a alleles lost is q. Therefore, even the most rigorous selection against aa accomplishes little once the frequency of a is low.

In spite of the inefficiency of selection against recessive genes, the frequency does decrease steadily. The number of generations required to accomplish a given decrease in gene frequency can be calculated by rearranging formula (6) in the form

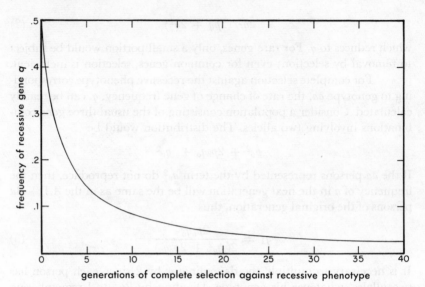

Figure 17–1. Change in gene frequency q of a recessive gene as a result of complete selection against homozygous recessives. The gene frequency approaches zero but theoretically never attains it. Eventually, the number of genes lost through selection will be so few that they may be replaced by mutation. At that point, the population would be in equilibrium.

$$n = \frac{1}{q_n} - \frac{1}{q_o} \tag{7}$$

In order to reduce the frequency of a gene from 0.1 to 0.05, ten generations of complete selection would be necessary. A reduction from 0.05 to 0.025 would require another twenty generations.

Incomplete selection against aa may also occur and can be readily treated mathematically by adding a $q_o{}^2w$ term to both numerator and denominator of equation (3), where again w is the genetic fitness of aa. Thus,

$$q_1 = \frac{2p_oq_o + 2q_o{}^2w}{2(p_o{}^2 + 2p_oq_o + q_o{}^2w)}$$

$$= \frac{q_o(1 - sq_o)}{1 - sq_o{}^2} \tag{8}$$

where $s = 1 - w$. As s, the coefficient of selection, approaches 1, (8) approaches (4). Iteration of this formula will give the new gene frequency for subsequent generations of selection. For $s < 1$, selection is less effective than total selection against the aa genotype. The frequency of a will decrease nevertheless to the equilibrium value at which removal of a by selection and addition of a by mutation are exactly balanced.

General Formula for Selection

The situations of selection against a dominant or a recessive genotype are special cases. A more general statement of selection does not require that some of the genotypes be of equal advantage. The Hardy-Weinberg distribution would be modified to

$$w_1 p^2 + w_2 2pq + w_3 q^2$$

where w_1, w_2, and w_3 are the relative fitnesses of the three genotypes. Where more than two alleles exist, additional terms can be added as needed. It is theoretically possible for the various w's to have any value from zero to one. It should be remembered that the fitness of a genotype is a function of environment and may change as environment changes.

Selection against Sex-Linked Traits

The effects of selection on sex-linked traits are different from those on autosomal traits only in that we must recognize the special patterns of transmission resulting from hemizygosity of the X chromosome in males. For traits with a high fitness, one third of the genes are in males, two thirds in females. But for recessive traits with a low fitness, a larger portion of genes are in males. This is because affected males do not transmit their X chromosomes, although heterozygous females transmit an X chromosome bearing an abnormal gene equally to sons and daughters. For recessive traits with zero fitness, half the genes are in males.

For rare recessive traits, selection occurs only in males, since homozygous recessive females are virtually nonexistent. Mathematical treatment assumes that heterozygous females are normal. If the fitness of affected males is zero, half of the genes are eliminated each generation because of affected males; the other half are transmitted to females and survive. This is analogous to the situation of an autosomal dominant gene with $w = \frac{1}{2}$. The gene frequency q after n generations of selection is

$$q_n = q_0 (1/2)^n \tag{9}$$

Selection is not as efficient as for an autosomal dominant trait of zero fitness, but it is efficient nevertheless.

The treatment for $w > 0$ is complicated by the fact that the proportion of genes carried by males is itself a function of w. The effect of selection on rare traits is expressed by the relation

$$q_n = q_0 (f + wm)^n$$

where f is the portion of genes carried by females, m is the portion carried by males, and w is the fitness of affected males. The values f and m are readily obtained for values of w by iteration of $f + wm$, keeping in mind that $f + m = 1$ and that, at equilibrium, f and m are constant. Table 17–1 gives values of f, m, and $f + wm$ for selected values of w. The ratio of affected males to heterozygous females can be used to estimate w, the fitness in males.

TABLE 17–1

Total Fitness for Sex-Linked Recessive Traits for Various Values of Fitness, w, in Males

| MALE FITNESS w | PROPORTION OF GENES IN | | TOTAL FITNESS $f + wm$ |
	MALES m	FEMALES f	
0	0.5000	0.5000	0.5000
0.1	0.4606	0.5394	0.5855
0.2	0.4336	0.5664	0.6531
0.3	0.4129	0.5871	0.7110
0.4	0.3961	0.6039	0.7623
0.5	0.3820	0.6180	0.8090
0.6	0.3698	0.6302	0.8521
0.7	0.3591	0.6409	0.8923
0.8	0.3496	0.6504	0.9301
0.9	0.3411	0.6589	0.9659
1.0	0.3333	0.6667	1.0000

No truly dominant sex-linked traits that are deleterious are known. This is understandable in view of the apparent inactivation of one X chromosome in females. The frequency of such a trait would be very rare in any event, since all persons with the gene would be subject to selection. The discussion of the difficulty in recognizing autosomal genes when $w = 0$ also applies to sex-linked genes. The only clue to the genetic nature of such a trait and to its location on the X chromosome would be the 2:1 ratio of affected females and males. On the other hand, nongenetic factors could also produce such a ratio by chance.

POLYMORPHIC TRAITS

The word *polymorphic* means existing in multiple forms. As applied to biology, it means that a trait under consideration occurs in two or more forms in a species. Geneticists further restrict the meaning of the word by requiring that the different forms be present in frequencies greater than can be maintained by mutation. In the previous section, we saw that the effects of selection were to reduce the frequency of an allele to a value so low that the allele is maintained in the population only because mutation continually replaces alleles lost through selection. Since mutation is infrequent, traits maintained solely by this mechanism are necessarily infrequent also.

There exist many loci, some of whose alleles occur with appreciable frequencies. The two common alleles of the MN blood group system each have frequencies about 0.5. There are four common alleles in the ABO blood group system, with frequencies among Caucasians of approximately 0.20 I^{A_1}, 0.05 I^{A_2}, 0.06 I^B, and 0.69 I^O. These are examples of true polymorphism.

A polymorphism may be unstable or it may be balanced. An unstable polymorphism is one in which selection leads to alteration of the gene frequencies. Such a situation might arise when two populations, each originally with a single allele, interbreed to form a new population. If the two alleles are not selectively identical, selection may cause one to displace the other. Before this has happened, the population is polymorphic but unstable. A similar situation could arise through a change in environment. If the relative fitness of the three common genotypes of a two-allele system is $w_3 > w_1$ and w_2, the homozygous genotype corresponding to w_3 will increase. If the order is changed so that $w_1 > w_3$ and w_2, the homozygous genotype corresponding to w_1 will displace the others.

One special situation arises theoretically when the heterozygote has lower fitness than either homozygote. The best known example is Rh incompatibility. For purposes of illustration, the rather complex Rh genetics may be simplified to a two-allele system, R and r, the genotypes RR and Rr being Rh+, and rr being Rh−. Mothers who are Rh− sometimes form antibodies against Rh+ fetuses. The antibodies enter the child's circulation, leading to the condition known as *erythroblastosis fetalis*. Most babies now born with this condition are saved by having their blood replaced by a compatible type. Formerly, the condition was usually fatal.

An erythroblastotic baby can arise from two types of matings: ♂ RR × ♀ rr and ♂ Rr × ♀ rr. In either case, in order for the child to be "incompatible" with the mother, it must have an R allele, and thus a genotype of Rr. Failure to survive would lead to the loss of equal numbers of R and r alleles. If the population frequencies of R and r were 0.5, then loss of Rr children would not alter the frequency of either allele. If the frequencies were other than 0.5, loss of Rr persons would cause a greater *relative* loss of the less frequent allele. Eventually, the less frequent allele should become rare. A system is said to be in equilibrium when selection does not alter the gene frequencies. This is an unstable equilibrium, however, since any deviation will lead to replacement of one allele. The exact point of equilibrium will depend on the relative advantages of the two homozygous genotypes. The Rh locus is characterized by very high and very low frequencies of r in different populations of the world. It has been suggested that these populations were in the process of eliminating R or r alleles, but modern migrations of populations have changed the picture.

The Rh system also illustrates another possibility in selection. The fitness of the heterozygote varies with the gene frequencies. The portion of Rr offspring originating from rr mothers decreases as the frequency of r decreases. With very high frequencies of r, most Rr children would come from $Rr \times rr$ matings, in half of which the mother would be the $Rh-$ parent. These cases would have the potential of producing erythroblastotic babies. If r is rare, most Rr persons would come from $RR \times Rr$ matings, which do not produce erythroblastotic babies.

Balanced Polymorphism

A polymorphism is said to be balanced if there exists a stable equilibrium maintained by selection. The most common situation would be when the heterozygote is more fit than either homozygote; that is, $w_2 > w_1$ and w_3. Under such circumstances, there exists a value of q such that chance deviations are counterbalanced by decreased fitness of the homozygotes. The effect is to restore q to its equilibrium value.

It can be shown that the equilibrium value of q is given by

$$q = \frac{s_1}{s_1 + s_3}$$

where s_2 is assumed to be zero ($w_2 = 1$). If the two homozygotes are equally fit, the equilibrium value of q is 0.5. If the coefficient of selection of aa is twice that of AA, equilibrium will be attained when $q = 0.33$.

Perhaps the best explored example of balanced polymorphism is found in the abnormal hemoglobins, particularly sickle cell hemoglobin. Persons homozygous for Hb S have very low fitness, few surviving to adulthood ($s_3 \simeq 1$). On the other hand, heterozygotes seem to have some protection from malaria. In some populations of Africa, the frequency of the Hb S gene is such that, if the populations have in fact achieved a balanced equilibrium, persons homozygous for normal Hb A are only 75 percent as fit as those heterozygous for Hb S. Whether this selection is due entirely to differences in susceptibilty to malaria has not been established.

REFERENCES AND SUGGESTED READING

ALLISON, A. C. 1954. Protection afforded by sickle-cell trait against subtertian malarial infection. *Brit. Med. J.* 1: 290–294.

CLARKE, C. A. 1961. Blood groups and disease. *Progr. Med. Genet.* 1: 81–119.

CROW, J. 1962. Population genetics: Selection. In *Methodology in Human Genetics* (W. J. Burdette, ed.). San Francisco: Holden-Day, pp. 53–75.

FISHER, R. A. 1958. *The Genetical Theory of Natural Selection*, 2d ed. New York: Dover, 291 pp.

GERSHOWITZ, H., BEHRMAN, S. J., and NEEL, J. V. 1958. Hemagglutinins in uterine secretions. *Science* 128: 719–720.

HALDANE, J. B. S. 1961. Natural selection in man. *Progr. Med. Genet.* 1: 27–37.

ROBERTS, D. F., and HARRISON, G. A. (eds.). 1959. *Natural Selection in Human Populations*. New York: Pergamon, 76 pp.

PROBLEMS

1. Define:

   fitness   prezygotic selection
   selection   polymorphism
   meiotic drive

2. *A* is a dominant normal gene; *a* is its recessive allele that is lethal when homozygous.
   a. Starting with an initial gene frequency for *a* of 0.1, what will be the frequency after ten generations?
   b. How many generations will be required to reduce the frequency to one fifth its initial value?

3. The complete selection against individuals homozygous for hemoglobin S is counterbalanced in many areas by the relative advantage enjoyed by the heterozygote, who is more resistant to malaria than homozygous normal individuals. With the control of malaria, this advantage should no longer be present. In a population in which 20

percent of the adult population are heterozygotes, what will be the *gene* frequency of Hb S after one generation of malaria control? After ten generations? After 100 generations? How many generations will be required to reduce the frequency to 0.001?

4. Hemophilia A is a rare sex-linked recessive trait. Assuming 10 percent fitness in males, what portion of the genes would be lost through selection in one generation?

5. In a certain balanced polymorphic system, the fitness of AA is 70 percent that of the heterozygote and the fitness of aa is 10 percent. At equilibrium, what is the frequency of a?

Chapter Eighteen

HUMAN POPULATIONS

All human beings are classed together into a single species, *Homo sapiens*. In spite of the diversity of human types, we are, after all, similar. No one has difficulty classifying persons, however primitive the persons may seem, into human versus nonhuman groups. One criterion commonly applied to determine if two groups of organisms are members of a single species is whether they are completely fertile in cross matings. By this criterion, all human beings obviously belong to the same species.

Much diversity does exist among human beings, nevertheless, and it exists at many different levels. Each of us as an individual differs from other individuals from the same background. Each family differs somewhat from other families; groups of families differ from other groups of families; and, finally, the major ethnic groups differ from each other.

Various terms have been used to designate the major groups of mankind. The most common term is *race*. A race may be defined as a group of historically related persons who share a gene pool that differs from the gene pool of other groups. The difficulty with this definition is that it does not tell us how discriminating we should be in recognizing differences. Since there are hundreds of populations that differ from all other populations, we might therefore claim that there are hundreds of races. Common usage of the term, however, has been more restrictive.

THE ORIGIN OF RACES

This discussion will consider the manner in which races can arise from a population that initially is in equilibrium. It is assumed that there are two or more alleles at each of many loci. Each allele will have a certain frequency. Formation of races would be the formation of subpopulations with gene frequencies different from each other.

In order for races to arise, there must exist isolating mechanisms.

In nearly every case, this has probably been geographic initially. One can imagine other isolating mechanisms, such as assortative mating, but these are more important in maintaining isolation than in giving rise to it. Geographic isolation would occur when any natural barrier, such as a river, mountain range, or ocean, separated two groups, making gene flow difficult. Complete isolation has undoubtedly been the exception rather than the rule. A common reason for separation might be migration of part of a population because of overcrowding. This could happen by mass migration of a portion of the population or by migration of individuals over a period of time. Having migrated, persons are more likely to seek mates among fellow emigrants than among the surrounding population.

Through variations on the preceding factors, isolated populations arise. It does not automatically follow, however, that the isolated population will in time be different. Differences will develop only if one or more of the following events also occur.

Genetic Drift

If two alleles, A and a, in a population have frequencies $p = 0.6$ and $q = 0.4$, respectively, the most probable values of p and q in a group of persons drawn from that population are $p = 0.6$ and $q = 0.4$. The expected deviation from those values is given by the standard deviation, $s = \sqrt{pq/2N}$, where N is the number of persons in the sample. Sixty-eight percent of the time, the value of p in the sample will not deviate more than one standard deviation; 95 percent of the time, p will not deviate more than two standard deviations. For large values of N, s is very small and the expected deviation is correspondingly small. If the sample of persons is small, the chances that p in the sample will differ from p of the parent population are much greater. For the gene frequencies given earlier, $p = 0.6$ and $q = 0.4$, a sample of 500 persons would have $s = 0.0155$. If 500 persons emigrated from this population, 68 percent of the time p would lie between 0.5845 and 0.6155 and 95 percent of the time p would be between 0.5690 and 0.6310. If only 50 persons emigrated, $s = 0.049$. Now, $0.551 < p < 0.649$ 68 percent of the time, and $0.502 < p < 0.698$ 95 percent of the time. Formation of a new population by migration of a small number of persons therefore may lead purely by chance to a different gene frequency in the emigrant population.

Comparable to these figures is the sampling of genes that occurs each time a new generation comes into being. If the parent population is large, chance fertility or infertility of a person with a particular combination of genes is counterbalanced by equal fertility or infertility of others of different genotypes. If the population is small, this may not be the case. One man whose genotype is *AA* may sire an undue proportion of the next generation, thus leading to an increase in the frequency of gene *A*. This is particularly evident in cultures where the harem system exists.

These chance fluctuations of genes are called *genetic drift*. The term implies that sampling error alone is responsible for changes in gene frequency. A consequence is that shifts are equally likely to occur in either direction, leading to either an increase or a decrease of *p*. Because Wright first explored the effects of genetic drift systematically, this phenomenon is sometimes called the *Sewell Wright* effect.

An example of genetic drift in a human population has been reported by Glass *et al.* in a study of the Dunkers. A religious isolate in Pennsylvania, they were founded in this country by a small group that immigrated from Germany. Analysis of a series of blood groups shows them to deviate considerably both from the German population and from the surrounding American population. Because of the small size of the group, it is postulated that the change in gene frequencies has resulted purely from genetic drift. A similar discrepancy in gene frequencies has been observed in a number of other small populations.

Selection

The effects of selection on gene frequency were treated in Chapter 17. In order for selection to lead to different gene frequencies in different populations, it must be supposed that the fitness of various genotypes differs in the populations. This variation, in turn, would usually reflect the action of different environments. Thus *AA* might be the favored genotype in one environment whereas *aa* would have an advantage in another. In more general terms, the fitness coefficients w_1, w_2, w_3, etc. must differ in the different populations.

Since selection is frequently a function of environment, populations that inhabit similar though widely separated environments may have similar types and frequencies of certain genes, even though the populations are otherwise different. Also, populations known to be unrelated but that occupy a common geographic area may have similar frequencies. Conversely, closely related populations in different environments may have diverged in their gene frequencies. It is thus hazardous to infer the relationships of populations on the basis of one genetic locus or only a few loci.

Even complexes of genes may be misleading. An example is found in skin pigmentation. For the most part, races that have inhabited tropical areas for thousands of years are darkly pigmented. Those that have lived in more temperate regions have less pigment. The dark pigment is thought to protect persons from the intense rays of the equatorial sun. Persons with little pigment cannot tolerate sun to the extent that highly pigmented persons can. On the other hand, in regions where there is very little sun, more of the radiation is thought to be available for conversion of ergosterol to vitamin D in persons without pigment. Several races are highly pigmented—Africans, Melanesians, Micronesians, and Australians. Selection has favored the development of pigment independently in these groups. The Africans and Australians seem to be no more closely related—indeed, perhaps they are less closely related—than are Africans and Caucasians. Yet from the point of view of pigment, they are similar.

Another physical trait thought to be controlled by selection is the ratio of body surface area to mass. In general, animals living in cold climates are larger and rounder; in hot climates they are smaller and thinner. Heat loss is largely a function of surface area. For this reason, it is thought that stocky persons are favored in cold climates, where the problem is to conserve heat, and thin persons are favored in hot climates, where the problem is to get rid of heat. The very thin populations are all tropical, while the arctic inhabitants are heavy-set. The inheritance of body form is very complex and many factors other than selection for heat economy undoubtedly influence selection for body types.

Not all selection is related to external environment. Particularly in the case of man, social factors may give rise to and perpetuate population differences that are inherited. Each culture has its own theories on the ideal types of mates. Although the ideal may rarely exist, there are usually some persons in the culture who approach the ideal more than do others. To the extent that these persons have a favored opportunity to reproduce, the gene pool of the population will shift in their direction. If the ideal type is sufficiently stable over a long period, the effect on the gene pool could be appreciable. On the other hand, during the past century in Western civilization, there have been frequent changes in the concept of ideal types.

The influence of social forces on mate selection tends to perpetuate the separation of populations that might otherwise blend. There are many examples, including the continued existence of separate white and Negro populations in America. The geographic isolation that permitted separate populations to arise no longer exists. Perpetuation of two populations by social factors alone is doomed to failure in the long run. There is a small but continued exchange of genes between the two populations, which will cause the gene pools gradually to converge. The speed with which this happens is influenced by social factors, but the ultimate outcome is not.

Mutation

Mutation is not generally considered to have a major role in formation of isolates. In a freely interbreeding population, a mutant gene either would be rapidly eliminated or, if it were favorable and escaped chance elimination, would spread through the entire population, displacing other alleles until an equilibrium frequency corresponding to its relative fitness was attained. The fact that only a part of the population possessed the mutant allele at some time would not be a basis for dividing the population into groups.

Once a population is isolated from others, mutations can then become an important factor in further increasing the isolation. A particular mutation always occurs in a particular population, and the population in which it occurs has the potential to change genetically. If specific mutations were frequent, then all populations would have the same potential. But mutations—particularly favorable mutations—are exceedingly rare. A normal gene mutates to a nonfunctional form approximately once per 100,000 gametes. Mutations that lead to a change in amino acid sequence of the protein product are rarer, and specific changes, as in hemoglobin A to S, must be much rarer, possibly only one in 10^7 or 10^8 gametes. In populations of a billion persons, even these rare mutations must occur occasionally, but prehistoric populations were much smaller, and most mutations did not occur in most populations. When a favorable mutation did occur, chances are that it occurred only once, and the population in which it occurred could therefore become different from other populations.

It is not possible to prove that single events of mutations gave rise to all of the alleles of a specific type now existing. However, for some alleles, the evidence points in that direction. Perhaps the best example is hemoglobin C. This β-chain variant is found only among persons of African origin. Furthermore, its distribution in Africa is very limited and reaches a maximum concentration in the Upper Volta (Fig. 18–1). Hemoglobin C seems to resemble Hb S in offering some protection against malaria in persons heterozygous for Hbs A and C. Persons homozygous for Hb C are anemic, but they do not die in childhood as do persons homozygous for Hb S. The Hb C gene therefore has some of the advantages of the Hb S but not all the disadvantages. Judging from its distribution, it is now in the process of displacing Hb S in those populations in which Hb S offers an advantage. The single focal point of distribution suggests that the Hb C mutation has occurred only once. If it occurred in other places and times, it was lost, either through chance (genetic drift) or because it offered no advantage in those environments.

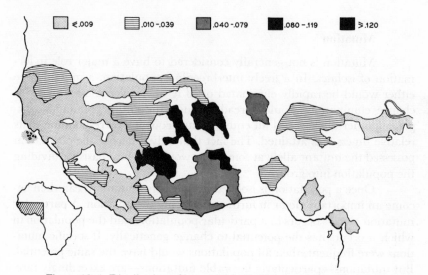

Figure 18–1. Distribution of hemoglobin C allele in Africa, showing the area of maximum concentration. Information is not available for blank areas. (From D. L. Rucknagel and J. V. Neel, 1961, *Progr. Med. Genet.* 1: 158–260, by permission.)

A gene that is favored in all environments will gradually displace its alleles, given sufficient time. So long as a tenuous contact is maintained among divergent groups, a pathway is present for the flow and exchange of genes. The human populations have probably been few indeed that were so isolated as never to give or receive genes from the outside. The time necessary for a gene to spread under primitive conditions was very long.

THE EVOLUTION OF HUMAN POPULATIONS

Knowledge of prehuman and early human populations comes primarily from the skeletal remains of individuals who happened to meet their end in a place favorable for the preservation of bony material. There have been many discoveries of fossil material in recent decades, and the idea of the "missing link" can now be disregarded. It is still not possible to specify a precise sequence of evolutionary forms, but there are enough early hominid forms known to account for the general pattern of evolution from apelike ancestors to modern man.

A discussion of the varieties of prehistoric man can be found in books on physical anthropology. The only question that will be considered here is how the present races of man are related to each other in terms of evolution. Two extreme possibilities can be imagined (Fig. 18–2).

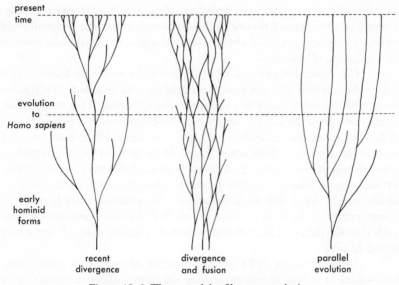

present
time

evolution
to
Homo sapiens

early
hominid
forms

recent
divergence

divergence
and fusion

parallel
evolution

Figure 18–2. Three models of human evolution.

The more generally accepted is that all of the existing races of man diverged after man had evolved to *Homo sapiens*. Divergence may have occurred earlier, but only a single line survived to give rise to modern man. At no time was the line homogeneous; there was always variability, although there was also opportunity for gene exchange among all parts of the population, at least until *Homo sapiens* appeared.

Another hypothesis is that the present major groups of man diverged prior to the final evolutionary process. Evolution to *Homo sapiens* would have been by parallel evolution. This occurs when similar environments cause two separate populations to evolve in the same manner to the same final product. Many examples of parallel evolution are known in lower organisms. There is no reason to suppose it could not have occurred in man also, given the same genetic variability in the various populations.

A third possibility is a combination of the first two. Fossil evidence favors coexistence of several forms of early man. Some of these forms undoubtedly became isolated and eventually extinct. Other forms could probably interbreed and exchange genes, although the skeletal remains are different among the groups. Particularly advantageous genes could be distributed among otherwise distinct groups without leading to a loss of the major group differences. Occasionally two groups might join, forming a new population.

The third idea is similar to the first in that it assumes that the ancestors of modern man were never completely isolated from each other. It resembles the second theory in that it assumes that the progenitors of presently existing races had already formed separate populations prior to the final steps of evolution.

The exact happenings of evolution may never be known. It is known though that all races now existing appear to be able to breed effectively with all other races to produce fertile offspring. This means that, unlike the case of the donkey and horse, the chromosome complements of all human races are equivalent. Whether the same alleles exist in every population is yet to be fully investigated. If the present racial groups had been divergent for a long evolutionary time, differences would almost certainly have arisen—as they have in other closely related species—which would have led to unbalanced chromosome complements in crosses, either in the F_1 or F_2 generations. It is therefore necessary to conclude that the different lines of man were never totally isolated over a long period of time.

Anthropologists differ on the number of races that exist today. Some think it is best to recognize only six races; others recognize up to two dozen races. The disagreement is not in whether these groups exist; it is in whether each should be assigned separate race status. The present classifications of man are based primarily on morphology. For centuries, this was the only readily observable variation. The term "morphology" today includes many aspects of body structure not readily observable without modern instruments, such as X-ray machines. Most of the traits used for classification are inherited, since it is only inherited differences that are biologically relevant. The traits that have been of greatest value are polygenic, although variations at specific loci are becoming more useful as knowledge of them increases. Many more loci will have to be known before characterizations based on frequencies of specific alleles can completely replace the present methods based largely on morphology.

Each of the major races is composed of many "local" races or populations. Perhaps none of the latter has all the features characteristic of the major racial group to which it belongs. As a group, the local races resemble each other in many ways but also differ. In some instances, local races may show features intermediate between major racial groups, suggesting an affinity with both and testifying to the arbitrariness with which lines between races are drawn.

Table 18–1 is a list of the major races as viewed by Garn. A few local races are included, although the list is very incomplete. Even the local races frequently are composed of groups of related but distinct populations. The grouping in Table 18–1 is somewhat arbitrary, in the sense that the major races may not be equivalent in terms of their separation from each other. Some have been more isolated and have evolved more independently than others. Furthermore, the list is not one with which all anthropologists agree. The differences among populations are weighed differently by some, leading to other classifications. Nevertheless, the list indicates the diversity of mankind and the population units into which man is divided.

TABLE 18–1

The Major Races of Man, Including Some Local Races (from Garn, 1961)

MAJOR RACE	LOCAL RACES
1. Amerindian	North American Indians
	Central American Indians
	South American Indians
2. Polynesian	
3. Micronesian	
4. Melanesian-Papuan	
5. Australian	
6. Asiatic	Japanese
	Chinese
	Filipino
7. Indian	Hindu
	Dravidian
8. European	North European
	Mediterranean
9. African	Sudanese
	Forest Negro
	Bantu
	Bushmen

Increasingly, Mendelian traits are being used to aid in the recognition and classification of human populations. For the most part, studies of gene frequencies have supported conclusions based on earlier techniques of physical anthropology. Examples of the type of variation observed among different groups are given in Table 18–2.

In assessing the biological potentials of various racial groups, much has been made of the superiority of one group or another in some trait. Examples of outstanding intellect among Jews and outstanding athletic ability among Negroes are plentiful. It should always be kept in mind that, for any measure, a population is described by two statistics— the mean and the variation about the mean. Two populations may differ slightly in means but have such wide variation about the means that the

TABLE 18-2

Frequencies of Alleles at Three Blood Group Loci for Selected Populations*

POPULATION	I^A	I^B	I^O	L^M	L^N	R	r
U. S. White	0.28	0.08	0.64	0.54	0.46	0.61	0.39
English	0.26	0.06	0.68	0.53	0.47	0.60	0.40
American Indian	0.10	0.00	0.90	0.76	0.24	1.00	0.00
Japanese	0.27	0.17	0.56	0.54	0.46	0.95	0.05
U. S. Negro	0.17	0.14	0.69	0.48	0.52	0.71	0.29
West African	0.18	0.16	0.66	0.51	0.49	0.74	0.26
Australian Aborigines	0.24-0.41	0.00	0.59-0.76	0.30	0.70	0.87	0.13
Indian (India)	0.18	0.26	0.56	0.66	0.34	0.70	0.30

* The values given are somewhat arbitrary because of the heterogeneity of the groups included in the population designations. These values do show the typical range among populations. In the case of the *Rh* locus, only two alleles have been indicated. These correspond to presence or absence of the factor Rh° (D).

distributions almost coincide (Fig. 18–3). On the other hand, they may have the same mean but differ in the variation about the mean, so that one has more extremes, both high and low. Comparison of populations on the basis of a few noted (or notorious) persons is therefore meaningless;

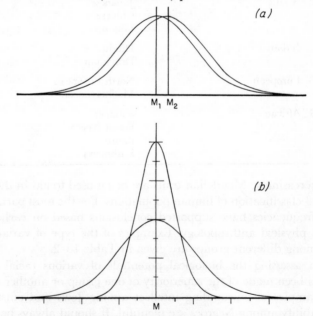

Figure 18–3. (a) Two normal distributions with the same areas and the same variation about the mean but with slightly different means. (b) Two normal distributions with the same mean and same areas but with different variation about the mean.

comparisons can only be done with large, statistically random samples. Statements about superiority require an arbitrary scale of good and bad, requiring value judgments which are outside the realm of science.

THE EFFECTS OF RACE CROSSING

If populations differ in their gene pool, then a legitimate question is whether matings between persons of different races are biologically equal to matings within racial groups. One might suppose that evolution has favored complexes of genes or special chromosome arrangements within races and that mating between races breaks up these complexes, leading to a less favorable genome. The offspring might be less fit and have reduced fertility. On the other hand, the effect of race crossing is to increase the heterozygosity in the F_1, and in some species, of which corn is an example, this leads to greater fitness of the F_1 (*hybrid vigor* or *heterosis*). With both increased and decreased fitness in other species to serve as examples, conclusions about human beings must be based on direct observations.

Opportunities for careful studies of crosses between races have not been frequent, in spite of the common occurrence of such crosses. Too often, the liaisons have been of a temporary or clandestine nature, with no way to assess fertility. The offspring of such matings have often been considered outcasts, belonging to neither parental group. Thus, they have not been exposed to environments that would permit comparison with the parental groups. For many of the attributes for which persons are evaluated, inequalities of environment can vitiate conclusions on the origin of differences.

One of the better opportunities for study of race crossing is found in Hawaii. Caucasians, Orientals, and Polynesians are all well represented. The absence of social barriers permits persons of different races to intermarry, and it is possible therefore to compare offspring from various parental combinations. Only a beginning has been made in this direction, but as yet no effects of interbreeding have been noted. The children of various crosses seem to be comparable for the measures used.

Although the observations are not properly controlled, it is apparent that other instances of race crossing also have produced offspring who are in the normal range of biological fitness, including abilities and fertility. Many of the present day ethnic groups are the result of a fusion of two or more separate groups. For example, the present American Negroes have about 30 percent European and 70 percent African genes.

It was at one time suggested that the effects of the sickle cell gene are more severe in American Negroes than in Africans. The consequences of homozygosity for Hb S were markedly deleterious in the United States, but comparable cases were not reported in Africa. It was thought that the Hb S genes interacted with the "European" genes of American Negroes to produce a severe disease but that in Africa combinations of genes had evolved that were not so deleterious. Subsequently, this difference was shown to be a fallacy based on inadequate medical reporting from Africa. Sickle cell disease occurs in Africa as well as in the United States, and the disease is just as severe in Africa. The two genetic backgrounds appear not to make a difference.

REFERENCES AND SUGGESTED READING

BOYD, W. C. 1950. *Genetics and the Races of Man.* Boston: Little, Brown, 454 pp.

DOBZHANSKY, T. 1951. *Genetics and the Origin of Species,* 3d ed. New York: Columbia University Press, 364 pp.

GARN, S. M. 1961. *Human Races.* Springfield, Ill.: Charles C Thomas, 137 pp.

GLASS, B. 1954. Genetic changes in human populations, especially those due to gene flow and genetic drift. *Advan. Genet.* 6: 95–139.

———, and LI, C. C. 1953. The dynamics of racial intermixture—an analysis based on the American Negro. *Am. J. Human Genet.* 5: 1–20.

———, SACKS, M. S., JAHN, E., and HESS, C. 1952. Genetic drift in a religious isolate: An analysis of the causes of variation in blood group and other gene frequencies in a small population. *Am. Naturalist* 86: 145–159.

HARRISON, G. A. (ed.). 1961. *Genetical Variation in Human Populations.* New York: Pergamon Press, 115 pp.

MORTON, N. E. 1962. Genetics of interracial crosses in Hawaii. *Eugen. Quart.* 9: 23–24.

MOURANT, A. E. 1954. *The Distribution of the Human Blood Groups.* Oxford: Blackwell, 438 pp.

RUCKNAGEL, D. L., and NEEL, J. V. 1961. The hemoglobinopathies. *Progr. Med. Genet.* 1: 158–260.

PROBLEMS

1. Define:

    race   parallel evolution
    genetic drift   hybrid vigor

2. There are two alleles at the haptoglobin locus, Hp^1 and Hp^2. The frequency of Hp^1 in Caucasians is 0.4 and in American Negroes is 0.6. Other genetic markers indicate that the latter population is 30 percent Caucasian. What was the frequency of Hp^1 in the African population that contributed to the American Negroes?

Chapter Nineteen

INBREEDING

Marriages of persons who are related through a common ancestor are consanguineous and their offspring are inbred. Since there are not enough ancestors for each of us to have arisen independently, most marriages are consanguineous. For example, each person has two parents, four grandparents, eight great-grandparents, etc. The number of ancestors at any preceding generation is given by 2^n, where n is the number of generations. For $n = 22$ (ca. 1000 A.D. for ancestors of the present generation), the number of ancestors would be 4,294,967,296. Since this figure is larger than the entire population of the world today, some persons served as ancestors through more than one line of descent.

Such remote consanguinity is of little genetic interest. So long as there is random mating and the size of the population is sufficient to maintain a large gene pool, the unavoidable remote consanguinity does little to alter the expected frequencies of gene combinations. The mating of close relatives is important, however, since it leads to a significant increase in homozygosity of offspring. To the extent that homozygosity for genes is deleterious, consanguineous marriages are deleterious. However, the deleterious effects are not shared equally by all offspring of consanguineous marriages, since the effects depend on homozygosity for specific alleles. Some matings show no deleterious effects; others show severe effects.

Rarely in history, particular families, usually of the ruling class, have practiced very close consanguinity over several generations. The best known example is found among the Pharaohs of Egypt, where brother-sister matings were the rule. In spite of this close inbreeding the progeny recorded appear not to have been defective.

THE INCREASE IN HOMOZYGOSITY IN CONSANGUINEOUS MARRIAGES

The most important consanguineous marriages, as measured by the number of marriages and the magnitude of consanguinity effect, are marriages of first cousins. Even in cultures or special groups within cultures in which such marriages are frowned on, they do occur, sometimes by special dispensation.

The frequency of cousin marriages varies both with the population structure and the cultural concepts of incest. In a population in which mobility is low, and particularly if the population is partitioned into small social groups—a situation found in societies composed of small

TABLE 19–1

Frequency of First Cousin Marriages in Several Populations (from Morton, 1961)

POPULATION	FREQUENCY, IN PERCENT
Japan, 3 cities	4.13
England	0.61
U. S., rural	0.00
Brazil, São Paulo	0.66
Germany, Münster	0.08
India, Marathas	10.00

villages—suitable mates are often related. Urbanization and increased mobility tend to decrease the proportion of consanguineous marriages. In some cultures, such as Japan, cousin marriages are regarded with favor. Table 19–1 is a summary of the frequency of cousin marriages in several cultures.

Consanguinity and Marriages of First Cousins

Formulas for treating the effects of consanguinity quantitatively have been developed, primarily by Dahlberg. Only autosomal genes will be considered, since genes on X chromosomes form a special situation. Males, with one X chromosome, cannot be inbred. Females can, and many of the relationships of autosomal genes apply also to X chromosomes of females. However, the strong selection exerted against deleterious genes on the X chromosome in hemizygous males reduces the problem of inbreeding for females.

Only first cousin marriages will be considered in this discussion, since the effect of inbreeding is much greater in these than in more distant consanguineous marriages. Figure 19–1 is a diagram of a first cousin mar-

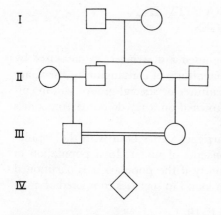

I

II

III

IV

Figure 19–1. Diagram of first cousin marriage. In this pedigree, the husband is related to his wife through his father's sister. There are three other possible paths of relationship—through his father's brother, his mother's sister, and his mother's brother. For autosomal genes, these relationships are equivalent. For genes on the X chromosome, they are not. The frequencies of the four types of cousin marriage vary among different cultures.

riage. The probability that a particular autosomal allele in generation I will be transmitted to the great-grandchild of generation IV is ⅛. The probability that the allele will be transmitted through both lines of descent is ⅛ × ⅛ = 1/64. However, there are four alleles at any locus in generation I, any of which might be transmitted with a probability of 1/64. Therefore, the total probability that both alleles of generation IV are derived from a single allele of generation I is 4 × 1/64 = 1/16. The probability that both alleles of generation IV had a different origin is 1 − 1/16 = 15/16.

For an allele a, the probability that the offspring in generation IV is homozygous aa because of common origin of a is $(1/16)q$, where q is the frequency of a. The probability of homozygosity if both alleles had a different origin is $(15/16)q^2$. Adding these together, the total probability of homozygosity, P_{aa}, for a is

$$P_{aa} = (15/16)q^2 + (1/16)q$$
$$= q^2 + (1/16)pq$$

Through similar reasoning, it can be shown that $P_{AA} = p^2 + (1/16)pq$. However, the frequency of heterozygotes, P_{Aa}, is decreased by an amount equal to the increase in homozygotes. Thus,

$$P_{Aa} = (15/16)2pq = 2pq − (2/16)pq$$

Table 19–2 shows the relative frequencies of homozygous recessives among offspring of first cousin marriages and among offspring of unrelated persons for selected values of q. If q is large, there is very little difference in frequency of aa; if q is very small, the likelihood of aa is relatively much larger for children of first cousin marriages.

The proportion, k, of first cousin parents of aa offspring among all parents of aa offspring can be calculated for a given q, provided the frequency of first cousin marriages in the general population is known. This is given by

TABLE 19-2

Frequencies of Homozygous Recessive Offspring from Marriages of Unrelated Persons and
from First Cousin Marriages for Various Values of the Gene Frequency

FREQUENCY OF RECESSIVE GENE q	FREQUENCY OF aa OFFSPRING FROM UNRELATED PARENTS q^2	FREQUENCY OF aa OFFSPRING FROM FIRST COUSIN MARRIAGES $q^2 + (\frac{1}{16})pq$	RATIO OF aa OFFSPRING: RELATED TO UNRELATED
0.5	0.25	0.2656	1.06
0.2	0.04	0.0500	1.25
0.1	0.01	0.0156	1.56
0.05	0.0025	0.00547	2.19
0.02	0.0004	0.00163	4.08
0.01	0.0001	0.000719	7.19
0.005	0.000025	0.000336	13.44
0.002	0.000004	0.000129	32.25
0.001	0.000001	0.000063	63.00

$$k = \frac{c(q + 15q^2)/16}{(1 - c)q^2 + c(q + 15 q^2)/16}$$

$$= \frac{c(1 + 15q)}{c(1 - q) + 16q}$$

where c is the frequency of first cousin marriages. The above formula can
be rearranged to

$$q = \frac{c(1 - k)}{16k - 15c - ck}$$

which permits calculation of the gene frequency q in terms of k and c only.

Coefficient of Inbreeding

A general formula for expressing the degree of inbreeding was
developed by Sewell Wright. The coefficient of inbreeding, F, is the
probability that both alleles in a person were derived from a single allele
in some common ancestor. For nonconsanguineous marriages, $F = 0$ in
the offspring. For offspring of a first cousin mating, $F = \frac{1}{16}$, as has been
shown in the previous section. The formula for F is

$$F = \Sigma (1/2)^N$$

NORTHWEST MISSOURI
STATE COLLEGE LIBRARY

where N is the number of persons in the path of relationship, starting with one parent, counting back to the common ancestor, then continuing down the line of descent to the other parent. The component values must be calculated for each common ancestor and summed to give F. In the usual first cousin marriage, there are two common ancestors, each contributing $(\frac{1}{2})^5$ to the value of F (Fig. 19–2). More complex relationships are readily handled with this formula.

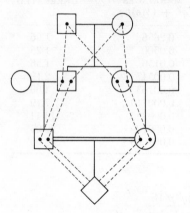

Figure 19–2. Diagram showing paths of relationship for the usual first cousin marriage. Since there are two common ancestors of the parents, there are two paths. The coefficient of inbreeding is therefore $F = (\frac{1}{2})^5 + (\frac{1}{2})^5 = \frac{1}{16}$.

If a common ancestor is himself inbred, there is increased likelihood that the alleles in an inbred descendant will be identical in origin. This can be evaluated by the more general expression,

$$F = \Sigma \, (1/2)^N (1 + F_a)$$

where F_a is the inbreeding coefficient of the ancestor.

The increase in homozygosity can be generalized in terms of F, since, in the specific case of first cousin marriages, the $\frac{1}{16}$ probability of identical origin of two alleles is merely the coefficient of inbreeding. Thus, in more general terms,

$$P_{AA} = (1 - F)p^2 + Fp$$

$$P_{Aa} = (1 - F)2pq$$

$$P_{aa} = (1 - F)q^2 + Fq$$

These formulas permit calculation of inbreeding effect for any degree of parental relationship.

NORTHWEST MISSOURI
STATE COLLEGE LIBRARY

Consanguinity in Isolates

Many small populations are known in which inbreeding is very much higher than in the general population. This will occur if a population is isolated as a result of geographic or social factors. Some small island populations number only a few hundred persons, and matings occur almost exclusively within this group. Inevitably, over several generations, the population becomes inbred. By chance, some alleles are lost and persons become homozygous for alleles having a common origin. A similar situation has occurred among several religious isolates. Where doctrine does not permit marriage outside the group and outsiders are not taken into the group, isolation and inbreeding occur.

There are several religious isolates in the United States that have been studied genetically. Most of these isolates were founded by immigration of a small group of persons, who then set up a closed organization in this country. Some of the groups prospered and consist now of thousands of persons. As the groups have become larger, the opportunities to avoid inbreeding would seem to have increased also. This reasoning is somewhat spurious, however, since the population is restricted to the original gene pool.

An example of the degree of inbreeding sometimes encountered in isolates is given in Figure 19–3. This pedigree is from a group living in Indiana. Although marriages do not always involve close relatives, the

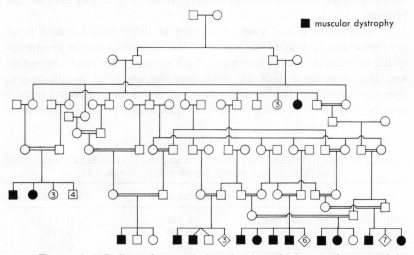

Figure 19–3. Pedigree from an isolate showing a high rate of consanguinity and the presence of a number of cases of muscular dystrophy inherited as an autosomal recessive trait. (Redrawn from Hammond and Jackson, 1958, by permission.)

number of consanguineous marriages that have occurred among ancestors of the most recent generation greatly increases the coefficients of inbreeding for these generations.

CONSANGUINITY AND CONCEALED DETRIMENTAL GENES

Not all genes can be identified in homozygous state, even though they may be detrimental. The effects may be on some complex attribute, such as body size, intelligence, or skeletal development. The effects may be minor or they may lead to death. Many of the defects may result from environmental as well as genetic causes or from interaction of specific genotypes and environments.

It is possible to test for the contribution of rare recessive genes to these complex traits by measuring their increase in offspring of consanguineous marriages. A number of studies have been designed to do this, a small portion of the results of which are presented in Table 19–3. Because of ease of assessment, the proportion of stillbirths and neonatal deaths has been studied frequently. Regardless of the population investigated, there is an increase in these events. The causes are heterogeneous. In many cases, homozygosity at a single locus may be the main factor; in other cases, simultaneous homozygosity at several loci may be important.

Estimates of the average number of deleterious recessive genes per person can be made from studies of the increase in defects among offspring of consanguineous marriages. Such estimates are crude; nevertheless, they provide a basis for estimating the ability of populations to tolerate mutations. The "genetic load" of deleterious recessive genes is usually expressed in terms of lethal equivalents. A lethal equivalent

TABLE 19–3

Mortality in Offspring of First Cousin Marriages Compared to Offspring of Unrelated Parents (from Various Sources, Summarized by Morton, 1961)

TRAIT	UNRELATED	FIRST COUSINS
Stillbirths and neonatal deaths	0.044	0.111
Infant and juvenile deaths	0.089	0.156
Early deaths, Hiroshima	0.031	0.050
Early deaths, Kure	0.035	0.041
Juvenile deaths	0.160	0.229
Postnatal deaths	0.024	0.081
Miscarriages	0.129	0.145

is one gene that, if present in homozygous combination, would cause death, or two genes, each of which in homozygous combination would cause death half the time, etc. Morton, Crow, and Muller have estimated, on the basis of studies of consanguinity in France by Sutter and Tabah, that each person has three to five lethal equivalents per genome. Other studies have produced similar results. This means that on the average each gamete has 1.5 to 2.5 genes that, if the gamete were to combine with an identical gamete, would lead to death. In addition to genes that are lethal, there are others that are detrimental even though they may not result in death.

Although future studies may cause a revision in the estimate of the number of detrimental genes per person, it is unlikely that new data will greatly alter the magnitude. Thus, most persons carry several genes that can be detrimental in appropriate combinations with other genes and the environment. Close inbreeding will often reveal these genes. Persons who survive close inbreeding have a slightly better chance of having fewer or none of the genes.

REFERENCES AND SUGGESTED READING

FREIRE-MAIA, N. 1957. Inbreeding in Brazil. *Am. J. Human Genet.* 9: 284–298.

HAMMOND, D. T., and JACKSON, C. E. 1958. Consanguinity in a midwestern United States isolate. *Am. J. Human Genet.* 10: 61–63.

MORTON, N. E. 1958. Empirical risks in consanguineous marriages: birth weight, gestation time, and measurements of infants. *Am. J. Human Genet.* 10: 344–349.

————. 1961. Morbidity of children from consanguineous marriages. *Progr. Med. Genet.* 1: 261–291.

————, CROW, J. F., and MULLER, H. J. 1956. An estimate of the mutational damage in man from data on consanguineous marriages. *Proc. Natl. Acad. Sci.* (U. S.) 42: 855–863.

SCHULL, W. J. 1958. Empirical risks in consanguineous marriages: Sex ratio, malformation, and viability. *Am. J. Human Genet.* 10: 294–343.

SLATIS, H. M., and HOENE, R. E. 1961. The effect of consanguinity on the distribution of continuously variable characteristics. *Am. J. Human Genet.* 13: 28–31.

————, REIS, R. H., and HOENE, R. E. 1958. Consanguineous marriages in the Chicago region. *Am. J. Human Genet.* 10: 446–464.

PROBLEMS

1. Define:

    consanguinity   inbreeding

2. A man is affected with the autosomal recessive form of muscular dystrophy. Two of his grandchildren (first cousins) marry.
    a. What is the probability that both are carriers of the disease?
    b. Assuming that both are carriers, what is the probability that any given child of theirs will be affected?
    c. If he had been affected with the sex-linked form, how would this have influenced your answer?

3. In a marriage involving first cousins, what is the probability that an offspring will be affected with a disease due to a rare recessive gene
    a. if the common grandfather of the couple is affected?
    b. if the husband's mother (the wife's aunt) is affected?
    c. if the husband's paternal uncle is affected?
    d. if there are no affected relatives?

4. In the pedigree below, what is the probability that the offspring of the first cousin marriage will be affected with galactosemia? What is the probability that this individual will be hemophilic? What is the probability that both conditions will be present? Both absent?

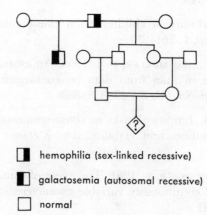

▌ hemophilia (sex-linked recessive)

▊ galactosemia (autosomal recessive)

☐ normal

5. In a population in which 1 percent of the marriages are between first cousins, it is observed that 30 percent of the matings that produce offspring affected with a rare excessive trait are between first cousins. What is the frequency of the gene responsible for the trait?

Chapter Twenty

HUMAN GENETICS AND HUMAN WELFARE

The preceding chapters have described many aspects of human genetics. In this chapter, some of the ways in which knowledge of human genetics can help mankind will be considered. The topics to be discussed were selected from a large number. There are others equally important.

MEDICAL GENETICS AND COUNSELING

One use of genetics is in counseling persons with real or imagined hereditary diseases on the prospects for transmission of their condition to their offspring. The need for such counseling has long been recognized, but too often in the past it has been provided by persons unequipped to give it. In some cases, these persons were nonprofessional; in others they were competent in other fields but ignorant of genetics. Their error, more often than not, has been to provide reassurance when such was not justified. The motivation in such cases usually has been to bring some peace of mind to parents who have produced a defective child and who wish to know the prospects for additional defective children. When such children subsequently have been produced contrary to the predictions of a well-meaning physician or other person, the result has been worse than a correct but less comforting answer would have been.

Persons seek counseling for a variety of reasons, and the first job of a counselor is to establish the real purpose of an inquiry. For this reason, it is necessary to relate the counseling to the total medical picture of the patient and his family. Ideally, counseling should be done by a physician familiar with the other problems a person may have. This frequently is not possible, but the counselor should work in association with the physician. The geneticist must remember that persons seeking advice may need psychiatric help rather than instruction in genetics, which they probably will ignore anyway.

In spite of these reservations, there are many ways in which genetic counseling can help persons. The most gratifying occurs when a person can be told that a dominant condition present in his parents but not in himself cannot be transmitted to offspring. A more common situation is when normal parents have produced an abnormal offspring and wish to know the prospects for other affected children. An appreciation for probability may be the best the geneticist has to offer.

Mendelian Systems

Many medical problems involve simple Mendelian traits, the inheritance of which has been covered in other chapters. Once the trait has been properly diagnosed, the prospects for additional affected persons can be readily assessed. A difficulty is sometimes encountered with diseases of late onset. For example, in Huntington's chorea, a degenerative disease of the central nervous system inherited as a simple dominant, the first signs of the disease may not appear until advanced age. Symptoms usually appear by the time an affected person is in his thirties, but cases have been observed in which the symptoms were delayed until age sixty. The offspring of an affected person is in a dilemma. He may wish to refrain from having children if he is to be affected, but by the time his risk for developing the disease is appreciably lowered from 1/2, he will be past the usual procreative age. For such persons, the geneticist can offer little comfort at present. Hopefully, when the disease is better understood biochemically, affected persons can be recognized at ages long before neurological symptoms appear.

More and more examples have been found of genes that are recessive with respect to production of disease but that nevertheless can be detected in heterozygous combination by changes in activity of a specific enzyme or metabolic pathway. Heterozygotes for phenylketonuria, galactosemia, sickle cell anemia, acatalasemia, and many other defects are healthy but can be recognized by appropriate chemical tests. For rare traits, testing the general population is not feasible. Close relatives of affected persons may find it to their advantage to check for heterozygosity if they are concerned about the possibility of transmitting the abnormal gene. This would be the case particularly if prospective parents each are related to persons with the same disorder.

Chromosomal Abnormalities

The prevalent abnormalities involving trisomy for chromosomes 21 and 18 appear to arise primarily from nondisjunction. The chances that a subsequent child also will be trisomic are very small. As stated earlier, there does appear to be a tendency for repeated nondisjunction in certain persons, reflected in a slight increase in risk of another non-disjunction involving the same or another chromosome. The basis for the increased risk is not understood, but it is small.

The risk of subsequently affected children from parents of whom one carries a balanced translocation is very much larger. Karyological examination of patients and their parents has provided the geneticist with a powerful tool for predicting the recurrence of abnormal offspring. Its primary application still is for trisomy 21 syndrome, but other uses will undoubtedly increase.

Empiric Risks

The precise modes of heredity for many conditions are not known. Diabetes and gout are examples of frequently occurring conditions in which there is clearly a strong genetic component, probably involving interaction with environment and other genetic systems. It is possible in such cases to predict recurrence entirely on the basis of frequency of recurrence in other families. A couple with no affected offspring will have a certain risk for a particular defect; a couple who has produced one affected child will have a higher risk; and a couple with two affected children will have perhaps a different risk for a third affected child. The amount of information available about a couple influences the predicted risk value. The more information available, the more accurate the predictions concerning future children.

Good empiric risk data are available only for a few conditions. For example, spontaneous abortions are due to many complex factors, some genetic and some environmental. In a large study, Warburton and Fraser found that the average risk of abortion is 15 percent. However, if a woman has already had one or more abortions, the risk increases to 25 percent. In spite of our lack of understanding of the etiology of abortion, the risk can be measured accurately and used in advising persons regarding their own risk.

With empiric figures, it should be kept in mind that a particular family may have a very different risk from the population as a whole. Among close relatives of cancer patients, the increased risk is of the order of 2 to 3 percent. There are very rare families in which the risk appears to be higher. Proper counseling should begin with a thorough investigation of the pedigree of the family under consideration.

Genetics and Diagnosis

In addition to usefulness in counseling, genetics can sometimes aid in diagnosis and in making a prognosis. A patient may have symptoms compatible with several conditions. Consideration of other family members may aid in making the correct diagnosis and in devising appropriate therapy. A diagnosis of the rare condition of Huntington's chorea in a young person would be made reluctantly unless it were known that a parent also had the condition. Even in common diseases, the knowledge that a patient has a high risk for certain inherited conditions will indicate tests that might otherwise not be included in a routine examination.

Phenylketonuria is one of the most dramatic examples of a direct application of genetics in the detection of a rare disease (p. 104). Many and perhaps most of the deleterious effects of this recessively inherited disease can be prevented if dietary management is instituted within the first few weeks of life *before* defects in the central nervous system occur. In order to detect the disease, a newborn must be tested at three to five weeks after birth. Testing is relatively simple and inexpensive, but since the disease occurs only once in 10- to 20,000 births and particularly since the test must be done after the child would normally have left the hospital, routine testing has rarely been done in the past. The exceptions have been newborn sibs of affected persons. These sibs have a 1/4 chance of being affected rather than the 1/10,000 chance of the general population. The initial demonstrations of the effectiveness of diet therapy were done on newborn sibs of patients who themselves were too old to derive appreciable benefit. In a number of states, there currently are programs to screen all newborns for phenylketonuria. How successful these programs will be is yet to be established.

There are many other examples in which knowledge of the genes present in other members of a family will help a physician decide to perform tests that might not be included in the early stages of diagnosis. Even with common diseases, such as diabetes, appreciation of the risk may help in more intelligent management of the environment for the prediabetic.

IATROGENIC DISEASES

The image of the physician as the healer of disease is well founded in general, but it does not follow that patients always improve under the care of a physician. Indeed, in a small portion of cases, the actions of the physician are detrimental to the patient. In the seventeenth century, this was frequently the case because the physician unknowingly carried germs from one patient to another. In the twentieth century, the dangers of infection are widely recognized, among laymen as well as physicians, and appropriate measures are observed. A new group of diseases has become much more common, however. These are the "drug idiosyncracy" diseases, in which persons show abnormal reaction to drugs. Since the agent is administered ordinarily by a physician, these diseases are said to be iatrogenic, or physician induced.

An example of an iatrogenic disease already discussed (p. 191) is the hemolysis associated with glucose-6-phosphate dehydrogenase deficiency. The enzyme deficiency was not recognized until it was observed that red blood cells of certain persons hemolyze following administration of the antimalarial drug primaquine. This trait has now been thoroughly investigated and is known to result from a gene on the X chromosome. It is possible to recogize persons with the variant gene by laboratory tests. Such persons are sensitive to many other drugs, a fact that must be considered when treating someone from a population, such as American Negroes, in which the gene frequency is high.

Several other types of drug sensitivity have been discovered. Atypical pseudocholinesterase was detected when several patients who were given succinylcholine prior to electroshock therapy developed prolonged apnea; this reaction is in contrast to that of most patients, who recover within a minute or two. These rare patients were found to be homozygous for a gene that leads to an abnormal form of the enzyme that breaks down succinylcholine. Heterozygous persons have both forms of the enzyme. Presence of the atypical enzyme is not associated with any recognized defect, apart from the inability to metabolize succinylcholine rapidly.

A third example of differential response to drugs is found in the inactivation of isoniazid, used in the treatment of tuberculosis. Some persons inactivate the drug rapidly, others slowly. Rapid inactivation appears to be a dominant trait.

As more drugs are administered to persons, more examples of genetic variation in individual capacity to tolerate drugs will be found. Investigations in this area have been given the name pharmacogenetics. The reason for this previously unsuspected genetic variation is unknown. For very rare traits, mutation may account for the frequency of variant alleles. For more common traits, such as the three described here, mutation is unlikely to be the major factor. Possibly, heterozygote advantage has led to an increase of the gene. Glucose-6-phosphate dehydrogenase deficiency, for example, is thought to have occurred because of better protection of the heterozygote against falciparium malaria. In any event, the disadvantage observed when persons are challenged with synthetic drugs cannot have existed prior to modern medical practice.

GENETICS AND EUGENICS

Interest in human heredity, and particularly human control over human heredity, antedates the discovery of the laws of heredity. Of particular importance was the eugenics movement in England in the last part of the nineteenth century. This movement, spearheaded by persons of outstanding intellect, such as Francis Galton and Karl Pearson, had as its objective the application of biologically sound principles to human populations. Since the biological basis of heredity was unknown, the first objective was to establish the nature of heredity.

Galton and Pearson chose to work with human beings and with what they considered important human traits, such as intelligence, stature, and special abilities. We now know these to be very complex traits under the control of many genes interacting with environmental variation. It is small wonder that these early investigators made little progress. They did make major contributions to the science of biometrics in the process, however.

Betterment of the human species through control of heredity has appealed to many persons. Unfortunately, some of the persons who followed Galton and Pearson were less committed to the principle that action should be based on sound observation. The largely fancied urgency for preserving the best qualities of man led to recommendations and in many cases actions that are now seen to have been futile and totally without scientific support. In the United States, the overpublicized story of the Jukes and Kallikaks, two families with a large number of mental defectives and criminals, is typical of the pseudoscience that attributed everything to heredity and that recommended sterilization as the only salvation. The movement reached its nadir in Nazi Germany, where the words of science were used to provide the basis for purely political deeds.

Largely in reaction to the excesses of the eugenicists of the first part of the twentieth century, attempts to control man's heredity came into disfavor. This is unfortunate, since control of his own well-being, both genetic and environmental, is a most worthwhile goal of man. This last point of view has gained in favor, particularly because of the increasing appreciation of the importance of genetics to medicine.

Even if one accepts the idea that eugenics is desirable, the proper course of action is not obvious. It is well to remember here that the only ethic of science is truth. Despite declarations to the contrary, science does not provide the basis for ethical and moral concepts of the rights of individuals versus the rights of communities. These come from other areas of our culture. Science can provide the means by which ethical objectives are achieved. The fact that eminent scientists have taken leading roles on occasion in advocating eugenic objectives does not mean that the goals themselves are scientifically arrived at. On the other hand, scientists are human beings and therefore are entitled to views on ethical and moral issues. Their special knowledge of certain areas of science may make them unusually well equipped to discuss the application of those areas to social problems.

The issue of eugenics that has been of concern to most persons is whether the human species is deteriorating genetically under the changed conditions (frequently called "relaxed" conditions) of selection that exist today. In Chapter 17, arguments were presented for the idea that selection is not relaxed. But is it possible that there is a deterioration of intelligence, which we generally value as the most important attribute distinguishing us from our near primate relatives? The basis for thinking there might be is the apparent fertility of persons of low intelligence compared to those of high intelligence. It is true that in most Western countries, persons with greater education do not have as many children as do persons of average or below average intelligence. It is usually forgotten that persons with very low intelligence are often infertile and that, when they are institutionalized, even the potential fertility is reduced to near zero.

Data on the rate of change of intelligence because of changing genetic constitution are not available. But there seems little basis for the attitude expressed by some concerning the urgency of corrective action. That there is no urgent need should not, however, deter a continuing evaluation of the status of the population and of changes that may be occurring. Nor should it deter discussion and experimentation on means of controlling the genetic destiny of a population.

The first problem would be a decision regarding what constitutes the best genotype. This problem is made more difficult by the possible conflict between the ideal genotype for the individual compared to the ideal genotype for the population. Even if it were possible to specify the ideal genotype for a person in a given environment, removal of genetic variability from the population as a whole would reduce the ability of the population to evolve rapidly with changing environment. Loss of

REFERENCES AND SUGGESTED READING   253

evolutionary flexibility has often led to extinction, a fate that most of us hope to delay.

REFERENCES AND SUGGESTED READING

HERNDON, C. N. 1962. Empiric risks. In *Methodology in Human Genetics* (W. J. Burdette, ed.). San Francisco: Holden-Day, pp. 144–155.

KALLMANN, F. J. 1956. Psychiatric aspects of genetic counseling. *Am. J. Human Genet.* 8: 97–101.

MOTULSKY, A. 1964. Pharmacogenetics. *Progr. Med. Genet.* 3: 49–74.

WARBURTON, D., and FRASER, F. C. 1964. Spontaneous abortion risks in man: Data from reproductive histories collected in a medical genetics unit. *Am. J. Human Genet.* 16: 1–25.

INDEX